MACMILLAN REEDS
WAYPOINT & MARINA GUIDE

The essential source directory for all sail & power boat owners.

© Nautical Data 2002

Nautical Data Ltd, The Book Barn,
Westbourne, Hampshire PO10 8RS
Tel: 01243 389352
Fax: 01243 379136
e-mail: info@nauticaldata.com

Cover photo: Derek Slatter
Cover design: Garold West

Section 1

The Waypoints, Marinas and Services Section is new for the 2003 season. These useful pages provide chartlets and facility details of over 150 marinas around the shores of the UK and Ireland, including the Channel Islands. Add to this a host of waypoints with associated waycharts, plus a regionally organised guide to services, and you have the perfect complement to any Macmillan Reeds almanac.

Section 2

The Marine Supplies & Services section lists more than 100 services which all owners will require from time to time. It provides a quick and easy reference to manufacturers and retailers of equipment, services and supplies both nationally and locally at coastal locations around the British Isles, together with emergency services. Many entries carry concise information for guidance.

Advertisement Sales

Enquiries about advertising space should be addressed to:
**MS Publications, 2nd Floor,
Ewer House, 44-46 Crouch Street,
Colchester, Essex, CO3 3HH
Tel: +44(0)1206 506223**
Fax: +44 (0)1206 500228

Section 1

Waypoints, Marinas and Services Guide

Section 2

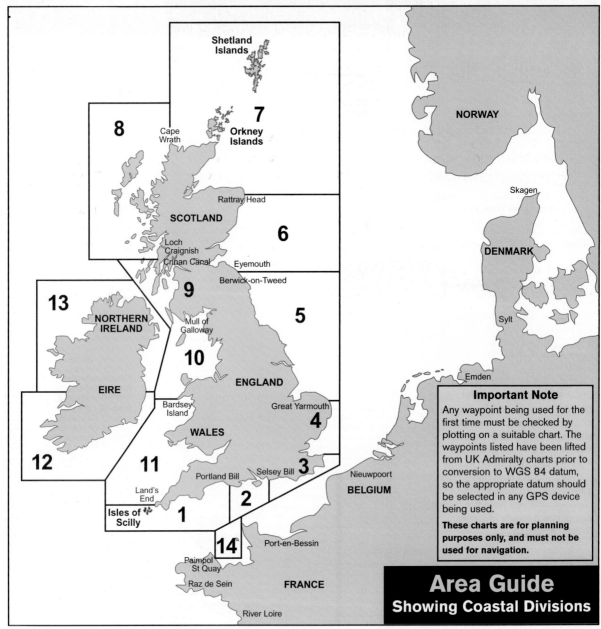

Important Note

Any waypoint being used for the first time must be checked by plotting on a suitable chart. The waypoints listed have been lifted from UK Admiralty charts prior to conversion to WGS 84 datum, so the appropriate datum should be selected in any GPS device being used.

These charts are for planning purposes only, and must not be used for navigation.

Area Guide
Showing Coastal Divisions

Area 1 ......**South West England** ....Isles of Scilly to Portland Bill		
Area 2 ......**Central Southern England** ....Portland Bill to Selsey Bill		
Area 3 ......**South East England**..............................Selsey Bill to North Foreland		
Area 4 ......**East England** ....North Foreland to Great Yarmouth		
Area 5 ......**North East England** ....Great Yarmouth to Berwick-upon-Tweed		
Area 6 ......**South East Scotland** ....Eyemouth to Rattray Head		
Area 7 ......**North East Scotland** ....Rattray Head to Cape Wrath including Orkney & Shetland Is		
Area 8 ......**North West Scotland**............................Cape Wrath to Crinan Canal		
Area 9 ......**South West Scotland** ....Crinan Canal to Mull of Galloway		
Area 10 ....**North West England** ....Isle of Man & N. Wales, Mull of Galloway to Bardsey Is		
Area 11 ....**South Wales & Bristol Channel** ....Bardsey Island to Lands End		
Area 12 ....**South Ireland** ....Malahide, south to Liscanor Bay		
Area 13 ....**North Ireland** ....Lambay Island, north to Liscanor Bay		
Area 14 ....**Channel Islands**....................................Guernsey, Jersey & Alderney		

SOUTH WEST ENGLAND - Isles of Scilly to Portland Bill

Planning a trip?

Met Office

Make it plain sailing
– for your free copy of
the *2002 Marine Weather Services* booklet
call the Met Office Customer Centre
on **0845 300 0300** or go to
www.metoffice.com/leisuremarine/mwsbooklet.html

For a five-day inshore forecast
for Lyme Regis – Land's End – Hartland Pt.,
dial **09060 100 458*** from your fax machine.

*09060 calls are charged at £1 per minute at all times.

Key to Marina Plans symbols

🔥	Calor Gas	**P**	Parking
🔧	Chandler	✕	Pub/Restaurant
♿	Disabled facilities	⇄	Pump out
🔌	Electrical supply		Rigging service
🔧	Electrical repairs		Sail repairs
🔧	Engine repairs		Shipwright
✚	First Aid	🛒	Shop/Supermarket
🚰	Fresh Water		Showers
D	Fuel - Diesel		Slipway
P	Fuel - Petrol	**WC**	Toilets
	Hardstanding/boatyard	☎	Telephone
◻	Laundry facilities	🛒	Trolleys
	Lift-out facilities	Ⓥ	Visitors berths

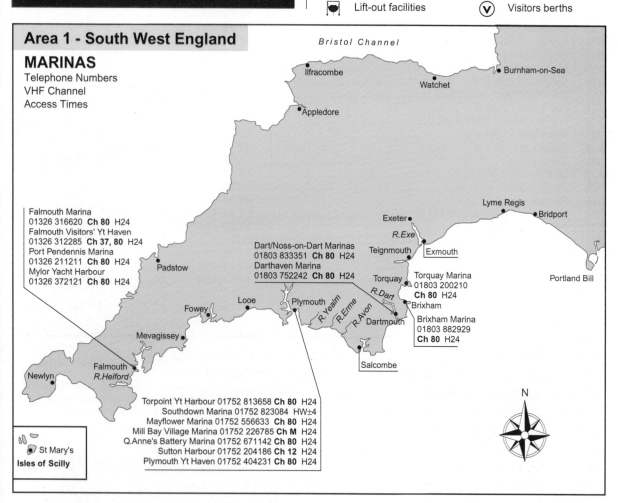

Area 1 - South West England

MARINAS
Telephone Numbers
VHF Channel
Access Times

Bristol Channel

Ilfracombe

Watchet

Burnham-on-Sea

Appledore

Falmouth Marina
01326 316620 **Ch 80** H24
Falmouth Visitors' Yt Haven
01326 312285 **Ch 37, 80** H24
Port Pendennis Marina
01326 211211 **Ch 80** H24
Mylor Yacht Harbour
01326 372121 **Ch 80** H24

Padstow

Lyme Regis
Bridport

Exeter
R.Exe
Teignmouth
Exmouth

Dart/Noss-on-Dart Marinas
01803 833351 **Ch 80** H24
Darthaven Marina
01803 752242 **Ch 80** H24

Torquay
R.Dart
Brixham
Dartmouth

Torquay Marina
01803 200210
Ch 80 H24

Portland Bill

Brixham Marina
01803 882929
Ch 80 H24

Looe
Plymouth
R.Yealm *R.Erme* *R.Avon*

Fowey

Mevagissey

Salcombe

Falmouth
R.Helford

Newlyn

Torpoint Yt Harbour 01752 813658 **Ch 80** H24
Southdown Marina 01752 823084 HW±4
Mayflower Marina 01752 556633 **Ch 80** H24
Mill Bay Village Marina 01752 226785 **Ch M** H24
Q.Anne's Battery Marina 01752 671142 **Ch 80** H24
Sutton Harbour 01752 204186 **Ch 12** H24
Plymouth Yt Haven 01752 404231 **Ch 80** H24

St Mary's
Isles of Scilly

N

A Blagdon Plymouth	01752 561830	**Bridport HM**	01308 423222
A Hooper Plymouth	01752 830411	**Bridport Police**	01308 422266
A Mathew Sail Loft (Ocean Blue Chandlery)		**Brigantine** Teignmouth	01626 872400
Penzance	01736 364004	**Brixham Chandlers** Brixham	01803 882055
Axe YC Axemouth	01297 20043	**Brixham HM**	01803 853321
Baltic Wharf Boatyard Totnes	01803 867922	**Brixham Marina** Brixham	01803 882929

Waypoint Guide Area 1 – South West England - Isles of Scilly to Portland Bill

No.	Name	Latitude	Longitude
34	**Portland Bill** - 5M S of	50°25'·82N	02°27'·30W
43	**Guernsey SW** - 1·8M W Les Hanois	49°26'·16N	02°45'·00W
60	**Roches Douvres Light** - 2·5M NE	49°08'·24N	02°45'·96W
	St Malo - 1·3M NW Grande Jardin Lt. Bn	48°41'·10N	02°06'·40W
	Cherbourg - 0·5M N of W ent	49°40'·95N	01°39'·35W
97	**Bridport** - 1M S of entrance	50°41'·50N	02°45'·70W
98	**Lyme Regis** - 1M SSE on ldg Lts	50°42'·80N	02°54'·80W
99	**River Exe** - 0·3M S of E Exe Lt By	50°35'·67N	03°22'·30W
100	**Teignmouth** - 1M E of Bar	50°32'·30N	03°27'·80W
101	**Torbay** - 1·7M NE of Berry Hd	50°25'·10N	03°27'·00W
102	**Dartmouth** - 2M 150° from ent	50°18'·25N	03°31'·60W
103	**Start Point** - 2M S of	50°11'·30N	03°38'·47W
104	**Salcombe** - 1·5M S of bar	50°11'·62N	03°46'·60W
105	**Bolt Tail** - 1·3M SW of R Avon	50°13'·60N	03°53'·60W
106	**River Erme** - 1·5M SSW of Battisborough Island	50°16'·80N	03°58'·50W
107	**River Yealm** -1·2M SW of Yealm Hd	50°17'·30N	04°05'·70W
108	**Plymouth** - 0·9M S of W end of brkwtr	50°19'·13N	04°09'·50W
109	**Rame Head** - 0·2M S of	50°18'·15N	04°13'·30W
110	**Eddystone** - 1M S of	50°09'·80N	04°15'·85W
111	**Looe** - 1·5M SE of entrance	50°19'·80N	04°25'·20W
112	**Polperro** - 0·7M S of	50°19'·00N	04°30'·80W
113	**Fowey** - 1·5M SSW of ent	50°18'·20N	04°39'·50W
114	**Charlestown** - 1M SE of	50°19'·00N	04°44'·10W
115	**Mevagissey** - 0·8M E of	50°16'·10N	04°45'·50W
116	**Gwineas Light Buoy** - 0·2M E of	50°14'·40N	04°45'·00W
117	**Dodman Point** - 1·3M SSE of	50°11'·90N	04°47'·00W
118	**Falmouth** - 0·8M S of St Anthony Hd	50°07'·64N	05°00'·90W
119	**Helford River** -1M E of ent	50°05'·70N	05°04'·00W
120	**Manacles** - 0·2M E of	50°02'·80N	05°01'·50W
121	**Coverack** - 1M E of	50°01'·30N	05°04'·30W
122	**Black Head** - 0·7M SE of	49°59'·70N	05°05'·30W
123	**Lizard** - 2M S of	49°55'·58N	05°12'·07W
124	**Porth Mellin** - 1·7M W of	50°00'·80N	05°18'·50W
125	**Porthleven** - 0·4M SW of	50°04'·50N	05°19'·70W
126	**Mountamopus Buoy** - 0·2M S	50°04'·40N	05°26'·20W
127	**Penzance** - 1·5M SE of and for Mousehole	50°06'·00N	05°30'·00W
128	**Tater Du Light** -1·5M ESE	50°02'·50N	05°32'·60W
129	**Runnel Stone Light Buoy** - 0·3M S	50°00'·85N	05°40'·30W
130	**Wolf Rock** - 2M S of	49°54'·65N	05°48'·50W
131	**St Mary's, Scilly** - 2M E of St Mary's Sound	49°54'·00N	06°15'·00W
	Treguier - 4·1M N of Pointe de Chateau	48°56'·20N	03°14'·30W
	Roscoff - 6M NNE of ent	48°49'·10N	03°54'·30W
	Ouessant Creac'h Light - 3·5M NW	48°30'·00N	05°11'·30W

Distance Table - South West England

Approximate distances in nautical miles are by the most direct route while avoiding dangers and allowing for Traffic Separation Schemes

		1	2	3	4	5	6	7	8	9	10	11	12	13	14	15	16	17	18	19	20
1.	Milford Haven	1																			
2.	Lundy Island	28	2																		
3.	Padstow	67	40	3																	
4.	Longships	100	80	47	4																
5.	Scilly (Crow Sound)	120	102	69	22	5															
6.	Penzance	115	95	62	15	35	6														
7.	Lizard Point	123	103	72	23	42	16	7													
8.	Falmouth	139	119	88	39	60	32	16	8												
9.	Mevagissey	152	132	99	52	69	46	28	17	9											
10.	Fowey	157	137	106	57	76	49	34	22	7	10										
11.	Looe	163	143	110	63	80	57	39	29	16	11	11									
12.	Plymouth (bkwtr)	170	150	117	70	92	64	49	39	25	22	11	12								
13.	R. Yealm (ent)	172	152	119	72	89	66	49	39	28	23	16	4	13							
14.	Salcombe	181	161	128	81	102	74	59	50	40	36	29	22	17	14						
15.	Start Point	186	166	135	86	103	80	63	55	45	40	33	24	22	7	15					
16.	Dartmouth	195	175	142	95	116	88	72	63	54	48	42	35	31	14	9	16				
17.	Torbay	201	181	150	101	118	96	78	70	62	55	50	39	38	24	15	11	17			
18.	Exmouth	213	193	162	113	131	107	90	82	73	67	61	51	49	33	27	24	12	18		
19.	Lyme Regis	226	206	173	126	144	120	104	96	86	81	74	63	62	48	41	35	30	21	19	
20.	Portland Bill	235	215	184	135	151	128	112	104	93	89	81	73	70	55	49	45	42	36	22	20

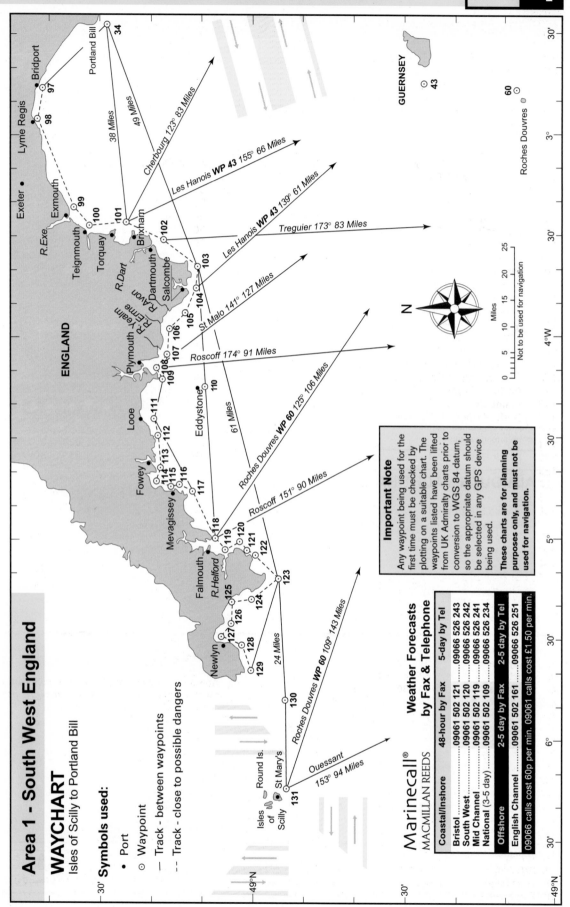

Area 1 - South West England

WAYCHART
Isles of Scilly to Portland Bill

Symbols used:
- ● Port
- ⊙ Waypoint
- — Track – between waypoints
- -- Track – close to possible dangers

Important Note

Any waypoint being used for the first time must be checked by plotting on a suitable chart. The waypoints listed have been lifted from UK Admiralty charts prior to conversion to WGS 84 datum, so the appropriate datum should be selected in any GPS device being used.

These charts are for planning purposes only, and must not be used for navigation.

Marinecall®
MACMILLAN REEDS

Weather Forecasts by Fax & Telephone

Coastal/Inshore	48-hour by Fax	5-day by Tel
Bristol	09061 502 121	09066 526 243
South West	09061 502 120	09066 526 242
Mid Channel	09061 502 119	09066 526 241
National (3-5 day)	09061 502 109	09066 526 234

Offshore	2-5 day by Fax	2-5 day by Tel
English Channel	09061 502 161	09066 526 251

09066 calls cost 60p per min. 09061 calls cost £1.50 per min.

FALMOUTH MARINA

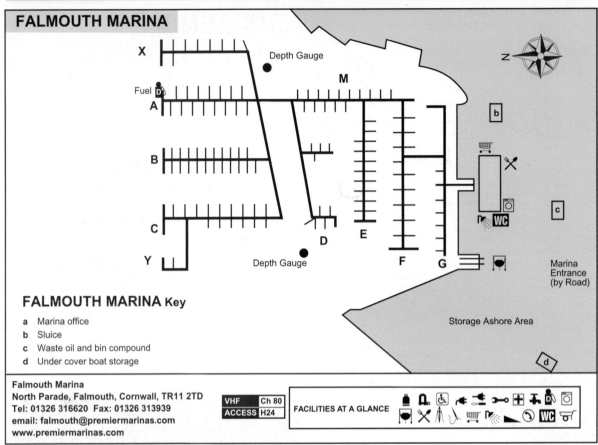

FALMOUTH MARINA Key

a   Marina office
b   Sluice
c   Waste oil and bin compound
d   Under cover boat storage

Falmouth Marina
North Parade, Falmouth, Cornwall, TR11 2TD
Tel: 01326 316620 Fax: 01326 313939
email: falmouth@premiermarinas.com
www.premiermarinas.com

VHF	Ch 80
ACCESS	H24

FACILITIES AT A GLANCE

FALMOUTH YACHT HAVEN

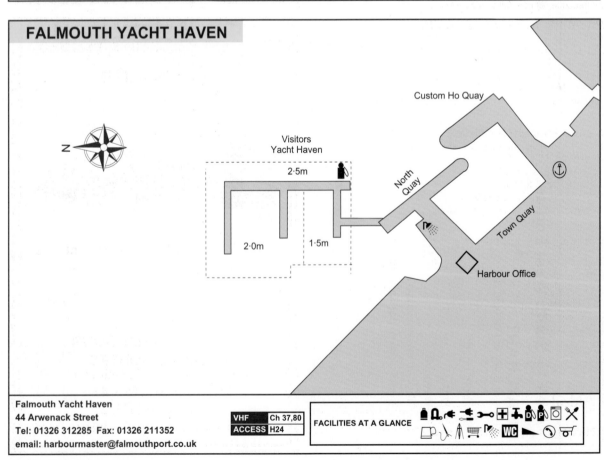

Falmouth Yacht Haven
44 Arwenack Street
Tel: 01326 312285 Fax: 01326 211352
email: harbourmaster@falmouthport.co.uk

VHF	Ch 37,80
ACCESS	H24

FACILITIES AT A GLANCE

ARIES VANE GEAR SPARES
48 Saint Thomas Street, Penryn, Cornwall TR10 8JW
Tel: (01326) 377467
Fax: (01326) 378117
e-mail: enquiries@ariesvane.com
www.ariesvane.com
Spare parts for original Aries gears.

FALMOUTH MARINA
North Parade, Falmouth, Cornwall TR11 2TD
Tel: (01326) 316620
Fax: (01326) 313939
e-mail: falmouth@premiermarinas.com
www.premiermarinas.com
Falmouth is an ideal starting point for a cruise to the Channel Islands, Brittany or the Scilly Isles. The marina offers first class facilities, including fully serviced berths, 24 hour security and an extensive boatyard. You can be guaranteed the professional and friendly service you would expect from any PREMIER MARINA.

MYLOR YACHT HARBOUR LTD
Mylor Yacht Harbour, Falmouth, Cornwall TR11 5UF
Tel: (01326) 372121
Fax: (01326) 372120
e-mail: enquiries@mylor.com
www.mylor.com
picturesque, all tide, full service marina.

PREMIUM LIFERAFT SERVICES
FALMOUTH
Tel: (01326) 374646
Freephone: 0800 243673
e-mail: info@liferafts.com
www.liferafts.com
Hire and sales of DoT and RORC approved liferafts and safety equipment.

SEAFIT MARINE SERVICES
Falmouth Marina, North Parade, Falmouth,
Cornwall TR11 2TD
Tel: (01326) 313713
Fax: (01326) 211521
Mobile: (07971) 196175
All repair and service work undertaken.

PORT PENDENNIS MARINA

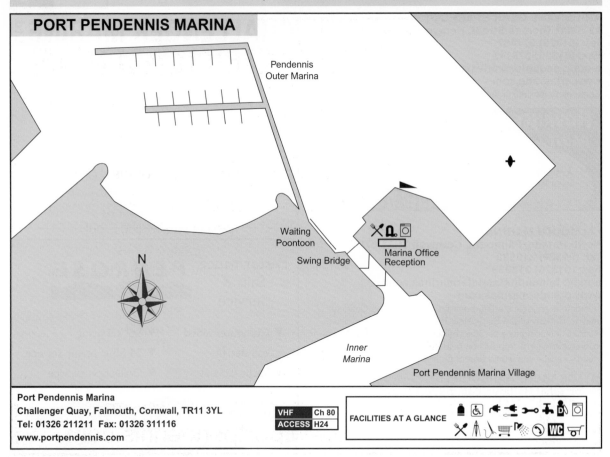

Port Pendennis Marina
Challenger Quay, Falmouth, Cornwall, TR11 3YL
Tel: 01326 211211 Fax: 01326 311116
www.portpendennis.com

VHF	Ch 80
ACCESS	H24

FACILITIES AT A GLANCE

MYLOR YACHT HARBOUR

MYLOR YACHT HARBOUR Key

a Harbour cafe and shops
b Showers/toilets/laundry
c Kingsmoor Cottage
d Club
e Rigging pontoon
f New public slipway
g Fueling pontoon
h Marine services and
   Harbour office
i LPG pontoon
j Water taxi pick up

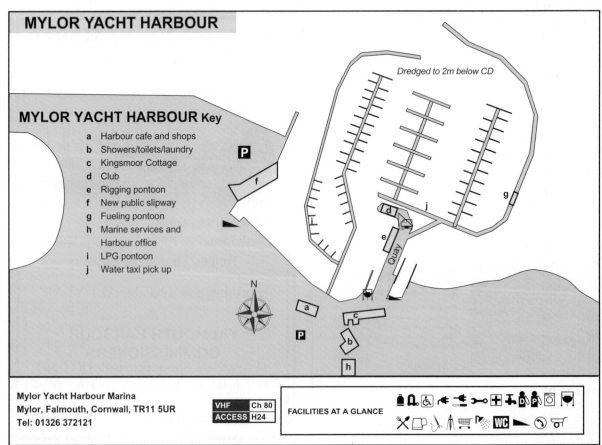

Mylor Yacht Harbour Marina
Mylor, Falmouth, Cornwall, TR11 5UR
Tel: 01326 372121

VHF	Ch 80
ACCESS	H24

FACILITIES AT A GLANCE

MYLOR YACHT HARBOUR LTD
Mylor Yacht Harbour, Falmouth, Cornwall TR11 5UF
Tel: (01326) 372121
Fax: (01326) 372120
e-mail: enquiries@mylor.com
www.mylor.com
picturesque, all tide, full service marina.

e-mail: dartsidequay@mdlmarinas.co.uk
www.marinas.co.uk
9 acre boat storage facility. Mud moorings. Fully serviced with power and water. Chandlery, 65 ton hoist, 16 ton trailer hoist and 25 ton crane. Pressure washing service. Various marine trades.

Brixham Police	0990 777444
Brixham Yacht Supplies Ltd Brixham	01803 882290
Brixham YC Brixham	01803 853332
C Toms and Son Ltd Fowey	01726 870232
Calibra Sails Dartmouth	01803 833094
Challenger Marine Penryn	01326 377222
Charlestown HM	01726 67526
Coverack HM	01326 280545
Creekside Boatyard (Old Mill Creek) Dartmouth	01803 832649
Dart Chandlers Dartmouth	01803 833772
Dart Marina Dartmouth	01803 833351
Darthaven Marina Dartmouth	01803 752242
Dartmouth Police	0990 777444
Dartmouth YC Dartmouth	01803 832305

DARTSIDE QUAY
Galmpton Creek, Galmpton, Brixham,
Devon TQ5 0EH
Tel: (01803) 845445
Fax: (01803) 843558

David Carne (Sales) Ltd Falmouth	01326 318314
David Carne (Sales) Ltd Penryn	01326 374177
Eland Exeter	01392 255788
Exe Leisure Exeter	01392 879055
Exe SC (River Exe) Exemouth	01395 264607
Falmouth Divers Ltd Penryn	01326 374736
Falmouth HM	01326 312285
Falmouth Marina Falmouth	01326 316620
Falmouth Town SC Falmouth	01326 373915
Falmouth Watersports Association Falmouth	01326 211223
Falmouth Yacht Haven Falmouth	01326 312285
Fathom Marine Bridport	01308 420988
Flushing SC Falmouth	01326 374043
Fowey Boatyard Fowey	01726 832194
Fowey Gallants SC Fowey	01726 832335
Fowey HM	01726 832471/2.
Fowey Police	0990 777444
Gweek Quay Boatyard Helston	01326 221657
Harbour Marine Plymouth	01752 204690/1

TORPOINT YACHT HARBOUR

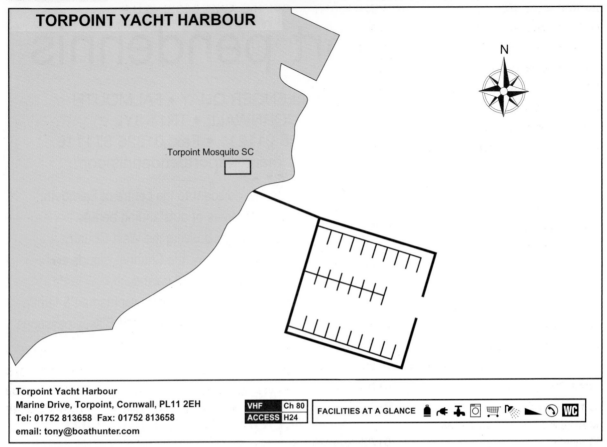

Torpoint Mosquito SC

N

Torpoint Yacht Harbour
Marine Drive, Torpoint, Cornwall, PL11 2EH
Tel: 01752 813658 Fax: 01752 813658
email: tony@boathunter.com

| VHF | Ch 80 |
| ACCESS | H24 |

FACILITIES AT A GLANCE

SOUTHDOWN MARINA

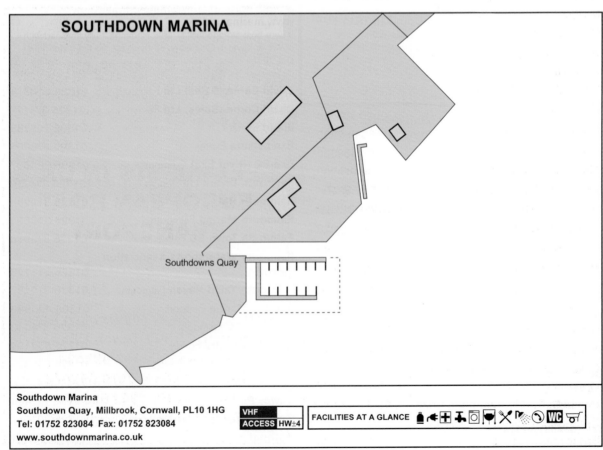

Southdowns Quay

Southdown Marina
Southdown Quay, Millbrook, Cornwall, PL10 1HG
Tel: 01752 823084 Fax: 01752 823084
www.southdownmarina.co.uk

| VHF | |
| ACCESS | HW±4 |

FACILITIES AT A GLANCE

Helford River HM	01326 250749
Helford River SC Helston	01326 231006
Island CC Salcombe	01548 531176
Isles of Scilly Police	01721 422444
Isles of Scilly Steamship Co St Mary's	01720 422710
J Moore & Son St Austell	01726 842964
Jimmy Green Marine Fore St Beer	01297 20744
John Alsop Sailmakers Salcombe	01548 843702
John Bridger Marine Exeter	01392 216420
Keith Buchanan St Mary's	01720 422037
Lincombe Boat Yard Salcombe	01548 843580
Looe Chandlery West Looe	01503 264355
Looe Divers Hannafore	01503 262727
Looe HM	01503 262839
Looe Police	01503 262233
Looe SC Looe	01503 262559
Lyme Regis HM	01297 442137
Lyme Regis Police	01297 442603
Lyme Regis Power BC Lyeme Regis	01297 443788
Lyme Regis SC Lyme Regis	01297 442800
Lympstone SC Exeter	01395 264152
Marine & Leisure Europe Ltd Plymouth	01752 268826
Marine Instruments Falmouth	01326 312414
Mayflower Chandlery Plymouth	01752 500121
Mayflower International Marina Plymouth	01752 556633
Mayflower SC Plymouth	01752 662526
Mevagissey HM	01726 843305
Mevagissey Police	0990 777444
Mill Bay Village Marina Plymouth	01752 226785
Mitchell Sails Fowey	01726 833731
Mojo Maritime Penzance	01736 762771
Mousehole HM	01736 731511
Mullion Cove HM	01326 240222
Mylor Chandlery & Rigging Falmouth	01326 375482
Mylor Yacht Harbour Falmouth	01326 372121
Mylor YC Falmouth	01326 374391
Newlyn HM	01736 362523
Norman Pearn and Co Looe	01503 262244
Noss-on-Dart Marina Dartmouth	01803 834582
Ocean Marine (Mayflower Marina) Plymouth	01752 500121
Ocean Sails Plymouth	01752 563666
Outriggers/Upper Deck Marine Fowey	01726 833233

OWEN CLARKE DESIGNS LLP
Lower Ridge Barns, PO Box 26, Dartmouth,
Devon TQ6 0YG
Tel: (01803) 770495
e-mail: info@owenclarkedesign.com
www.owenclarkedesign.com
Yacht design, naval architects, surveyors.

PADSTOW HARBOUR COMMISSIONERS
Tel: 01841 532239 Fax: 01841 533346
E-mail: padstowharbour@compuserve.com
Services include showers, toilets, diesel, water
and ice, CCTV security.
Inner harbour controlled by tidal gate – open
HW ±2hours – minimum depth 3 metres
Harbour Office, Padstow, Cornwall PL28 8AQ.
Website: www.padstow-harbour.co.uk

Paignton SC Paignton	01803 525817
Par HM	01726 818337
Paul Green Sailmakers Plymouth	01752 660317
Penrose Sailmakers Falmouth	01326 312705
Penzance Dry Dock and Engineering Co Ltd. Penzance	01736 363838
Penzance HM	01736 366113
Penzance Police	01736 362395
Penzance YC Penzance	01736 364989
Peter Dixon Chandlery Exmouth	01395 273248

MAYFLOWER MARINA

MAYFLOWER MARINA Key

a   Marina office, surveyors office

b   Brokerage, charter office, chandlery

c   Cafe

d   Bar

e   Brasserie

f   Berth holders toilets and showers

g   Harbour masters office

h   Riggers shop

i   Engineers shop

j   Picnic/BBQ area

k   Tourist information booth

Mayflower International Marina
Ocean Quay, Richmond Walk, Plymouth, PL1 4LS
Tel: 01752 556633 Fax: 01752 606896
email: mayflower@mayflower.co.uk

VHF	Ch 80
ACCESS	H24

FACILITIES AT A GLANCE

MILL BAY VILLAGE MARINA

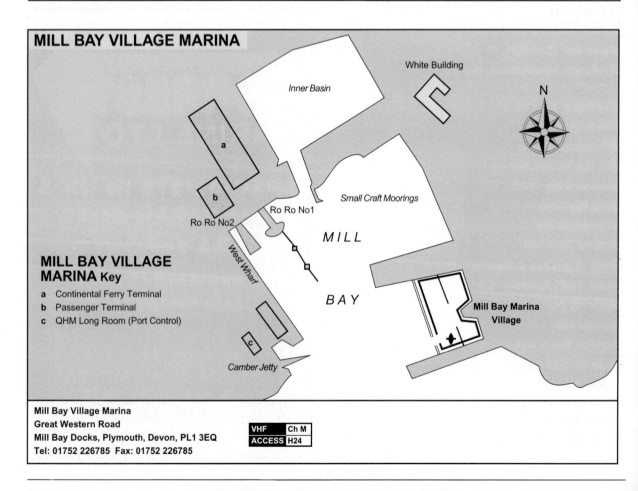

Inner Basin

White Building

N

Small Craft Moorings

Ro Ro No1

Ro Ro No2

West Wharf

M I L L

B A Y

Mill Bay Marina Village

Camber Jetty

MILL BAY VILLAGE MARINA Key

a   Continental Ferry Terminal

b   Passenger Terminal

c   QHM Long Room (Port Control)

Mill Bay Village Marina
Great Western Road
Mill Bay Docks, Plymouth, Devon, PL1 3EQ
Tel: 01752 226785 Fax: 01752 226785

VHF	Ch M
ACCESS	H24

Philip & Son Dartmouth	01803 833351
Plym YC Plymouth	01752 404991
Plymouth Police	01752 701188
Plymouth Yacht Haven Plymouth	01752) 404231
Ponsharden Boatyard Penryn	01326 372215
Port Navas YC Falmouth	01326 340065
Port of Falmouth Sailing Association Falmouth	01326 372927
Port Pendennis Marina Falmouth	01326 211211
Porthleven HM	01326 574207

PREMIUM LIFERAFT SERVICES DARTMOUTH
Tel: (01803) 833094
e-mail: info@liferafts.com
www.liferafts.com
Hire and sales of DoT and RORC approved liferafts and safety equipment.

PREMIUM LIFERAFT SERVICES SALCOMBE
Tel: (01548) 842777
Freephone: 0800 243673
e-mail: info@liferafts.com
www.liferafts.com
Hire and sales of DoT and RORC approved liferafts and safety equipment.

Queen Anne's Battery Marina Plymouth	01752 671142
Rat Island Sailboat Company (Yard) St Mary's	01720 423399

REED'S NAUTICAL
The Barn, Ford Farm, Bradford Leigh, Bradford-on-Avon, Wilts. BA15 2RP
Tel: (01225) 868821
Fax: (01225) 868831
e-mail: sales@abreed.demon.co.uk
www.reedsnautical.com
Specialists in worldwide mail order of nautical books, charts and prints for boating people everywhere - book & chart catalogues available.

Reg Landon Marine Truro	01872 272668
Restronguet SC Falmouth	01326 374536
Retreat Boatyard Ltd Exeter	01392 874270/875934
River Dart HM	01803 832337

QUEEN ANNE'S BATTERY MARINA

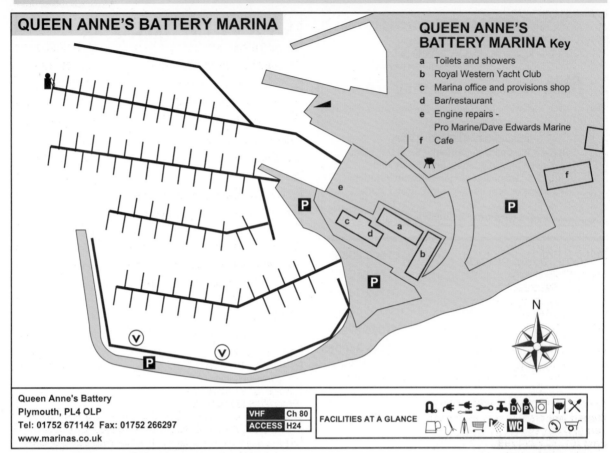

QUEEN ANNE'S BATTERY MARINA Key

a Toilets and showers
b Royal Western Yacht Club
c Marina office and provisions shop
d Bar/restaurant
e Engine repairs -
   Pro Marine/Dave Edwards Marine
f Cafe

Queen Anne's Battery
Plymouth, PL4 OLP
Tel: 01752 671142 Fax: 01752 266297
www.marinas.co.uk

VHF	Ch 80
ACCESS	H24

FACILITIES AT A GLANCE

SUTTON HARBOUR

SUTTON HARBOUR Key

a Fish market
b National Marine Aquarium
c Customs House
d The Cove
e Marina office
f Lock tower

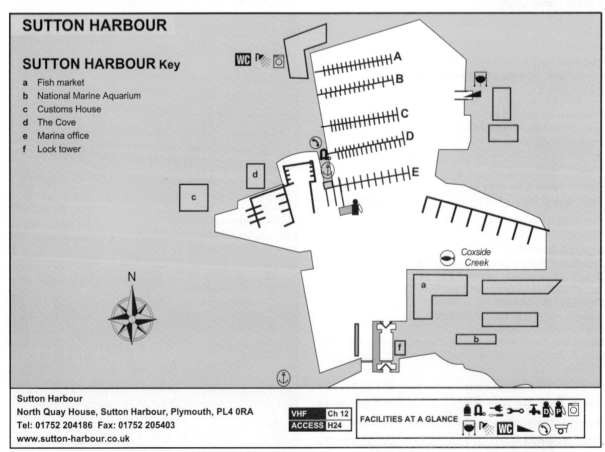

Coxside Creek

Sutton Harbour
North Quay House, Sutton Harbour, Plymouth, PL4 0RA
Tel: 01752 204186 Fax: 01752 205403
www.sutton-harbour.co.uk

VHF	Ch 12
ACCESS	H24

FACILITIES AT A GLANCE

EUROSPARS LTD
Queen Anne Works, Queen Anne's Battery, Plymouth PL4 0LT
Tel: (01752) 550550
Fax: (01752) 565005
e-mail: espars@aol.com
www.eurospars.com
Yacht mast manufacturer & rigging specialist.

PLYMOUTH SAILING SCHOOL
Queen Anne's Battery, Plymouth PL4 0LP
Tel: (01752) 667170
Fax: (01752) 257162
e-mail: school@plymsail.co.uk
www.plymsail.co.uk
One of the oldest established sailing schools in the country. Shorebased navigation, practical sailing, power cruising and power boating courses all the year round from a sheltered base in Plymouth Sound.

QUEEN ANNE'S BATTERY
Plymouth, Devon PL4 0LP
Tel: (01752) 671142
Fax: (01752) 266297
e-mail: qab@mdlmarinas.co.uk
www.marinas.co.uk
260 berth marina with fully serviced pontoons for boats up to 19 metres. 24 hour security. Shower, toilet and laundry facilities. On site restaurant and bar, café and cycle hire. Chandlery, petrol and diesel fuel. Boat lifting and hard standing area. 25 ton boat hoist and boat repairs. Yacht club, yacht brokerage and new boat sales.

ROYAL WESTERN YACHT CLUB
Queen Anne's Battery, Plymouth, Devon PL4 0TW.
Tel: (01752) 660077
Fax: (01752) 224299
e-mail: admin@rwyc.org
www.rwyc.org
Home of shorthanded sailing. Visiting yachtsmen welcome. Mooring facilities available.

SUTTON HARBOUR MARINA
North Quay House, Sutton Harbour, Plymouth PL4 0RA
Tel: (01752) 204186
Fax: (01752) 205403
Our historic harbour is a firm favourite with today's yachtsmen. Our friendly staff pride themselves on giving our visitors a warm welcome and offer excellent facilities including chandlery, boat repairs, fuel, servicing and car parking.

River Exe Dockmaster	01392 274306
River Yealm HM	01752 872533
River Yealm Police	0990 777444
RNSA (Plymouth) Plymouth	01752 55123/83
Rob Perry Marine Axminster	01297 631314
Royal Dart YC Dartmouth	01803 752496
Royal Cornwall YC (RCYC) Falmouth	01326 312126
Royal Fowey YC Fowey	01726 833573

Royal Plymouth Corinthian YC Plymouth	01752 664327
Royal Torbay YC Torquay	01803 292006
Royal Western YC Plymouth	01752 660077
Sails & Canvas Exeter	01392 877527
Salcombe Boatstore Salcombe	01548 843708
Salcombe HM	01548 843791
Salcombe Police	01548 842107
Salcombe YC Salcombe	01548 842593
Saltash SC Saltash	01752 845988
Scillonian Sailing and BC St Mary's	01720 277229
Sea Chest Nautical Bookshop Plymouth	01752 222012
Shipmates Chandlery Dartmouth	01803 839292
Shipmates Chandlery Salcombe	01548 844555
South Devon Sailing School Newton Abbot	01626 52352
South West Sails Penryn	01326 375291
Southdown Marina Millbrook	01752 823084

SP SYSTEMS
St. Cross Business Park, Newport, Isle of Wight PO30 5WU
Tel: (01983) 828000
Fax: (01983) 828100
Epoxy resins for laminating, bonding, coating and filling. Usable with wood, GRP, ferrocement, GRP/FRP materials including glass, carbon and Kevlar fibres. Structural engineering of GRP and composite materials. Technical advice service.

St Mary's HM	01720 422768
St Mawes SC St Mawes	01326 270686
Starcross Fishing & CC (River Exe) Starcross	01626 891996

PLYMOUTH YACHT HAVEN

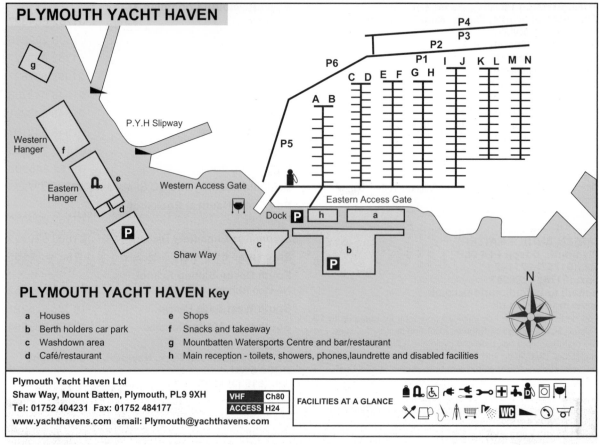

PLYMOUTH YACHT HAVEN Key

a Houses	**e** Shops
b Berth holders car park	**f** Snacks and takeaway
c Washdown area	**g** Mountbatten Watersports Centre and bar/restaurant
d Café/restaurant	**h** Main reception - toilets, showers, phones, laundrette and disabled facilities

Plymouth Yacht Haven Ltd
Shaw Way, Mount Batten, Plymouth, PL9 9XH
Tel: 01752 404231 Fax: 01752 484177
www.yachthavens.com email: Plymouth@yachthavens.com

VHF	Ch80
ACCESS	H24

FACILITIES AT A GLANCE

NOSS-ON-DART MARINA

NOSS-ON-DART Key

a Marina office
b Amenities

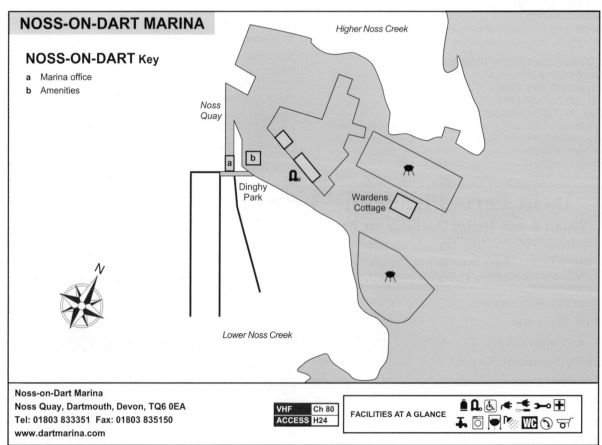

Noss-on-Dart Marina
Noss Quay, Dartmouth, Devon, TQ6 0EA
Tel: 01803 833351 Fax: 01803 835150
www.dartmarina.com

VHF	Ch 80
ACCESS	H24

FACILITIES AT A GLANCE

DART MARINA

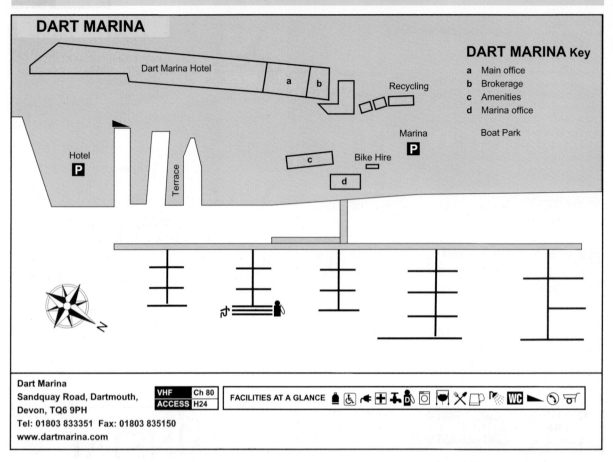

DART MARINA Key

- **a** Main office
- **b** Brokerage
- **c** Amenities
- **d** Marina office

Boat Park

Dart Marina
Sandquay Road, Dartmouth,
Devon, TQ6 9PH
Tel: 01803 833351 Fax: 01803 835150
www.dartmarina.com

VHF	Ch 80
ACCESS	H24

FACILITIES AT A GLANCE

DARTHAVEN MARINA

DARTHAVEN MARINA Key

- **a** Main office
  Chandlery
  Electricians
- **b** Shipwrights
- **c** Engineers
- **d** Passenger ferry pontoon
- **e** Berthing office

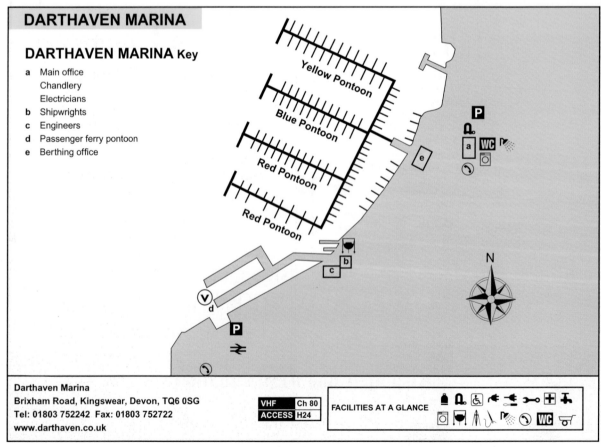

Darthaven Marina
Brixham Road, Kingswear, Devon, TQ6 0SG
Tel: 01803 752242 Fax: 01803 752722
www.darthaven.co.uk

VHF	Ch 80
ACCESS	H24

FACILITIES AT A GLANCE

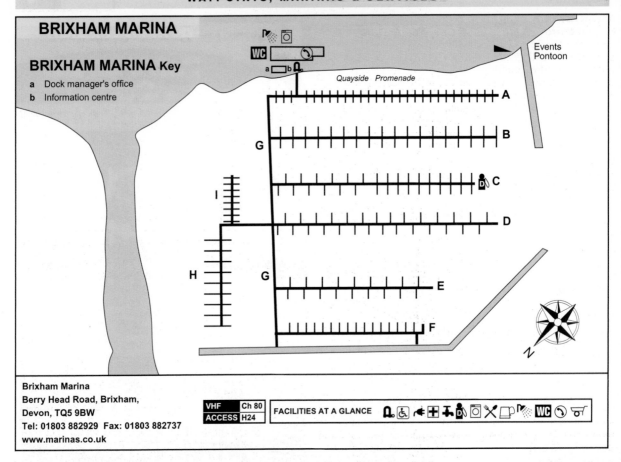

BRIXHAM MARINA

BRIXHAM MARINA Key

a Dock manager's office
b Information centre

Brixham Marina
Berry Head Road, Brixham,
Devon, TQ5 9BW
Tel: 01803 882929 Fax: 01803 882737
www.marinas.co.uk

VHF	Ch 80
ACCESS	H24

FACILITIES AT A GLANCE

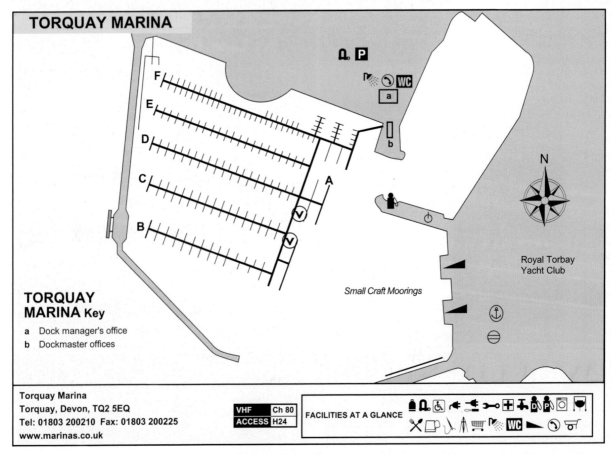

TORQUAY MARINA

TORQUAY MARINA Key

a Dock manager's office
b Dockmaster offices

Torquay Marina
Torquay, Devon, TQ2 5EQ
Tel: 01803 200210 Fax: 01803 200225
www.marinas.co.uk

VHF	Ch 80
ACCESS	H24

FACILITIES AT A GLANCE

ATLANTIC SPARS LTD

Hatton House, Bridge Road, Churston Ferrers,
Brixham, Devon TQ5 0JL
Tel: (01803) 843322
Fax: (01803) 845550
e-mail: atlantic@spars.co.uk
www.spars.co.uk

Regional centre for SELDEN integrated sailing systems. Services include standing and running rigging, repairs, custom spars and furling systems. Aluminium design and fabrications for industry. Official suppliers to the BT Global Challenge.

BRIXHAM MARINA

Berry Head Road, Brixham, Devon TQ5 9BW
Tel: (01803) 882929
Fax: (01803) 882737
e-mail: brixham@mdlmarinas.co.uk
www.marinas.co.uk

480 berth marina with fully serviced pontoons and a special events pontoon. Berths for boats up to 18 metres. Larger vessels by arrangement. 24 hour security. Shower, toilet and laundry facilities. Bar, restaurant and provisions shop. Chandlery, car park and diesel fuel. Yacht and power boat brokerage. Sea school and yacht charter.

DARTSIDE QUAY

Galmpton Creek, Galmpton, Brixham, Devon TQ5 0EH
Tel: (01803) 845445
Fax: (01803) 843558
e-mail: dartsidequay@mdlmarinas.co.uk
www.marinas.co.uk

9 acre boat storage facility. Mud moorings. Fully serviced with power and water. Chandlery, 65 ton hoist, 16 ton trailer hoist and 25 ton crane. Pressure washing service. Various marine trades.

Starcross YC Exeter	01626 890470
Sutton Harbour Plymouth	01752 204186
Tamar River SC Plymouth	01752 362741
Teign Corinthian YC Teignmouth	01626 772734
Teign Diving Centre Teignmouth	01626 773965
Teignmouth HM	01626 773165
Teignmouth Police	01626 772433
The Foc'sle Exeter	01392 874105
Topsham SC Topsham	01392 877524
Torbay Boating Centre Paignton	01803 558760
Torpoint Mosquito SC - Plymouth Plymouth	01752 812508
Torpoint Yacht Harbour Plymouth	01752 813658
Torquay Chandlers Torquay	01803 211854
Torquay HM	01803 292429
Torquay Marina Torquay	01803 200210
Torquay Police	0990 777444
Trouts Boatyard (River Exe) Topsham	01392 873044
UK Customs Nationwide	0845 0109000
Upper Deck Marine and Outriggers Fowey	01726 832287
W Trout and Son Topsham	01392 873044/875176
Weir Quay Boatyard Bere Alston	01822 840474

Yacht Parts (Plymouth) Plymouth	01752 252489
Yealm YC Newton Ferrers	01752 8722

Planning a trip?

Make it plain sailing
– for your free copy
of the *2002 Marine Weather Services* booklet
call the Met Office Customer Centre
on **0845 300 0300** or go to
www.metoffice.com/leisuremarine/mwsbooklet.html

For a five-day inshore forecast
for Selsey Bill – Lyme Regis,
dial **09060 100 457*** from your fax machine.

*09060 calls are charged at £1 per minute at all times.

Key to Marina Plans symbols

	Calor Gas	P	Parking
	Chandler	✕	Pub/Restaurant
	Disabled facilities		Pump out
	Electrical supply		Rigging service
	Electrical repairs		Sail repairs
	Engine repairs		Shipwright
+	First Aid		Shop/Supermarket
	Fresh Water		Showers
	Fuel - Diesel		Slipway
	Fuel - Petrol	WC	Toilets
	Hardstanding/boatyard		Telephone
	Laundry facilities		Trolleys
	Lift-out facilities	V	Visitors berths

Area 2 - Central Southern England

MARINAS
Telephone Numbers
VHF Channel
Access Times

Port Hamble Marina
023 8045 2741
Ch 80 H24
Hamble Point Marina
023 8045 2464
Ch 80 H24

Emsworth Yacht
Harbour
01243 377727
Ch 80 HW±2

Shamrock Quay
023 8022 9461
Ch 80 H24
Saxon Wharf Marina
023 8033 9490
Ch 80 H24

Northney Marina
023 9246 6321
Ch 80 H24

Town Quay Marina
023 8023 4397
Ch 10 H24

Ocean Village Marina
023 8022 9385
Ch 80 H24

Kemp's Marina
023 8063 2323
Ch M HW±3½

Southampton

Mercury Yt Hbr
023 8045 5994
Ch 80 H24

Gosport Marina
023 9252 4811
Ch 80 H24

Thornham
Marina
01243 375335
HW±3

Sunseeker Marina
01202 381111
Ch 80 H24

Poole Quay -
Dolphin Boat Haven
01202 649488
Ch 80 H24

Hythe 023 8020 7073 **Ch 80** H24

*Hamble
River*

Port Solent Marina
023 9221 0765
Ch 80 H24

Chichester
Marina
01243 512731
Ch M
HW±4

Buckler's Hard
01590 616200
Ch 80 HW H24

Swanwick Mna
01489 885000
Ch 80 H24

Cobbs Quay
Marina
01202 674299
Ch 80 HW±5

Parkstone Haven
01202 743610
Ch M H24

Lymington Yt Haven
01590 677071
Ch 80 H24
Lymington Marina
01590 673312
Ch 80 H24

Beaulieu

Portsmouth
Hbr

Langstone
Hbr

Chichester
Hbr

Salterns Marina
01202 709971
Ch 37, 80 H24

Christchurch

Lymington

Haslar Marina
023 9260 1201
Ch 80 H24

Southsea Marina
023 9282 2719
Ch 80 HW±3

Poole Harbour

Cowes

*Newtown
Creek*

*Wootton
Creek*

Bembridge

Birdham Pool
01243 512310
HW±3

Ridge Wharf
01929 552650
HW±2

Weymouth

Yarmouth

Nab Tower

Sparkes Yacht
Harbour
023 9246 3572
Ch 80 H24

Yarmouth Harbour
01983 760321
Ch 68 H24

Isle of Wight

Ryde Leisure Hbr
01983 613879
Ch 80 HW±2

St Catherines Pt

N

Shepards Wharf Mna 01983 297821 **Ch 80 H24**
E Cowes Marina 01983 293983 **Ch 80** H24
Cowes Yt Hvn 01983 299975 **Ch 80** H24

Bembridge Marina
01983 872828
Ch 80

Weymouth Marina
01305 767576
Ch 80 H24
Weymouth Harbour
01305 206423

Island Hbr Marina
01983 822999
Ch 80 HW±4

Waypoint Guide Area 2 – Central Southern England - Portland Bill to Selsey Bill

1	**Nab Tower** - 0·5M NW of	50°40'·38N	00°57'·55W
2	**West Pole Bn** - 0·3M S of	50°45'·38N	00°56'·37W
3	**Langstone Fairway Buoy** - 0·5M S of	50°45'·78N	01°01'·27W
4	**Main Passage** - Dolphin gap off Southsea	50°45'·98N	01°04'·02W
5	**Horse Sand Buoy** - Portsmouth ch	50°45'·49N	01°05'·18W
6	**Forts** - midway between the two	50°44'·70N	01°05'·00W
7	**Gilkicker Point** - 0·3M S of	50°46'·00N	01°08'·40W
8	**Bembridge Tide Gauge**	50°42'·43N	01°04'·93W
9	**Bembridge Ledge Buoy**	50°41'·12N	01°02'·72W
10	**West Princessa Buoy** - S of Bembridge	50°40'·12N	01°03'·58W
11	**Dunnose Head** - 1M off	50°35'·00N	01°10'·00W
12	**St Catherine's Point** - 1M S of	50°33'·52N	01°17'·80W
13	**Wootton Beacon**	50°44'·51N	01°12'·05W
14	**Peel Bank Buoy** - east Solent	50°45'·58N	01°13'·25W
15	**Old Castle Point** - 0·3M N of	50°46'·30N	01°16'·50W
16	**Cowes entrance**	50°46'·20N	01°17'·85W
17	**Egypt Point** - 0·4M N of	50°46'·20N	01°18'·70W
18	**Hamble Point Buoy**	50°50'·12N	01°18'·58W
19	**Beaulieu Spit Beacon** - 0·3M off	50°46'·83N	01°21'·50W
20	**Newtown** - 0·5M NW of ent	50°43'·87N	01°25'·20W
21	**Yarmouth ent** - 0·4M N of	50°42'·80N	01°30'·00W
22	**Lymington, Jack in the basket** - seaward mark	50°44'·24N	01°30'·48W
23	**Hurst Narrows** - midway	50°42'·20N	01°32'·40W
24	**Keyhaven** - 0·2M E of entrance	50°42'·80N	01°32'·80W
25	**Fairway Buoy** - Needles channel	50°38'·20N	01°38'·90W
26	**Christchurch** - 0·3M E of ent	50°43'·44N	01°43'·80W
27	**Poole No 1 Buoy** - 1M E of	50°38'·32N	01°53'·57W
28	**Swanage** - 0·7M NE of pier	50°37'·00N	01°56'·00W
29	**Anvil Point** - 1·5M SE of	50°34'·30N	01°56'·00W
30	**St Albans Head** - 1·5M S of	50°33'·20N	02°03'·30W
31	**East Shambles** - 1M SE of	50°30'·00N	02°18'·90W
32	**Lulworth Cove** - 0·1M S of ent	50°36'·87N	02°14'·80W
33	**Weymouth** - 1M E of ent	50°36'·60N	02°25'·00W
34	**Portland Bill** - 5M S of	50°25'·82N	02°27'·30W
35	**Alderney - Bray Harbour** - 1M NNE of	49°45'·00N	02°10'·75W
37	**Casquets** - 1M W of	49°43'·38N	02°24'·06W
93	**Cap de La Hague** - 2M W of	49°43'·37N	02°00'·00W
	Cherbourg - 0·5M N of W ent	49°40'·95N	01°39'·35W
103	**Start Point** - 2M S of	50°11'·30N	03°38'·47W
	Le Havre - 0·5M NE of Le Havre LHA	49°32'·00N	00°09'·20W
	St-Vaast-la-Hougue - 3·0 M ENE of entrance	49°36'·40N	01°11'·00W

Distance Table - Central Southern England

Approximate distances in nautical miles are by the most direct route while avoiding dangers and allowing for Traffic Separation Schemes

		1	2	3	4	5	6	7	8	9	10	11	12	13	14	15	16	17	18	19	20
1.	Exmouth	**1**																			
2.	Lyme Regis	21	**2**																		
3.	Portland Bill	36	22	**3**																	
4.	Weymouth	46	32	8	**4**																
5.	Swanage	58	44	22	22	**5**															
6.	Poole Hbr ent	65	51	28	26	6	**6**														
7.	Needles Lt Ho	73	58	35	34	14	14	**7**													
8.	Lymington	79	64	42	40	20	24	6	**8**												
9.	Yarmouth (IOW)	77	63	40	39	18	22	4	2	**9**											
10.	Beaulieu R. ent	84	69	46	45	25	29	11	7	7	**10**										
11.	Cowes	86	71	49	46	28	27	14	10	9	2	**11**									
12.	Southampton	93	78	55	54	34	34	20	16	16	9	9	**12**								
13.	R. Hamble (ent)	90	75	53	51	32	34	18	12	13	6	6	5	**13**							
14.	Portsmouth	96	81	58	57	37	35	23	19	19	12	10	18	13	**14**						
15.	Langstone Hbr	98	84	61	59	39	39	25	21	21	14	12	21	18	5	**15**					
16.	Chichester Bar	101	86	63	62	42	42	28	23	24	17	15	23	18	8	5	**16**				
17.	Bembridge	97	81	59	58	38	39	24	18	19	13	10	18	15	5	6	8	**17**			
18.	Nab Tower	102	86	64	63	43	44	29	23	24	18	15	24	19	10	7	6	6	**18**		
19.	St Catherine's Pt	82	68	45	44	25	25	12	19	21	27	15	36	29	20	20	19	17	15	**19**	
20.	Littlehampton	117	102	79	79	60	61	46	44	45	38	36	45	42	31	28	25	28	22	35	**20**

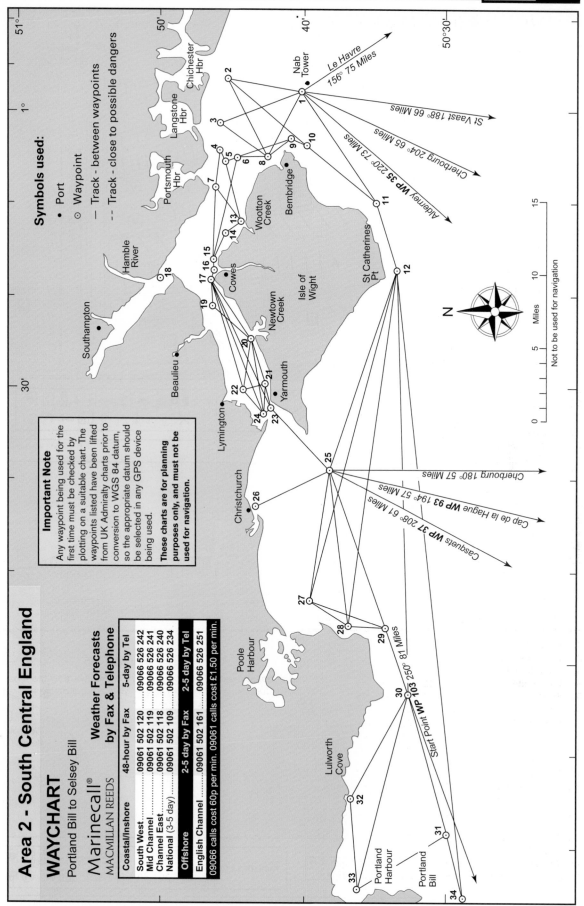

Area 2 - South Central England

WAYCHART
Portland Bill to Selsey Bill

Marinecall®
MACMILLAN REEDS

Weather Forecasts
by Fax & Telephone

Coastal/Inshore	48-hour by Fax	5-day by Fax
South West..................	09061 502 120	09066 526 242
Mid Channel...............	09061 502 119	09066 526 241
Channel East.............	09061 502 118	09066 526 240
National (3-5 day).......	09061 502 109	09066 526 234

Offshore	2-5 day by Fax	2-5 day by Tel
English Channel........	09061 502 161	09066 526 251

09066 calls cost 60p per min. 09061 calls cost £1.50 per min.

Important Note

Any waypoint being used for the first time must be checked by plotting on a suitable chart. The waypoints listed have been lifted from UK Admiralty charts prior to conversion to WGS 84 datum, so the appropriate datum should be selected in any GPS device being used.

These charts are for planning purposes only, and must not be used for navigation.

Symbols used:

- ● Port
- ⊙ Waypoint
- — Track - between waypoints
- -- Track - close to possible dangers

Le Havre 156° 75 Miles

St Vaast 188° 66 Miles

Cherbourg 204° 65 Miles

Alderney WP 35 220° 73 Miles

Cherbourg 180° 57 Miles

Cap de la Hague WP 93 194° 57 Miles

Casquets WP 37 208° 61 Miles

Start Point WP 103 250° 81 Miles

Nab Tower

Chichester Hbr

Langstone Hbr

Portsmouth Hbr

Hamble River

Southampton

Beaulieu

Wootton Creek

Bembridge

St Catherines Pt

Isle of Wight

Newtown Creek

Cowes

Yarmouth

Lymington

Christchurch

Poole Harbour

Lulworth Cove

Portland Harbour

Portland Bill

N

Miles

Not to be used for navigation

WEYMOUTH MARINA

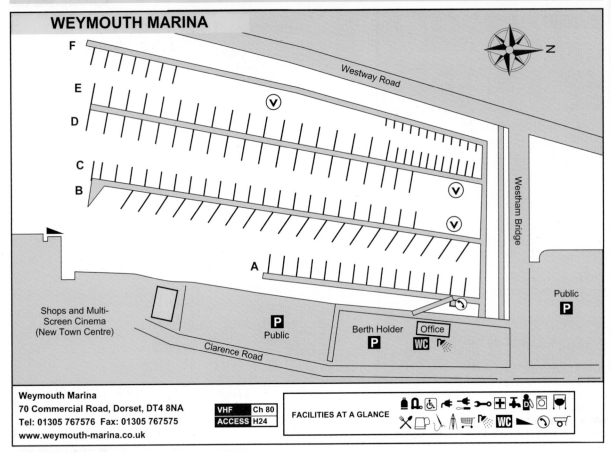

Weymouth Marina
70 Commercial Road, Dorset, DT4 8NA
Tel: 01305 767576 Fax: 01305 767575
www.weymouth-marina.co.uk

VHF	Ch 80
ACCESS	H24

FACILITIES AT A GLANCE

WEYMOUTH HARBOUR

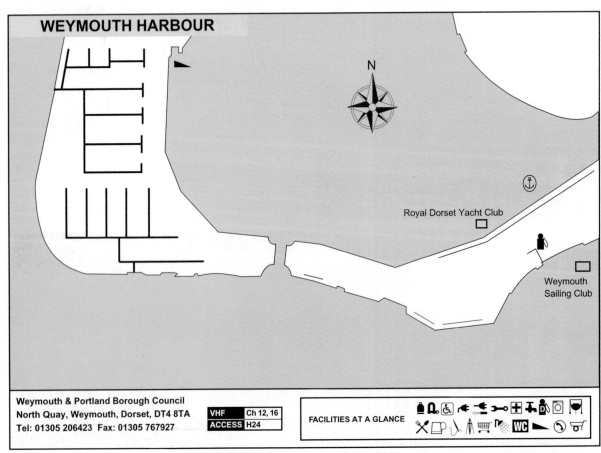

Weymouth & Portland Borough Council
North Quay, Weymouth, Dorset, DT4 8TA
Tel: 01305 206423 Fax: 01305 767927

VHF	Ch 12, 16
ACCESS	H24

FACILITIES AT A GLANCE

**DEAN & REDDYHOFF LTD
- WEYMOUTH MARINA**
**70 Commercial Rd,
Weymouth,
Dorset DT4 8NA
Tel: (01305) 767576
Fax: (01305) 767575
e-mail:
sales@weymouth-marina.co.uk
www.weymouth-marina.co.uk**
Located in the centre of town only minutes from local pubs & restaurants, the marina has proven a great success with berth holders and visitors alike. Weymouth's recent regeneration programme has been a complete success, making Weymouth a must visit port, whilst cruising the South Coast.

**PREMIUM LIFERAFT SERVICES
WEYMOUTH
Tel: (01305) 821040
Freephone: 0800 243673
e-mail:
info@liferafts.com
www.liferafts.com**
Hire and sales of DoT and RORC approved liferafts and safety equipment.

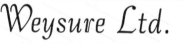

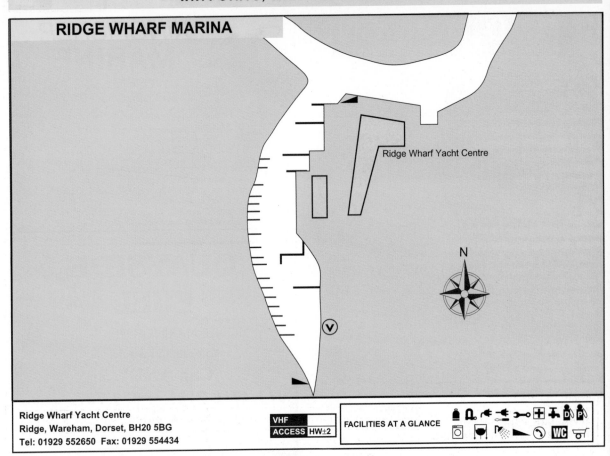

RIDGE WHARF MARINA

Ridge Wharf Yacht Centre

Ridge Wharf Yacht Centre
Ridge, Wareham, Dorset, BH20 5BG
Tel: 01929 552650 Fax: 01929 554434

VHF
ACCESS HW±2

FACILITIES AT A GLANCE

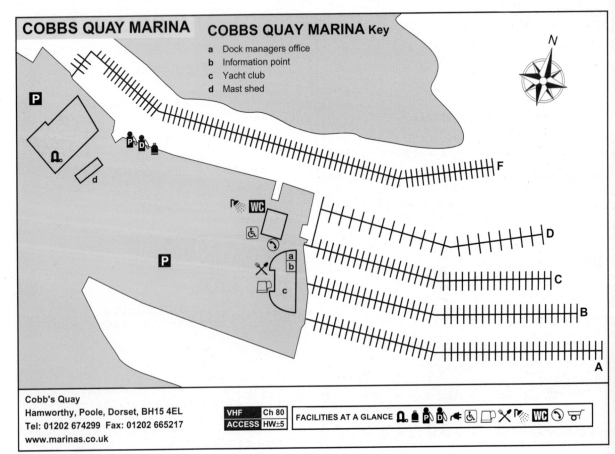

COBBS QUAY MARINA

COBBS QUAY MARINA Key

a   Dock managers office
b   Information point
c   Yacht club
d   Mast shed

Cobb's Quay
Hamworthy, Poole, Dorset, BH15 4EL
Tel: 01202 674299 Fax: 01202 665217
www.marinas.co.uk

VHF   Ch 80
ACCESS HW±5

FACILITIES AT A GLANCE

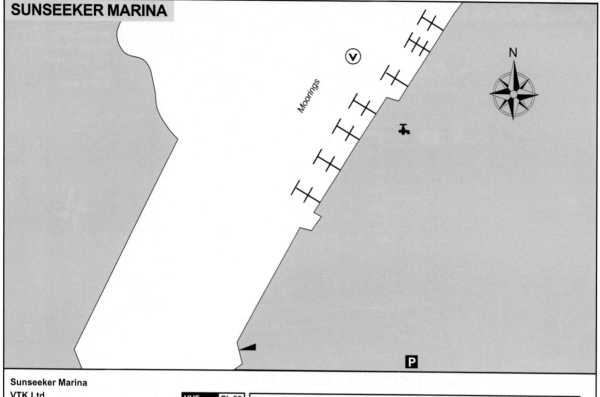

SUNSEEKER MARINA

Moorings

N

Sunseeker Marina
VTK Ltd
27 West Quay, Poole, BH15 1HX
Tel: 01202 381111 Fax: 01202 382222

VHF	Ch 80
ACCESS	H24

FACILITIES AT A GLANCE

COBB'S QUAY MARINA
Hamworthy, Poole, Dorset BH15 4EL
Tel: (01202) 674299
Fax: (01202) 665217
e-mail: cobbsquay@mdlmarinas.co.uk
www.marinas.co.uk

850 berth marina with fully serviced pontoons for boats up to 25 metres. 24 hour security. Shower, toilet and laundry facilities. Yacht club and restaurant. Chandlery, car park and fuel. Boat lifting and hard standing area for maintenance and storage ashore. Slipping & boat repairs. Dry stack facility and under cover storage. Brokerage and new boat sales.

AA Coombes Bembridge — 01983 872296

Acamar Marine Services/Sirius Yacht Training
Christchurch — 01202 488030

Aladdin's Cave Chandlery Ltd (Port Hamble)
Southampton — 023 80454858

Aladdins Cave Chandlery Ltd (Deacons)
Bursledon — 023 8040 2182

Aladdin's Cave Chandlery Ltd (Hamble Point)
Southampton — 023 80455058

Aladdins Cave Chandlery Ltd (Mercury)
Southampton — 023 80454849

Aladdins Cave Chandlery Ltd (Swanwick)
Swanwick — 01489 575828

Aladdin's Cave Camper Nicholsons
Gosport — 023 80402182

Andark Diving Southampton — 01489 581755

Arun Sails Chichester — 01243 573185

AQUA TOGS/SHIPMATES GROUP
115 High Street, Cowes, Isle of Wight PO31 7AX
Tel: (01983) 295071
Fax: (01983) 290169
e-mail: sales@chandlery.co.uk
www.chandlery.co.uk

Leading suppliers of brand name technical marine clothing, leisurewear, safety kit and footwear, specialist chandleries in Cowes and Dartmouth, book and chart agents, mail order available. Branches in Cowes, Lymington, Dartmouth, Salcombe, Seaview and Ryde.

POOLE DOLPHIN BOAT HAVEN

POOLE DOLPHIN BOAT HAVEN Key

a Berthing office
b Showers/Toilets
c The Quay Hotel
d Fish
landing area

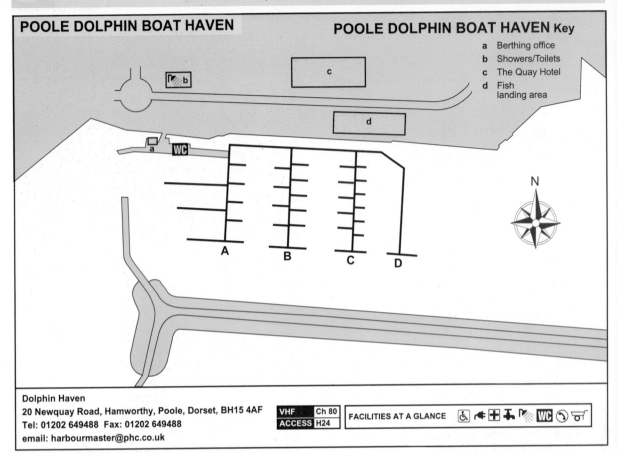

Dolphin Haven
20 Newquay Road, Hamworthy, Poole, Dorset, BH15 4AF
Tel: 01202 649488 Fax: 01202 649488
email: harbourmaster@phc.co.uk

VHF	Ch 80
ACCESS	H24

FACILITIES AT A GLANCE

PARKSTONE HAVEN

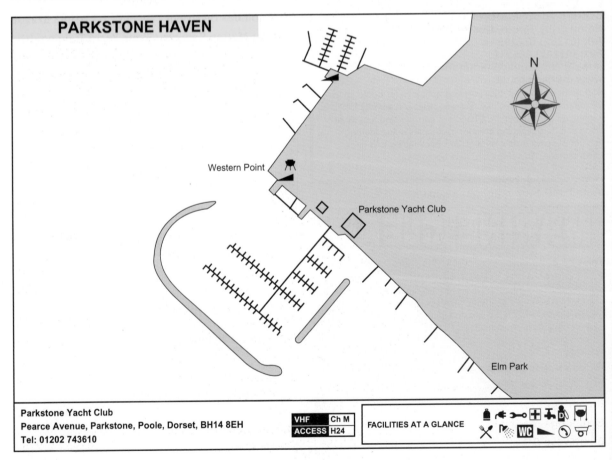

Parkstone Yacht Club
Pearce Avenue, Parkstone, Poole, Dorset, BH14 8EH
Tel: 01202 743610

VHF	Ch M
ACCESS	H24

FACILITIES AT A GLANCE

ATKIN & ASSOCIATES
2 Pippin Close, Lymington, Hampshire UK
SO41 3TP
Tel: (01590) 688633
Fax: (01590) 677793
e-mail: mike.atkin@ukonline.co.uk
Sailing & motor yacht surveyors.

B P S C MARINE SERVICES
Unit 4 Part Business Centre, 1 Park Road,
Freemantle, Southampton, Hampshire SO15 3US
Tel: 023 8023 0045
BPSC offer a fast efficient repair service on a wide range of nautical and survey instruments. Free estimates and advice. A comprehensive range of spares are carried, most of which can be despatched same day. Instruments commissioned. Compass adjusting service.

Beaulieu River HM	01590 616200
Beaulieu River Police	023 80335444
Beaulieu River SC Brockenhurst	01590 616273
Bembridge HM	01983 872828
Bembridge Marina Bembridge	01983 872828
Bembridge SC Isle of Wight	01983 872686

Berthon Boat Co Lymington	01590 673312
Birdham Shipyard Ltd Birdham	01243 512310
Birdham Shipyard Chichester	01243 512310
Bluecastle Chandlers Portland	01305 822298
Bosham SC Chichester	01243 572341
Brading Haven YC Isle of Wight	01983 872289
Bruce Bank Sails Southampton	01489 582444
Bucklers Hard Boat Builders Ltd Brockenhurst	01590 616214
Bucklers Hard Marina Brockenhurst	01590 616200
C Lallow Isle of Wight	01983 292112
C Q Chandlers Ltd Poole	01202 682095
Camber Berthing Offices - Portsmouth	023 92297395
Castle Cove SC Weymouth	01305 783708
Chichester Cruiser and Racing Club	01483 770391
Chichester Harbour HM	01243 512301
Chichester Marina Chichester	01243 512731
Chichester YC Chichester	01243 512918
Chris Hornsey (Chandlery) Ltd Southsea	02392 734728
Christchurch Boat Shop Christchurch	01202 482751

SALTERNS MARINA

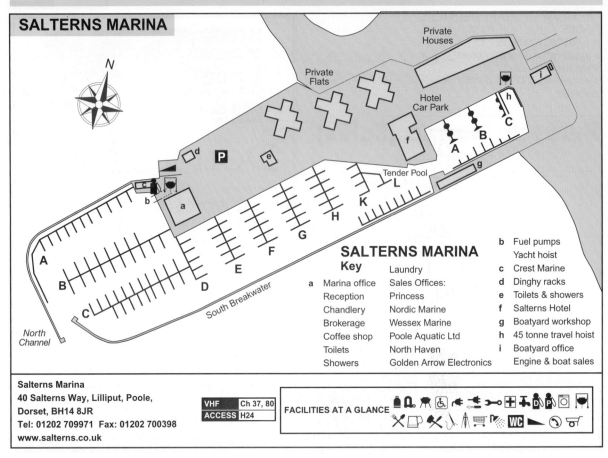

SALTERNS MARINA
Key

a Marina office
  Reception
  Chandlery
  Brokerage
  Coffee shop
  Toilets
  Showers
  Laundry
  Sales Offices:
  Princess
  Nordic Marine
  Wessex Marine
  Poole Aquatic Ltd
  North Haven
  Golden Arrow Electronics

b Fuel pumps
  Yacht hoist
c Crest Marine
d Dinghy racks
e Toilets & showers
f Salterns Hotel
g Boatyard workshop
h 45 tonne travel hoist
i Boatyard office
  Engine & boat sales

Salterns Marina
40 Salterns Way, Lilliput, Poole,
Dorset, BH14 8JR
Tel: 01202 709971 Fax: 01202 700398
www.salterns.co.uk

VHF	Ch 37, 80
ACCESS	H24

FACILITIES AT A GLANCE

YARMOUTH HARBOUR

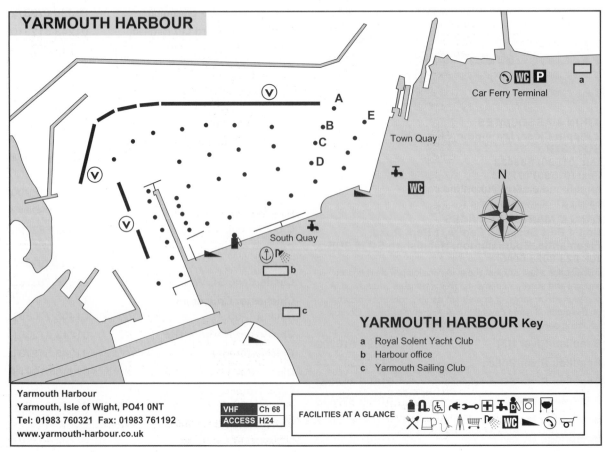

YARMOUTH HARBOUR Key

a Royal Solent Yacht Club
b Harbour office
c Yarmouth Sailing Club

Yarmouth Harbour
Yarmouth, Isle of Wight, PO41 0NT
Tel: 01983 760321 Fax: 01983 761192
www.yarmouth-harbour.co.uk

VHF	Ch 68
ACCESS	H24

FACILITIES AT A GLANCE

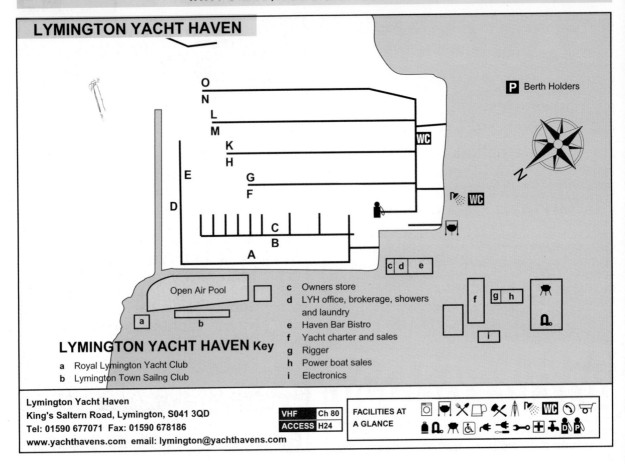

LYMINGTON YACHT HAVEN

P Berth Holders

LYMINGTON YACHT HAVEN Key

a Royal Lymington Yacht Club
b Lymington Town Sailng Club

c Owners store
d LYH office, brokerage, showers and laundry
e Haven Bar Bistro
f Yacht charter and sales
g Rigger
h Power boat sales
i Electronics

Lymington Yacht Haven
King's Saltern Road, Lymington, SO41 3QD
Tel: 01590 677071 Fax: 01590 678186
www.yachthavens.com email: lymington@yachthavens.com

VHF	Ch 80
ACCESS	H24

FACILITIES AT A GLANCE

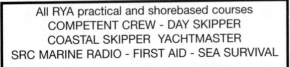

LYMINGTON CRUISING SCHOOL
24 Waterloo Road, Lymington, Hampshire
SO41 9DB
Tel: (01590) 677478
Fax: (01590) 689210
e-mail: lymingtoncruisin@aol.com
www.lymingtoncruising.co.uk
All RYA practical and shorebased courses including:
Yachtmaster preparation, Coastal Skipper, Day Skipper,
Competant Crew, SRC and First Aid. Relaxed, friendly, caring
service. Courses structured to suit the individuals needs.
Adventure and fun but safety paramount.

MARINE GLEAM
14 Fromond Close, Lymington, Hants SO41 9LQ
Tel: 0800 074 4672
e-mail: enquiries@marinegleam.biz
www.marinegleam.biz
A full cleaning programme to meet your specific requirements
from a one off, or a regular clean to a full exterior polish, teak,
canopy and covers, anti-fouling, full interior, engine & bilges
cleaned.

NICK COX YACHT CHARTER LTD
Kings Saltern Road, Lymington, Hampshire
SO41 3QD
Tel: (01590) 673489
Fax: (01590) 673489
Lymington's hardware & technical specialist.

PREMIUM LIFERAFT SERVICES
LYMINGTON
Tel: (01590) 688407
Freephone: 0800 243673
e-mail: info@liferafts.com
www.liferafts.com
Hire and sales of DoT and RORC approved liferafts and safety
equipment.

Christchurch HM	01202 495061
Christchurch Police	01202 486333
Christchurch SC Christchurch	01202 483150
Cobbs Quay Marina Poole	01202 674299
Cobnor Activities Centre Trust	01243 572791
Compass Point Chandlery Southampton	023 80452388

CONVOI EXCEPTIONNEL LTD
Castleton House, High Street,
Hamble, Southampton, Hampshire SO31 4HA.
Tel: (023) 8045 3045
Fax: (023) 8045 4551
e-mail: info@convoi.co.uk
International marine haulage and abnormal load consultants.
European abnormal load permits obtained and escort car
service. Capacity for loads up to 100 tons.

Coombes Boatyard Chichester	01243 866663
Cowes Combined Clubs	01983 295744
Cowes Corinthian YC Isle of Wight	01983 296333
Cowes HM	01983 293952
Cowes Yacht Haven Isle of Wight	01983 299975
Cowes Yachting	01983 280770
Crusader Sails Poole	01202 670580
Davis's Boatyard Poole	01202 674349
Dell Quay SC Chichester	01243 785080
Diverse Yacht Services Hamble	023 80453399

LYMINGTON MARINA

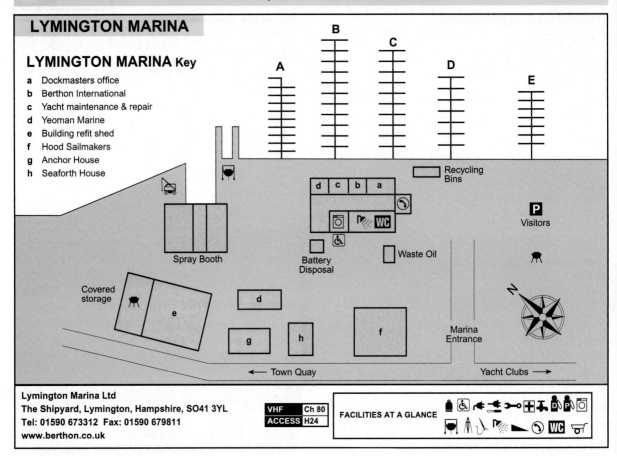

LYMINGTON MARINA Key

- **a** Dockmasters office
- **b** Berthon International
- **c** Yacht maintenance & repair
- **d** Yeoman Marine
- **e** Building refit shed
- **f** Hood Sailmakers
- **g** Anchor House
- **h** Seaforth House

Recycling Bins

Visitors

Spray Booth

Battery Disposal

Waste Oil

Covered storage

Marina Entrance

Town Quay ←

Yacht Clubs →

Lymington Marina Ltd
The Shipyard, Lymington, Hampshire, SO41 3YL
Tel: 01590 673312 Fax: 01590 679811
www.berthon.co.uk

VHF	Ch 80
ACCESS	H24

FACILITIES AT A GLANCE

BUCKLER'S HARD MARINA

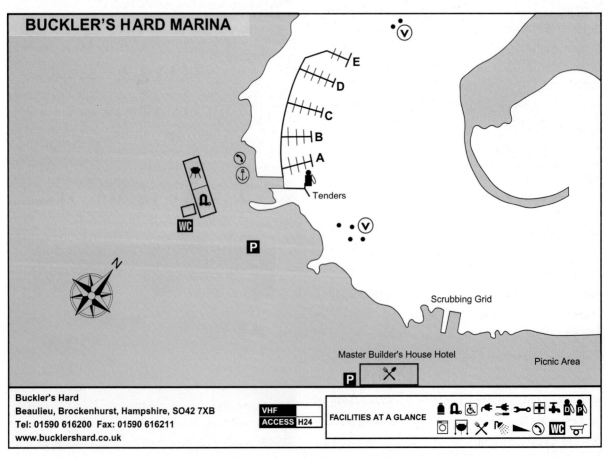

Tenders

Scrubbing Grid

Master Builder's House Hotel

Picnic Area

Buckler's Hard
Beaulieu, Brockenhurst, Hampshire, SO42 7XB
Tel: 01590 616200 Fax: 01590 616211
www.bucklershard.co.uk

VHF	
ACCESS	H24

FACILITIES AT A GLANCE

**PREMIUM LIFERAFT SERVICES
LYMINGTON**
Tel: (01590) 688407
Freephone: 0800 243673
e-mail: info@liferafts.com
www.liferafts.com
Hire and sales of DoT and RORC approved liferafts and safety equipment.

Dolphin Haven Poole	01202 649488
Dorset Yachts Poole	01202 674531
East Cowes Marina Isle of Wight	01983 293983
East Cowes SC Isle of Wight	01983 531687
East Dorset SC Poole	01202 706111
Eastney Cruising Association Portsmouth	023 92734103
Elephant Boatyard Southampton	023 80403268
Eling SC	023 80863987
Emsworth Chandlery Emsworth	01243 375500
Emsworth SC Emsworth	01243 372850
Emsworth Slipper SC Emsworth	01243 372523
Emsworth Yacht Harbour Emsworth	01243 377727
Epic Ventures Ltd Cowes	01983 291292
Fareham Marina Fareham	01329 822445
Fareham Sailing & Motor BC Fareham	01329 233324
Ferrybridge Marine Services Ltd Weymouth	01305 781518
Fishbourne Quay Boatyard Ryde	01983 882200

**GENACIS
Dolphin House, 2 Allens Lane, Hamworthy,
Poole Dorset, BH16 5DA**
Tel: (01202) 624356
Fax: (01202) 625842
e-mail: enquiries@genacis.com
www.genacis.com
Dolphin water-cooled diesel generators
3-16 CVA.

George Haines Ltd Chichester	01243 512228
Gosport CC Gosport	02392 586838
Greenham Marine Emsworth	01243 378314
Haines Boatyard Chichester	01243 512228
Hamble Point Marina Southampton	023 8045 2464
Hamble River HM	01489 576387
Hamble River Police	023 80335444
Hamble River SC Southampton	023 80452070
Hardway Marine Store Gosport	023 92580420
Hardway SC Gosport	02392 581875
Harold Hayles Yarmouth	01983 760373

Harwoods Yacht Chandlers Yarmouth	01983 760258
Haslar Marina Gosport	023 9260 1201
Hayling Ferry SC; Locks SC Hayling Island	023 80829833
Hayling Island SC Hayling Island	023 92463768
Highcliffe SC Christchurch	01425 274874

**HOLMAN RIGGING
Chichester Marina, Chichester,
West Sussex PO20 7EJ.**
Tel/Fax: (01243) 514000
e-mail: enquiries@holmanrigging.co.uk
www.holmanrigging.co.uk
Agent for major suppliers in this field we offer a specialist mast and rigging service. Purpose designed mast trailer for quick and safe transportation. Installation for roller headsail and mainsail reefing systems. Insurance reports and quotations.

Hood Sailmakers Lymington	01590 675011
Hornet SC Gosport	02392 580403
Hythe Marina Southampton	023 8020 7073
Hythe SC Southampton	023 80846563
Island Harbour Marina Newport	01983 822999
Island SC Isle of Wight	01983 296621
Itchen Marina Southampton	023 8063 1500
Itchenor SC Chichester	01243 512400

**JP SERVICES -
MARINE SAFETY & TRAINING
The Old Police House, Arundel Road, Tangmere,
Chichester, West Sussex PO18 0DZ**
Tel: (01243) 537552
Fax: (01243) 531471
e-mail: training@jpservices.co.uk
www.jpservices.co.uk
RYA and professional training for motor yachts and work boats.
Max 2 students per practical course. Sea survival courses.
Safety Training and risk awareness to MCA standards.
Consultancy following on the water accidents.

K Latham Poole	01202 748029
Kelvin Hughes Ltd Southampton	023 80634911
Kelvin Hughes Southampton	023 8063 4911
Kemp Sails Ltd Wareham	01929 554308/554378
Kemps Quay Marina Southampton	023 8063 2323
Keyhaven Police	01590 615101
Keyhaven YC Keyhaven	01590 642165
Kingfisher Marine Weymouth	01305 766595
Lake Yard	01202 674531
Langstone Harbour HM	023 9246 3419
Langstone SC Havant	023 92484577
Lilliput SC Poole	01202 740319
Locks SC Portsmouth	023 92829833
Lymington HM	01590 672014
Lymington Marina Lymington	01590 673312
Lymington Town SC Lymington	0159 674514
Lymington Yacht Haven Lymington	01590 677071
Marchwood YC Marchwood	023 80666141

COWES YACHT HAVEN

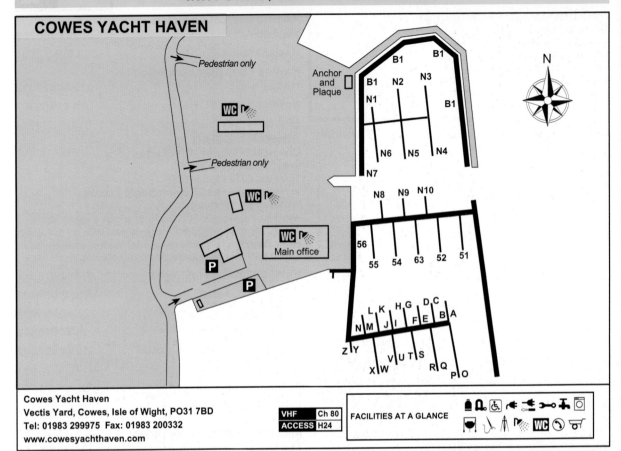

Cowes Yacht Haven
Vectis Yard, Cowes, Isle of Wight, PO31 7BD
Tel: 01983 299975 Fax: 01983 200332
www.cowesyachthaven.com

VHF	Ch 80
ACCESS	H24

FACILITIES AT A GLANCE

CAFÉ MOZART
48 High Street, Cowes,
Isle of Wight PO31 7RR
Tel: (01983) 293681
Fax: (01983) 293681
e-mail: cafemozart@hotmail.com
www.cafemozart.co.uk
From sticky buns to fine dining!

COWES YACHT HAVEN
Vectis Yard, High Street, Cowes,
Isle of Wight PO31 7BD
Tel: (01983) 299975
Fax: (01983) 200332
e-mail: info@cowesyachthaven.com
www.cowesyachthaven.com
Marina and yachting event centre.

KEVIN MOLE OUTBOARDS
Unit 10, Medina Court, Arctic Road, Cowes,
Isle of Wight PO31 7XD
e-mail: kevinmole@outboards.uk.com
www.outboards.uk.com
Outboard servicing & repairs, part accessories, oils & lubricants, marine finance. Main agents for Yamaha inflatables, Ribeye, Fletcher, Terhi, Powercat, Hydrive.

MARI LYNCH
The Annex of Keystone House, Plaistow Road,
Dunsfold, Godalming, Surrey GU8 4PT
Tel: (01483) 201085
www.mariart.co.uk
Yacht portraits and marine art by Mari Lynch. Visit my virtual gallery at: www.mariart.co.uk for photo-samples & commissions phone Mari +44 (0)1483 201085.

Marine Connections Bitterne	023 803 36200
Marine Force (Poole) Poole	01202 723311
Marine Force Chichester	01243 771111
Marine Force Lymington	01590 673698

MARINEFORCE LTD
Unit 6, Waterloo Industrial Estate, Flanders Rd,
Hedge End, Hampshire SO30 2QT
Tel: (0870) 010 4877
Fax: (0870) 010 4885
e-mail: enquiries@marineforce.com
www.marineforce.com
The UK's leading marine retailer, featuring 10 retail outlets, a huge mail order catalogue and a full trading website. Thousands of stock lines available across clothing, electronics, general chandlery, boats and engines, books and charts.

Marine Superstore Port Solent Chandlery Portsmouth	023 92219843
McWilliams Sailmakers Cowes	01983 281100
Mengham Marine Hayling Island	023 92464333
Mengham Rythe SC Hayling Island	023 92463337
Mercury Yacht Harbour Southampton	023 8045 5994

MICHAEL SHANLY INVESTMENTS LTD
Sorbon, Aylesbury End, Beaconsfield, Bucks
HP27 9LB
Tel: (01494) 671331
Fax: (01494) 683912
Saxon moorings Old Windsor - Moorings available.

Mitchell's Boatyard Poole	01202 747857
Netley SC Netley	023 80454272
New Dawn Dive Centre Lymington	01590 675656
Newtown Creek HM	01983 525994
Newtown Creek Police	01983 528000
Nick Cox Yacht Chandlery Ltd Lymington	01590 673489
North Haven YC Poole	01202 708830
Northney Marina Hayling Island	023 9246 6321
Northrop Sails Ramsgate	01843 851665
Northshore Yacht Yard Chichester	01243 512611
Ocean Village Marina Southampton	023 8022 9385
Ocean World Ltd Cowes	01983 291744

EAST COWES

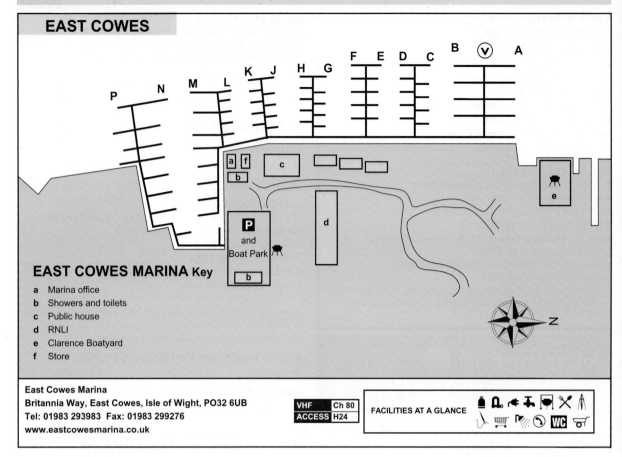

EAST COWES MARINA Key

a Marina office
b Showers and toilets
c Public house
d RNLI
e Clarence Boatyard
f Store

East Cowes Marina
Britannia Way, East Cowes, Isle of Wight, PO32 6UB
Tel: 01983 293983 Fax: 01983 299276
www.eastcowesmarina.co.uk

VHF	Ch 80
ACCESS	H24

FACILITIES AT A GLANCE

SHEPHARDS WHARF MARINA

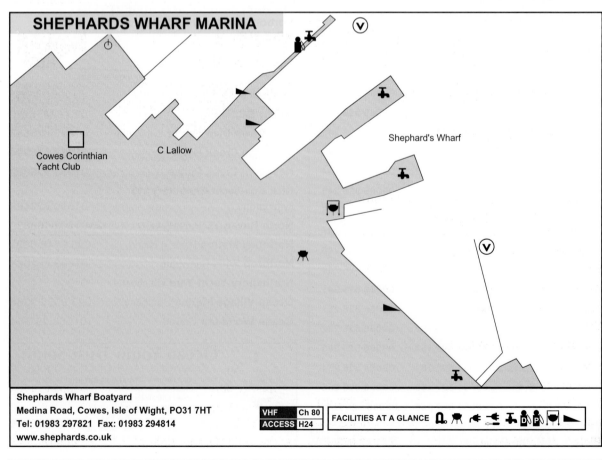

Cowes Corinthian
Yacht Club

C Lallow

Shephard's Wharf

Shephards Wharf Boatyard
Medina Road, Cowes, Isle of Wight, PO31 7HT
Tel: 01983 297821 Fax: 01983 294814
www.shephards.co.uk

VHF	Ch 80
ACCESS	H24

FACILITIES AT A GLANCE

DEAN & REDDYHOFF LTD
- EAST COWES MARINA
Britannia Way, East Cowes,
Isle of Wight PO32 6HA
Tel: (01983) 293983
Fax: (01983) 299276
e-mail: sales@eastcowesmarina.co.uk
www.eastcowesmarina.co.uk
Perfectly situated up stream of Cowes town centre, the marina has undergone a complete revamp both in and out of the water. New features include pontoons and services, lifting dock, public house, landscaping and much more. All visitors more than welcome.

KEVIN MOLE OUTBOARDS
Unit 10, Medina Court, Arctic Road, Cowes,
Isle of Wight PO31 7XD
e-mail: kevinmole@outboards.uk.com
www.outboards.uk.com
Outboard servicing & repairs, part accessories, oils & lubricants, marine finance. Main agents for Yamaha inflatables, Ribeye, Fletcher, Terhi, Powercat, Hydrive.

POWERSAIL AND ISLAND CHANDLERS LTD
East Cowes Marina, Clarence Road, East Cowes,
Isle-of-Wight PO32 6YB
Tel: (01983) 299800
Fax: (01983) 299800
Chandlery provisions, all boating needs.

Offshore Marine Services Ltd Bembridge	01983 873125	**Poole Harbour** Police	01202 223954
Old Harbour Dive School Portland	01305 861000	**Poole HM**	01202 440233
Parker & Kay Sailmakers - South Hamble	023 8045 8213	**Poole YC** Poole	01202 672687
		Port Hamble Marina Southampton	023 8045 2741
Parkstone YC (Haven) Ltd Poole	01202 743610	**Port Solent Marina** Portsmouth	023 9221 0765
Parkstone YC Poole	01202 743610	**Portchester SC** Portchester	01329 376375
Pascall Atkey & Sons Ltd Isle of Wight	01983 292381	**Portland HM**	01305 824044
		Portland Police	01305 821205
Peters PLC Chichester	01243 511033	**Portsmouth Harbour Commercial Docks HM**	023 92297395
Piplers of Poole Poole	01202 673056	**Portsmouth Harbour Control**	023 92723694

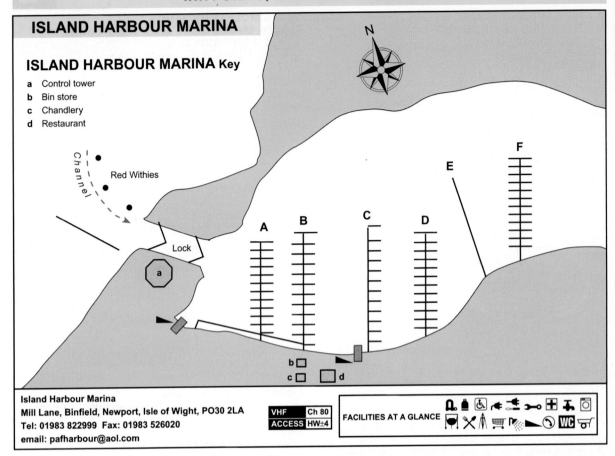

ISLAND HARBOUR MARINA

ISLAND HARBOUR MARINA Key

a Control tower
b Bin store
c Chandlery
d Restaurant

Island Harbour Marina
Mill Lane, Binfield, Newport, Isle of Wight, PO30 2LA
Tel: 01983 822999 Fax: 01983 526020
email: pafharbour@aol.com

| VHF | Ch 80 |
| ACCESS | HW±4 |

FACILITIES AT A GLANCE

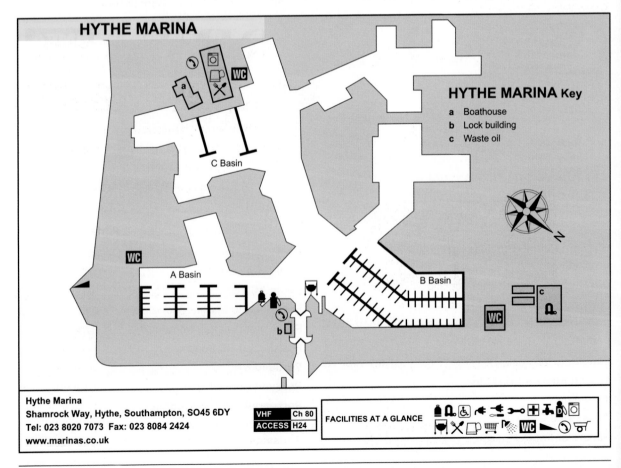

HYTHE MARINA

HYTHE MARINA Key

a Boathouse
b Lock building
c Waste oil

Hythe Marina
Shamrock Way, Hythe, Southampton, SO45 6DY
Tel: 023 8020 7073 Fax: 023 8084 2424
www.marinas.co.uk

| VHF | Ch 80 |
| ACCESS | H24 |

FACILITIES AT A GLANCE

HYTHE MARINA VILLAGE
Shamrock Way, Hythe, Southampton,
Hampshire SO45 6DY
Tel: (023) 8020 7073
Fax: (023) 8084 2424
e-mail: hythe@mdlmarinas.co.uk
www.marinas.co.uk

210 berth marina with fully serviced pontoons for boats up to 20 metres. Access by lock manned 24 hours. 24 hour security. Shower, toilet and laundry facilities. Chandlery, brokerage, shops, hairdresser, bar and restaurants. Car park, petrol and diesel fuel. Boat lifting and hard standing area. Slipway, 30 ton hoist and boat repairs.

Portsmouth Harbour HM	023 92723124
Portsmouth SC Portsmouth	02392 820596
Quay Sails (Poole) Ltd Poole	01202 681128

QUAY WEST CHANDLERS
Mitchells Boatyard, Turks Lane, Parkstone, Poole, Dorset
BH14 8EW
Tel: (01202) 742488
Fax: (01202) 742489

General yacht chandlers, covering all aspects of water useage, with practical hands on experience and loads of patience!!

R. ARTHURS CHANDLERY
59-61 Forton Road, Gosport, Hampshire PO12 4TD
Tel: (023) 9252 6522
Fax: (023) 9252 6522
e-mail: arthurschandlery@aol.com

For all your marine chandlery. International, Blakes, XM, Coopers, Sikkens, Epifanes, Jabsco, Rule, Whale, Attwood, Aquasignal, Hella, Stanfords, Imray, Admiralty, Liros Ropes. Ocean Safety Rigging Service.

R K Marine Ltd Swanwick	01489 583572

RACECOURSE YACHT BASIN (WINDSOR) LTD
Maidenhead Road, Windsor, Berkshire SL4 5HT
Tel: (01753) 851501
Fax: (01753) 868172
e-mail: marina@ryb.co.uk
www.ryb.co.uk

Marina - full facilities - shop - sales - brokerage.

RAFYC	023 80452208
Ratsey & Lapthorn Isle of Wight	01983 294051
Redclyffe YC Poole	01929 557227

RHP Marine Cowes	01983 290421
Richardson Sails Southampton	023 80403914
Richardsons Boatbuilders Binfield Newport	01983 821095
Ridge Wharf Yacht Centre Wareham	01929 552650
Rockall Sails Chichester	01243 573185
Ron Davis Marine Portland	01305 821175
Ron Hale Marine Portsmouth	023 92732985

ROSSITER YACHTS LTD
Rossiters Quay, Bridge St, Christchurch, Dorset
BH23 1DZ
Tel: (01202) 483250
Fax: (01202) 490164
e-mail: rossiteryachts@hotmail.com
www.rossiteryachts.co.uk

Builders of Curlew and Pontail + repairs & restorations in wood and GRP, osmosure treatment centre. Marine engineering: diesel, petrol, inboard, outboard, marine diesel sales, rigging service, cranage & storage, chandlery, brokerage, moorings.

Royal Motor YC Poole	01202 707227
Royal Corinthian YC (Cowes) Cowes	01983 292608
Royal Dorset YC Weymouth	01305 786258
Royal London YC Isle of Wight	019 83299727
Royal Lymington YC Lymington	01590 672677
Royal Motor YC Poole	01202 707227
Royal Naval Club and Royal Albert YC Portsmouth	023 9282 5924

TOWN QUAY MARINA

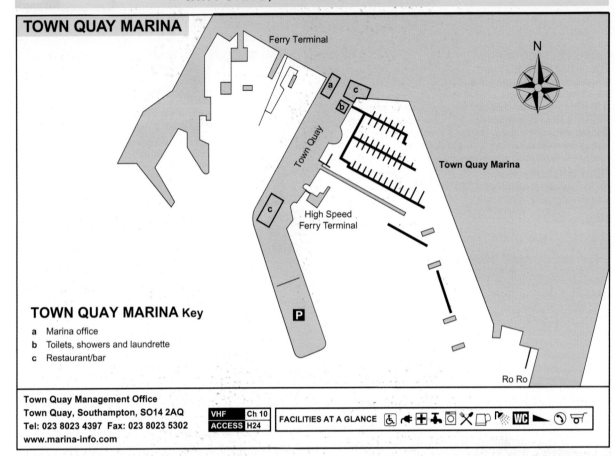

TOWN QUAY MARINA Key

a Marina office
b Toilets, showers and laundrette
c Restaurant/bar

Town Quay Management Office
Town Quay, Southampton, SO14 2AQ
Tel: 023 8023 4397 Fax: 023 8023 5302
www.marina-info.com

| VHF | Ch 10 |
| ACCESS | H24 |

FACILITIES AT A GLANCE

OCEAN VILLAGE MARINA

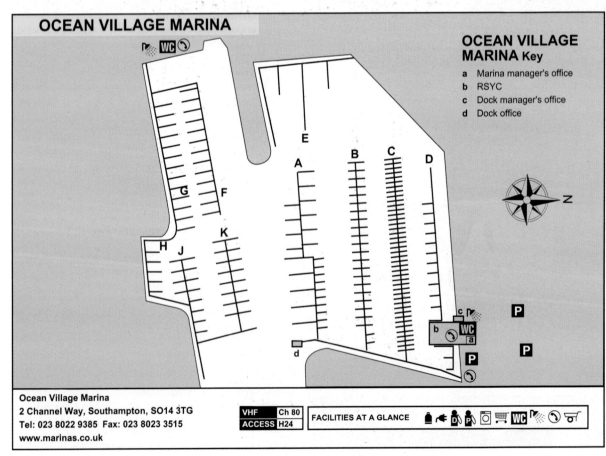

OCEAN VILLAGE MARINA Key

a Marina manager's office
b RSYC
c Dock manager's office
d Dock office

Ocean Village Marina
2 Channel Way, Southampton, SO14 3TG
Tel: 023 8022 9385 Fax: 023 8023 3515
www.marinas.co.uk

| VHF | Ch 80 |
| ACCESS | H24 |

FACILITIES AT A GLANCE

OCEAN VILLAGE MARINA
2 Channel Way, Southampton, Hampshire SO14 3TG
Tel: (023) 8022 9385
Fax: (023) 8023 3515
e-mail: oceanvillage@mdlmarinas.co.uk
www.marinas.co.uk
Situated in the centre of Southampton. 450 berth marina with fully serviced pontoons for boats up to 90 metres. 24 hour security. Shower, toilet and laundry facilities. Car park. Yacht brokerage. Adjacent shopping and entertainment complex including cinema and restaurants. Boat lifting and hard standing area at nearby Shamrock Quay and Hamble Point Marina.

Royal Naval Sailing Association
Gosport   023 92521100
Royal Solent YC Yarmouth   01983 760256
Royal Southampton YC Southampton 023 8022 3352
Royal Southern YC Southampton   023 8045 0300
Royal Victoria YC Fishbourne   01983 882325
Royal Yacht Squadron Isle of Wight   01983 292191
Ryde HM   01983 613879

Ryde Leisure Harbour Ryde   01983 613879
Saltern Sail Co West Cowes   01983 280014
Saltern Sail Company Yarmouth   01983 760120
Salterns Chandlery Poole   01202 701556
Salterns Marina Boatyard & Hotel
Poole   01202 707321
Sandbanks Yacht Company Poole   01202 707500
Saxon Wharf Marina Southampton   023 8033 9490
Sea Teach Ltd Emsworth   01243 375774
Seaview YC Isle of Wight   01983 613268
Shamrock Chandlery Southampton   023 806 32725
Shamrock Quay Marina Southampton 023 8022 9461
Shepherds Wharf Boatyard Ltd
Cowes   01983 297821
Shepherds Wharf Boatyard Ltd
Cowes   01983 297821

SHERATON MARINE CABINET
White Oak Green, Hailey, Witney, Oxfordshire OX8 5XP
Tel/Fax: (01993) 868275
Manufacturers of quality teak and mahogany marine fittings, louvre doors, grating and tables. Special fitting-out items to customer specification. Colour catalgoue available on request.

Ship and Shore Hayling Island   023 924637373
Shorewater Sports Chichester   01243 672315
Solent Marine Chandlery Ltd Gosport 023 92584622
South Coast Marine Christchurch   01202 482695
Southampton HM   023 8033 9733
Southampton Police   023 80845511
Southampton SC Southampton   023 80446575
Southampton Yacht Services Ltd
Southampton   023 803 35266
Southern Cylinder Services Fareham   01329 221125
Southern Sails Poole   01202 677000
Southsea Marina Southsea   023 9282 2719

SP SYSTEMS
St. Cross Business Park, Newport, Isle of Wight PO30 5WU
Tel: (01983) 828000
Fax: (01983) 828100
Epoxy resins for laminating, bonding, coating and filling. Usable with wood, GRP, ferrocement, GRP/FRP materials including glass, carbon and Kevlar fibres. Structural engineering of GRP and composite materials. Technical advice service.

Sparkes Boatyard Hayling Island   023 92463572
Sparkes Marina Hayling Island   023 92463572
Spinnaker Yacht Chandlery Bembridge 01983 874324

STONE PIER YACHT SERVICES
Stone Pier Yard, Shore Road, Warsash, Hampshire SO31 9FR
Tel: (01489) 885400
Fax: (01489) 482049
e-mail: jgale82246@aol.com
High quality workmanship at reasonable prices, friendly and professional repair, refit and restoration facilities for GRP and timber vessels in our spacious workshop. Call Jon Gale for personal solutions to your problems, large or small.

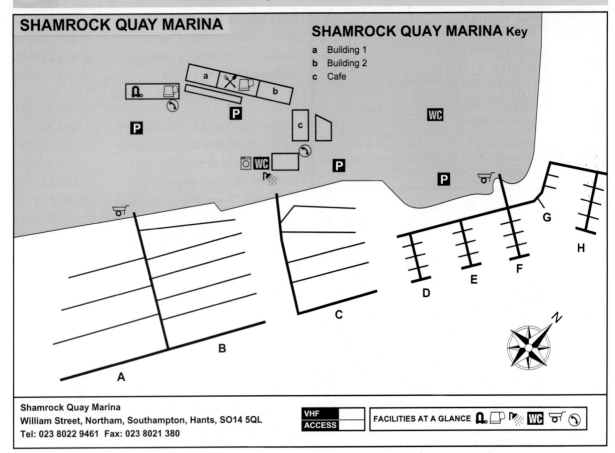

SHAMROCK QUAY MARINA

SHAMROCK QUAY MARINA Key

a Building 1
b Building 2
c Cafe

Shamrock Quay Marina
William Street, Northam, Southampton, Hants, SO14 5QL
Tel: 023 8022 9461 Fax: 023 8021 380

VHF
ACCESS

FACILITIES AT A GLANCE

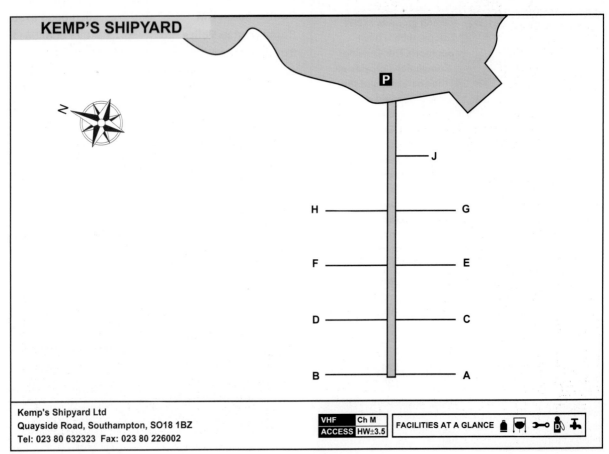

KEMP'S SHIPYARD

Kemp's Shipyard Ltd
Quayside Road, Southampton, SO18 1BZ
Tel: 023 80 632323 Fax: 023 80 226002

VHF Ch M
ACCESS HW±3.5

FACILITIES AT A GLANCE

SAXON WHARF MARINA

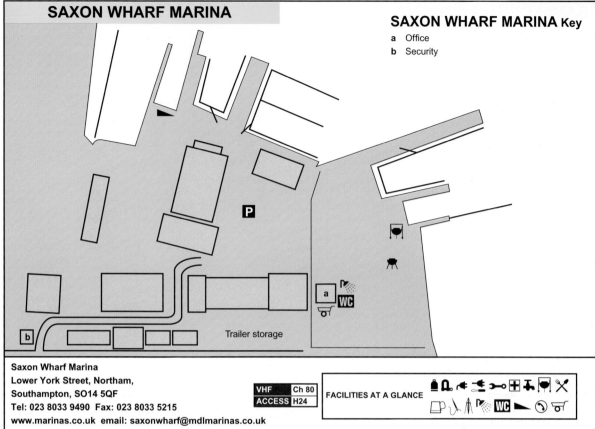

SAXON WHARF MARINA Key
a Office
b Security

Trailer storage

Saxon Wharf Marina
Lower York Street, Northam,
Southampton, SO14 5QF
Tel: 023 8033 9490 Fax: 023 8033 5215
www.marinas.co.uk email: saxonwharf@mdlmarinas.co.uk

| VHF | Ch 80 |
| ACCESS | H24 |

FACILITIES AT A GLANCE

GREENHAM REGIS MARINE ELECTRONICS
Shamrock Quay, William Street, Southampton
SO14 5QL
Tel: 023 8063 6555
Fax: 023 8023 1426
e-mail: sales@greenham-regis.co.uk
www.greenham-regis.co.uk
Sales & service + installation of top quality marine electronic
equipment via our waterfront sales & service centres in Poole,
Lymington, Cowes, Southampton, Emsworth and Itchenor.
Contact us for a competitive quotation - you could be surprised.

SAXON WHARF
Lower York Street, Northam, Southampton,
Hampshire SO14 5QF
Tel: (023) 8033 9490
Fax: (023) 8033 5215
e-mail: saxonwharf@mdlmarinas.co.uk
www.marinas.co.uk
Marine trade centre with capacity for lifting boats up to 50 metres.
200 ton boat hoist and storage ashore. Extensive marine trades
and services. Extra facilities available at nearby Shamrock Quay.

SHAMROCK QUAY
William Street, Northam, Southampton,
Hampshire SO14 5QL
Tel: (023) 8022 9461
Fax: (023) 8021 3808
e-mail: shamrockquay@mdlmarinas.co.uk
www.marinas.co.uk
250 berth marina with fully serviced pontoons for boats up to 60
metres. 24 hour security. Shower, toilet and laundry facilities.
Shops, bars and restaurant. Chandlery. Boat lifting and hard
standing area. 63 ton hoist and 12 ton mobile crane. Extensive
marine trades and services. Yacht brokerage, new boat sales
and yacht charters.

HAMBLE POINT MARINA

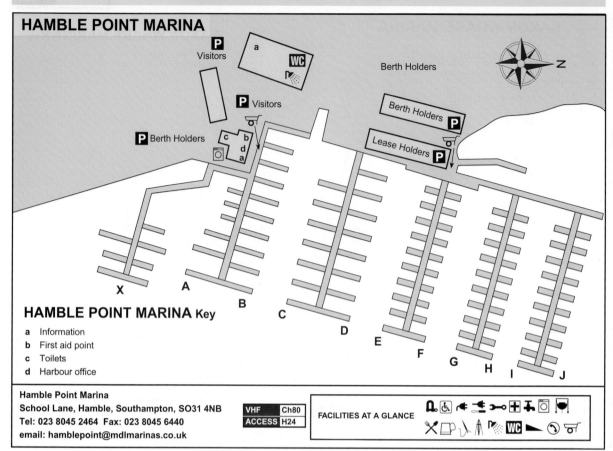

HAMBLE POINT MARINA Key

a Information
b First aid point
c Toilets
d Harbour office

Hamble Point Marina
School Lane, Hamble, Southampton, SO31 4NB
Tel: 023 8045 2464 Fax: 023 8045 6440
email: hamblepoint@mdlmarinas.co.uk

VHF	Ch80
ACCESS	H24

FACILITIES AT A GLANCE

PORT HAMBLE MARINA

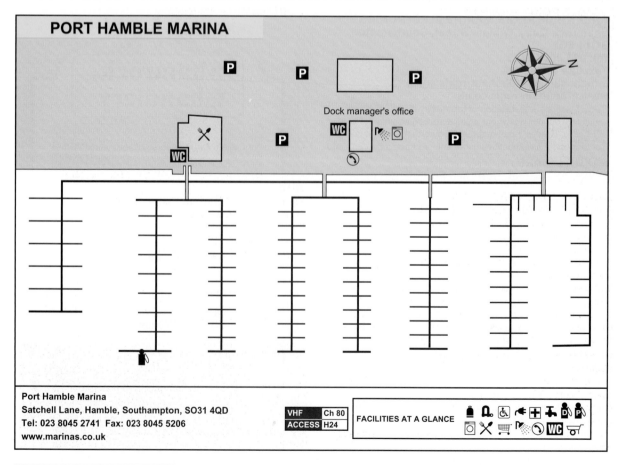

Port Hamble Marina
Satchell Lane, Hamble, Southampton, SO31 4QD
Tel: 023 8045 2741 Fax: 023 8045 5206
www.marinas.co.uk

VHF	Ch 80
ACCESS	H24

FACILITIES AT A GLANCE

MERCURY YACHT HARBOUR

MERCURY YACHT HARBOUR Key

a Toilets
b Laundrette
c Chandlery
d Restaurant and bar
e Brokerage
f Dockmaster,
marina managers office
g Waste disposal
h Recycling area

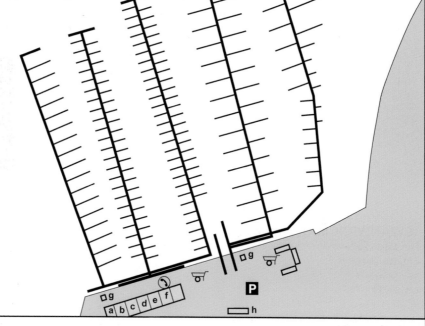

Mercury Yacht Harbour
Satchell Lane, Hamble, Southampton, SO31 4HQ
Tel: 023 8045 5994 Fax: 023 8045 7369
www.marinas.co.uk email: mercury@mdlmarinas.co.uk

VHF   Ch 80
ACCESS H24

FACILITIES AT A GLANCE

HAMBLE POINT MARINA
**School Lane, Hamble, Southampton,
Hampshire SO31 4NB
Tel: (023) 8045 2464
Fax: (023) 8045 6440
e-mail: hamblepoint@mdlmarinas.co.uk
www.marinas.co.uk**

Situated at the mouth of the River Hamble. 229 berth marina
with fully serviced pontoons for boats up to 20 metres. 24 hour
security. Shower, toilet and laundry facilities. Bar and restaurant.
Chandlery, car park and ice. Lifting for boats up to 62 tons, hard
standing area and slipway. Boat repairs and electronic services.
Boat storage and winter lay-up. 4 ton crane for masts/engines.
Yacht brokerage, new boat sales and dry sailing facility.

MERCURY YACHT HARBOUR
**Satchell Lane, Hamble, Southampton,
Hampshire SO31 4HQ
Tel: (023) 8045 5994
Fax: (023) 8045 7369
e-mail: mercury@mdlmarinas.co.uk
www.marinas.co.uk**

350 berth marina with fully serviced pontoons for boats up to 24
metres. 24 hour security. Shower, toilet and laundry facilities.
Bar and restaurant. Chandlery and car park. Boat lifting and
hard standing area. Sailmakers and electronic services. Sailing
schools, yacht charters and yacht brokerage.

PREMIUM LIFERAFT SERVICES
HAMBLE
**Tel: 023 8045 7316
Freephone: 0800 243673
e-mail: info@liferafts.com
www.liferafts.com**

Hire and sales of DoT and RORC approved liferafts and safety
equipment.

PORT HAMBLE MARINA
**Satchell Lane, Hamble, Southampton,
Hampshire SO31 4QD
Tel: (023) 8045 2741
Fax: (023) 8045 5206
e-mail: porthamble@mdlmarinas.co.uk
www.marinas.co.uk**

Close to Hamble Village. 310 berth marina with fully serviced pontoons
for boats up to 24 metres. 24 hour security. Shower, toilet and laundry
facilities. Bar and restaurant. Chandlery, car park, petrol and diesel fuel.
Boat lifting and hard standing area. Yacht repair yard, brokerage,
sailmakers and electronic services. Divers, salvage and towing launch.

QUANTUM-PARKER & KAY SAILMAKERS - SOUTH
**Hamble Point Marina, School Lane,
Hampshire SO31 4JD
Tel: 023 8045 8213
Fax: 023 8045 8228
e-mail: pkay@quantumsails.com
www.quantumsails.com**

A complete sail making service, from small repairs to the
construction of custom designed sails for racing or cruising
yachts. Covers constructed for sail and powercraft, plus the
supply of all forms of sail handling hardware.

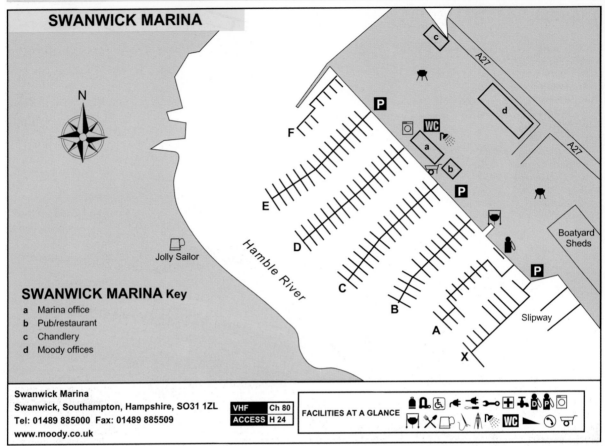

SWANWICK MARINA

F

E

D

C

B

A

X

Jolly Sailor

Hamble River

Boatyard Sheds

Slipway

c

d

P

WC

a

b

P

P

SWANWICK MARINA Key

a   Marina office
b   Pub/restaurant
c   Chandlery
d   Moody offices

Swanwick Marina
Swanwick, Southampton, Hampshire, SO31 1ZL
Tel: 01489 885000 Fax: 01489 885509
www.moody.co.uk

VHF	Ch 80
ACCESS	H 24

FACILITIES AT A GLANCE

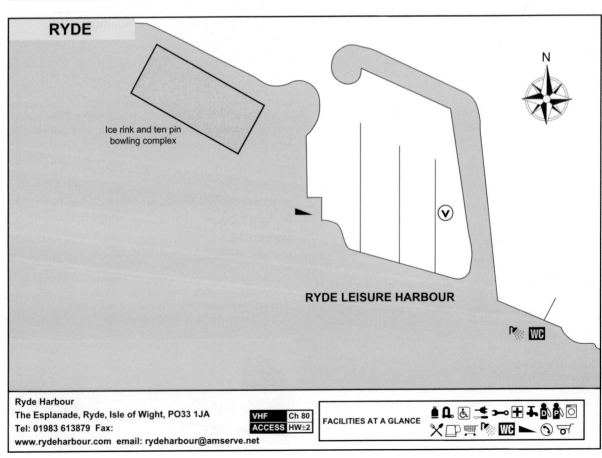

RYDE

Ice rink and ten pin
bowling complex

RYDE LEISURE HARBOUR

WC

Ryde Harbour
The Esplanade, Ryde, Isle of Wight, PO33 1JA
Tel: 01983 613879 Fax:
www.rydeharbour.com email: rydeharbour@amserve.net

VHF	Ch 80
ACCESS	HW±2

FACILITIES AT A GLANCE

SWANWICK YACHT SURVEYORS
Swanwick Marina, Lower Swanwick,
Southampton SO31 12L
Tel: (01489) 564822
Fax: (01489) 564828
e-mail: swanwickys@aol.com
www.swanwickys.co.uk
Pre-purchase surveys. MIIMS & BMF member.

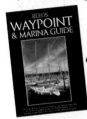

SHORE
SAILMAKERS

Sail loft in the Marina for
• Sail Repairs
• New Sails
• Sail Graphics
• Fast Service

2003M&WM94/jd

SWANWICK MARINA, SWANWICK, SOUTHAMPTON SO31 7ZL
Tel: 01489 589450   Fax: 01489 885917

**Dinghies to Ocean racers
Speedboats to Flybridge cruisers**

Design &
manufacture
of...

...Canopies
Spray hoods
Winter covers

Sailormade...

J B Yacht Services
01489 572487
Repairs & replacements
The Birches, Sarisbury
Court, Sarisbury Green,
Southampton SO31 6AG

2003M&WM93/jd

Sunsail Portsmouth	023 92222224
Sunseeker International Marina Poole	01202 381111
Swanage Police	01929 422004
Swanage SC Swanage	01929 422987
Swanwick Marina Southampton	01489 885000
Tarquin Boat Co Emsworth	01243 375211
Tarquin Marina Emsworth	01243 377727
The Gosport Marina Ltd Gosport	023 92524811
Thorney Island SC Thorney Island	01243 371731
Thornham Marina Emsworth	01243 375335
Town Quay Marina Southampton	023 8023 4397
Trafalgar Yacht Services Fareham	01329 823577
Tudor SC Portsmouth	023 92662002
UK Customs Nationwide	0845 0109000

VETUS DEN OUDEN LTD
39 South Hants Ind. Park, Totton, Southampton
SO40 3SA
Tel: 023 8086 1033
Fax: 023 8066 3142
e-mail: sales@vetus.co.uk
www.vetus.co.uk
Wholesalers of diesel engines, generators, exhaust systems,
propellers, shafts, bow thrusters, hatches, portlights, windlasses,
ventilators, fuel and water tanks, hydraulics systems, air
conditioning, wipers, pumps, seats, hoses and much much
more.

vetus ®
BOAT EQUIPMENT
VETUS DEN OUDEN LTD
*39 South Hants Industrial Park,
Totton, Southampton,
Hants SO40 3SA*
FOR VETUS BOAT EQUIPMENT INCLUDING DIESEL EQUIPMENT,
HYDRAULIC STEERING, BOW PROPELLERS AND HUNDREDS
OF OTHER PRODUCTS - ASK FOR FREE COLOUR CATALOGUE
*TEL: SOUTHAMPTON 023 8086 1033   FAX: 023 8066 3142
E-mail: sales@vetus.co.uk   Website: vetus.co.uk*

2003.M&WMD2/c

W L Bussell & Co Weymouth	01305 785633
Warsash Nautical Bookshop Southampton	01489 572384
Warsash SC Southampton	023 80583575
West Solent Boatbuilders Lymington	01590 642080
Weston CC Southampton	07905 557298
Weston SC Southampton	023 80452527
Weymouth HM	01305 206423
Weymouth Marina Weymouth	01305 767576
Weymouth Police	01305 250512
Weymouth SC Weymouth	01305 785481
Wicor Marine Fareham	01329 237112
Yacht & Sports Gear Ltd Chichester	01243 784572
Yachtmail Ltd Lymington	01590 672784
Yarmouth Harbour Yarmouth	01983 760321
Yarmouth HM	01983 760321
Yarmouth Police	01983 528000
Yarmouth SC Yarmouth	01983 760270

BEMBRIDGE MARINA

BEMBRIDGE MARINA Key

a Marina office
b Brading Haven YC

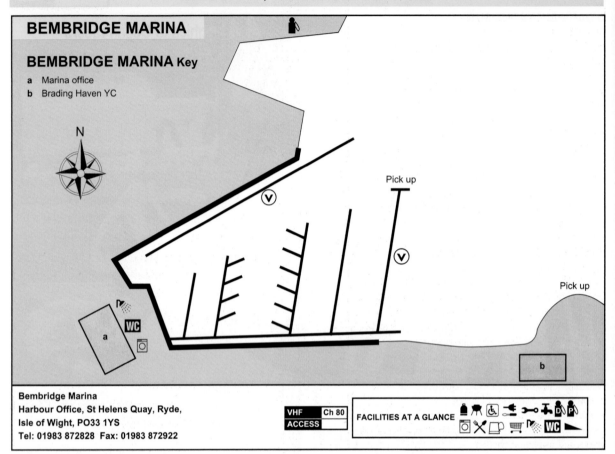

Bembridge Marina
Harbour Office, St Helens Quay, Ryde,
Isle of Wight, PO33 1YS
Tel: 01983 872828 Fax: 01983 872922

VHF	Ch 80
ACCESS	

FACILITIES AT A GLANCE

HASLAR MARINA

HASLAR MARINA
Key

a Admin. offices,
security, toilets,
showers, weather,
soft drinks machine
b Rubbish skips,
security gate
c Bistro/bar and
independent operators,
trolleys
d Security, car park
e Superloo: toilets,
showers, trolleys
f Bar, restaurant, toilets,
public telephone,
shower, laundry
g The Millenium
Timespace
h Public slipway

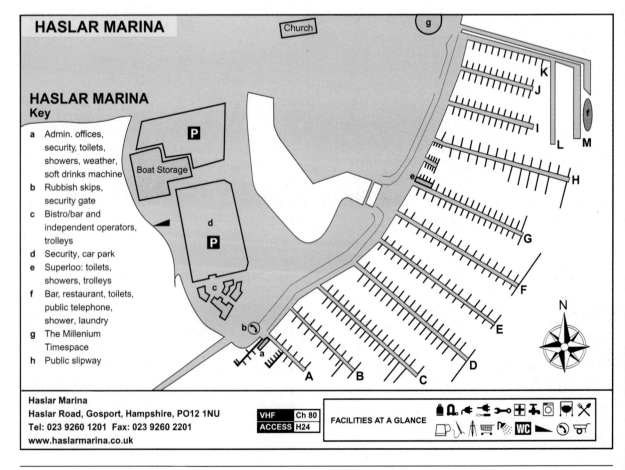

Haslar Marina
Haslar Road, Gosport, Hampshire, PO12 1NU
Tel: 023 9260 1201 Fax: 023 9260 2201
www.haslarmarina.co.uk

VHF	Ch 80
ACCESS	H24

FACILITIES AT A GLANCE

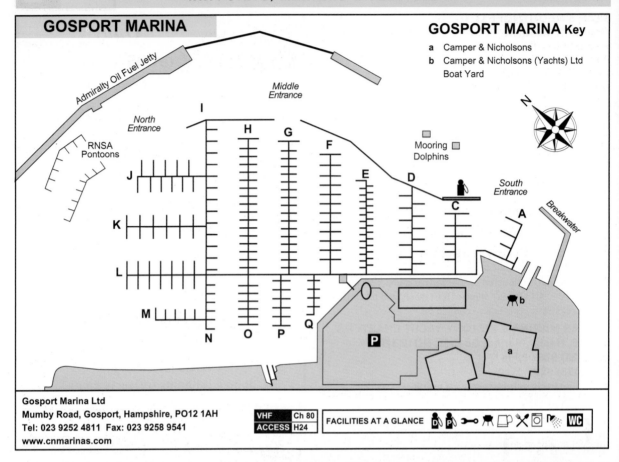

GOSPORT MARINA

GOSPORT MARINA Key

a Camper & Nicholsons
b Camper & Nicholsons (Yachts) Ltd Boat Yard

Admiralty Oil Fuel Jetty

Middle Entrance

North Entrance

RNSA Pontoons

Mooring Dolphins

South Entrance

Breakwater

Gosport Marina Ltd
Mumby Road, Gosport, Hampshire, PO12 1AH
Tel: 023 9252 4811 Fax: 023 9258 9541
www.cnmarinas.com

| VHF | Ch 80 |
| ACCESS | H24 |

FACILITIES AT A GLANCE

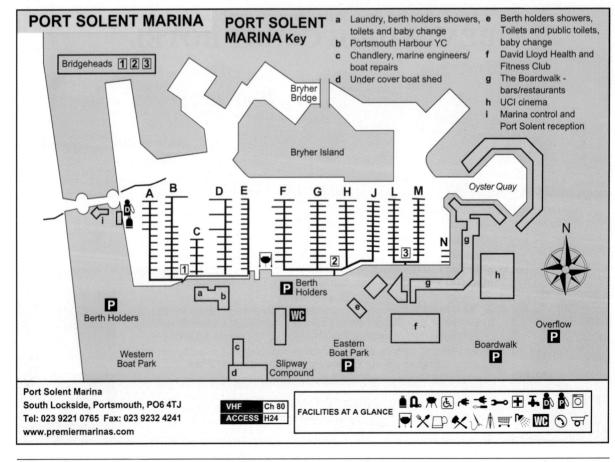

PORT SOLENT MARINA

PORT SOLENT MARINA Key

a Laundry, berth holders showers, toilets and baby change
b Portsmouth Harbour YC
c Chandlery, marine engineers/ boat repairs
d Under cover boat shed
e Berth holders showers, Toilets and public toilets, baby change
f David Lloyd Health and Fitness Club
g The Boardwalk - bars/restaurants
h UCI cinema
i Marina control and Port Solent reception

Bridgeheads 1 2 3

Bryher Bridge

Bryher Island

Oyster Quay

Berth Holders

Berth Holders

WC

Western Boat Park

Eastern Boat Park

Slipway Compound

Boardwalk

Overflow

Port Solent Marina
South Lockside, Portsmouth, PO6 4TJ
Tel: 023 9221 0765 Fax: 023 9232 4241
www.premiermarinas.com

| VHF | Ch 80 |
| ACCESS | H24 |

FACILITIES AT A GLANCE

PORT SOLENT MARINA
South Lockside, Port Solent, Portsmouth,
Hampshire PO6 4TJ
Tel: (023) 9221 0765
Fax: (023) 9232 4241
e-mail: portsolent@premiermarinas.com
www.premiermarinas.com
From a huge chandlery and outstanding marine services to restaurants, bars, a fitness centre and multiscreen cinema, Port Solent offers visitors and berth holders superb facilities, unsurpassed by any other UK marina. Port Solent is a PREMIER MARINA.

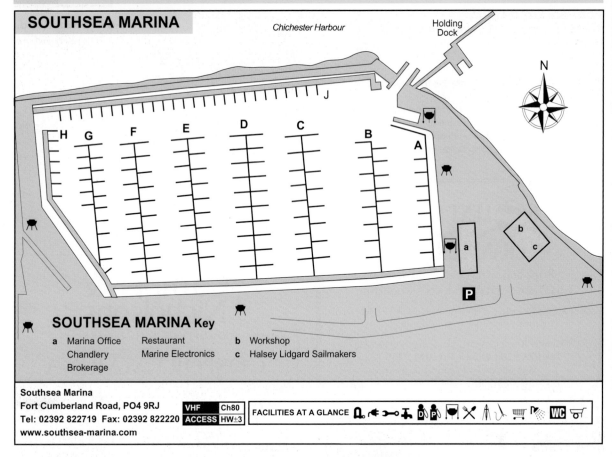

SOUTHSEA MARINA

Chichester Harbour

Holding Dock

N

J

H G F E D C B A

a b c

P

SOUTHSEA MARINA Key

a Marina Office
Chandlery
Brokerage

Restaurant
Marine Electronics

b Workshop

c Halsey Lidgard Sailmakers

Southsea Marina
Fort Cumberland Road, PO4 9RJ
Tel: 02392 822719 Fax: 02392 822220
www.southsea-marina.com

VHF Ch80
ACCESS HW±3

FACILITIES AT A GLANCE

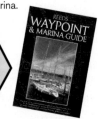

Marinecall®

WEATHER AT SEA

Accurate. Reliable. Conclusive.
Marinecall, forecasting you can depend on.

DETAILED FORECASTS BY TELEPHONE AND FAX

Coastal/Inshore Areas	5-Day Forecast by Telephone 09066 526 PLUS	48-Hour Forecast by Fax 09061 502 PLUS
National Inshore Waters (3-5 day forecast)	234	109
Scotland North	235	110
Scotland East	236	114
North East	237	115
East	238	116
Anglia	239	117
Channel East	240	118
Mid Channel	241	119
South West	242	120
Bristol	243	121
Wales	244	122
North West	245	123
Clyde	246	124
Caledonia	247	125
Minch	248	126
N. Ireland	249	127
Channel Islands	250	-
Offshore Areas	**2-5 Day Planner by Telephone 09066 526 PLUS**	**2-5 Day Planner by Fax 09061 502 PLUS**
English Channel	251	161
Southern North Sea	252	162
Irish Sea	253	163
Biscay	254	164
Nth West Scotland	255	165
Northern North Sea	256	166

09066 calls cost 60p/min. 09061 calls cost £1.50/min. Marinecall, iTouch (UK) Ltd, EC2A 4PF.
Customer Helpdesk 0870 600 4219. E-mail: Marinecall@iTouch.co.uk Visit: www.marinecall.co.uk
Information supplied by Met Office

For a FREE 2002 Marinecall Met Book write to:-
Marinecall, iTouch (UK) Ltd /Weather Dept, FREEPOST LON13551, London, EC2B 2DR

SPARKES MARINA

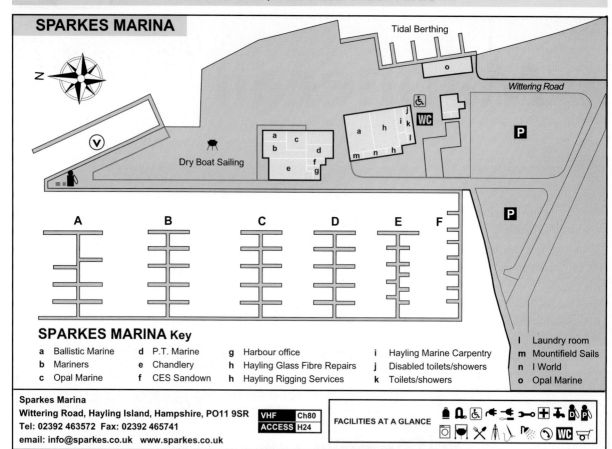

Tidal Berthing

Wittering Road

Dry Boat Sailing

A   B   C   D   E   F

SPARKES MARINA Key

a	Ballistic Marine	d	P.T. Marine
b	Mariners	e	Chandlery
c	Opal Marine	f	CES Sandown

g	Harbour office
h	Hayling Glass Fibre Repairs
h	Hayling Rigging Services

i	Hayling Marine Carpentry
j	Disabled toilets/showers
k	Toilets/showers

l	Laundry room
m	Mountifield Sails
n	I World
o	Opal Marine

Sparkes Marina
Wittering Road, Hayling Island, Hampshire, PO11 9SR
Tel: 02392 463572 Fax: 02392 465741
email: info@sparkes.co.uk www.sparkes.co.uk

VHF	Ch80
ACCESS	H24

FACILITIES AT A GLANCE

NORTHNEY MARINA

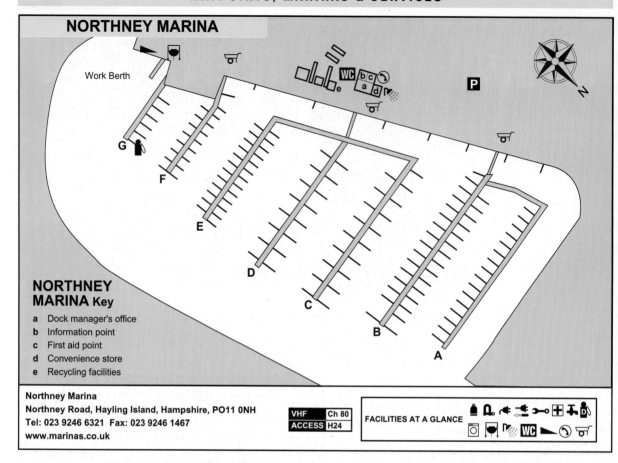

Work Berth

G
F
E
D
C
B
A

NORTHNEY MARINA Key

a Dock manager's office
b Information point
c First aid point
d Convenience store
e Recycling facilities

Northney Marina
Northney Road, Hayling Island, Hampshire, PO11 0NH
Tel: 023 9246 6321 Fax: 023 9246 1467
www.marinas.co.uk

VHF	Ch 80
ACCESS	H24

FACILITIES AT A GLANCE

EMSWORTH YACHT HARBOUR

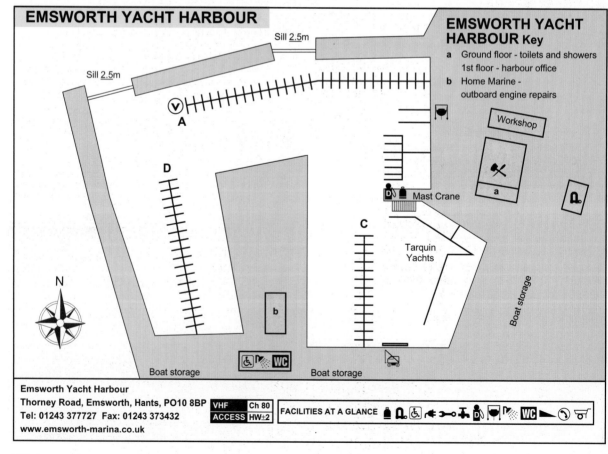

Sill 2.5m
Sill 2.5m
A
D
C
b
a
Mast Crane
Workshop
Tarquin Yachts
Boat storage
Boat storage
Boat storage
N

EMSWORTH YACHT HARBOUR Key

a Ground floor - toilets and showers
1st floor - harbour office
b Home Marine -
outboard engine repairs

Emsworth Yacht Harbour
Thorney Road, Emsworth, Hants, PO10 8BP
Tel: 01243 377727 Fax: 01243 373432
www.emsworth-marina.co.uk

VHF	Ch 80
ACCESS	HW±2

FACILITIES AT A GLANCE

CHICHESTER MARINA

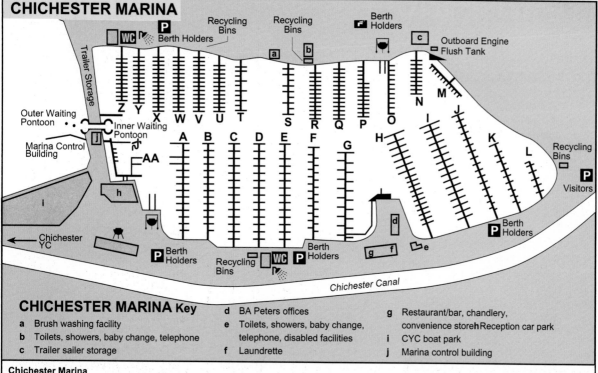

CHICHESTER MARINA Key

a Brush washing facility

b Toilets, showers, baby change, telephone

c Trailer sailer storage

d BA Peters offices

e Toilets, showers, baby change, telephone, disabled facilities

f Laundrette

g Restaurant/bar, chandlery, convenience store **h** Reception car park

i CYC boat park

j Marina control building

Chichester Marina
Birdham, Chichester, West Sussex, PO20 7EJ
Tel: 01243 512731 Fax: 01243 513472
email: chichester@premiermarinas.com
www.premiermarinas.com

VHF	Ch 80
ACCESS	HW ±4

FACILITIES AT A GLANCE

NORTHNEY MARINA
Northney Road, Hayling Island, Hampshire PO11 0NH
Tel: (023) 9246 6321 Fax: (023) 9246 1467
e-mail: northney@mdlmarinas.co.uk
www.marinas.co.uk
Situated within Chichester Harbour. 228 berth marina with fully serviced pontoons for boats up to 24 metres. 24 hour security. Shower and toilet facilities. Car park and diesel fuel. Boat lifting and hard standing area with 35 ton hoist. Yacht repair and boatyard services. Yacht brokerage.

CHICHESTER MARINA
Birdham, Chichester, West Sussex PO20 7EJ
Tel: (01243) 512731 Fax: (01243) 513472
e-mail: chichester@premiermarinas.com
www.premiermarinas.com
Situated in the north east corner of Chichester harbour, Chichester Marina enjoys one of the most attractive locations in the country. With 1071 berths, Chichester offers a unique combination of service, facilities, security and friendliness, unparalleled in UK marinas. Chichester Marina is a PREMIER MARINA.

PREMIUM LIFERAFT SERVICES CHICHESTER
Tel: (01243) 262666 Freephone: 0800 243673
e-mail: info@liferafts.com
www.liferafts.com
Hire and sales of DoT and RORC approved liferafts and safety equipment.

EMSWORTH YACHT HARBOUR LTD
Thorney Road, Emsworth, Hampshire PO10 8BP.
Tel: (01243) 377727
Fax: (01243) 373432
www.emsworth-marina.co.uk
Friendly marina in Chichester harbour. Water, electricity, diesel, Calor gas, 40-tonne mobile crane, slipways, hard-standing and storage areas. Showers and toilets, car parking, chandlery, engineers and boat repairs.

BIRDHAM POOL MARINA

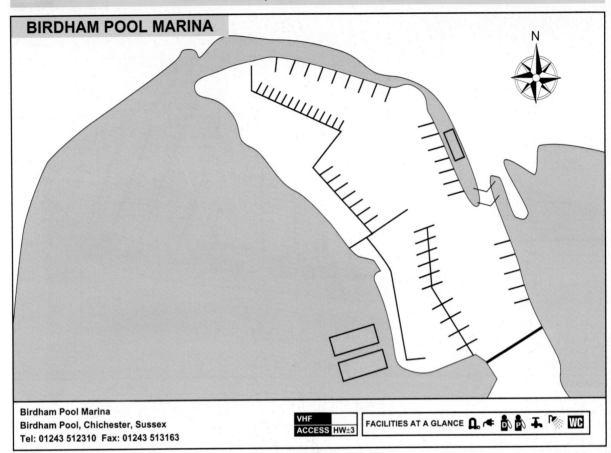

Birdham Pool Marina
Birdham Pool, Chichester, Sussex
Tel: 01243 512310 Fax: 01243 513163

VHF	
ACCESS	HW±3

FACILITIES AT A GLANCE

Planning a trip?

Make it plain sailing
– for your free copy
of the *2002 Marine Weather Services* booklet
call the Met Office Customer Centre
on **0845 300 0300** or go to
www.metoffice.com/leisuremarine/mwsbooklet.html

For a Five-day inshore forecast
for North Foreland – Selsey Bill,
dial **09060 100 456*** from your fax machine.

*09060 calls are charged at £1 per minute at all times.

Met Office

Key to Marina Plans symbols

🔔	Calor Gas	P	Parking
♺	Chandler	✗	Pub/Restaurant
♿	Disabled facilities		Pump out
	Electrical supply	📐	Rigging service
	Electrical repairs		Sail repairs
🔧	Engine repairs	✗	Shipwright
✚	First Aid	🛒	Shop/Supermarket
⚓	Fresh Water		Showers
	Fuel - Diesel		Slipway
	Fuel - Petrol	WC	Toilets
	Hardstanding/boatyard	☎	Telephone
	Laundry facilities		Trolleys
	Lift-out facilities	Ⓥ	Visitors berths

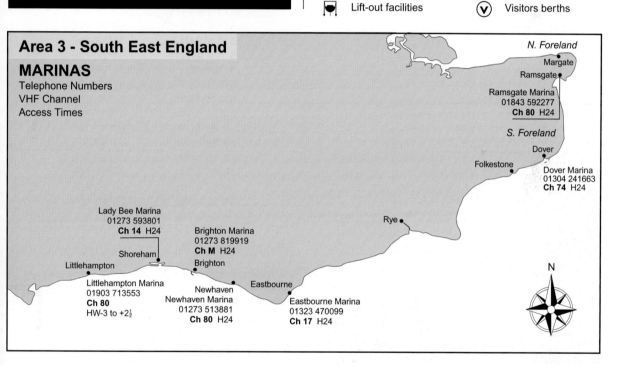

Area 3 - South East England

MARINAS

Telephone Numbers
VHF Channel
Access Times

N. Foreland
Margate
Ramsgate
Ramsgate Marina
01843 592277
Ch 80 H24

S. Foreland
Dover
Folkestone
Dover Marina
01304 241663
Ch 74 H24

Lady Bee Marina
01273 593801
Ch 14 H24

Brighton Marina
01273 819919
Ch M H24

Rye

Shoreham
Brighton
Littlehampton

Littlehampton Marina
01903 713553
Ch 80
HW-3 to +2½

Newhaven
Newhaven Marina
01273 513881
Ch 80 H24

Eastbourne

Eastbourne Marina
01323 470099
Ch 17 H24

N

A & P Ship Care Ramsgate ,Ramsgate 01843 593140

ADEC MARINE LTD
4 Masons Avenue, Croydon, Surrey
CR0 9XS.
TEL: 020 8686 9717
FAX: 020 8680 9912
e-mail: sales@adecmarine.co.uk
www.adecmarine.co.uk
Approved liferaft service station for south east UK. Additionally
we hire and sell new rafts and sell a complete range of safety
equipment for yachts including pyrotechnics, fire extinguishers,
lifejackets, lifebuoys & lights.

Arun Aquasports Littlehampton 01903 713553

Arun Canvas and Rigging Ltd
Littlehampton 01903 732561

Arun Nautique Littlehampton — 01903 730558

Aruncraft Chandlers Littlehampton — 01903 723667

Bosun's Locker Ramsgate — 01843 597158

Brighton HM — 01273 819919

Brighton Marina Boatyard Brighton — 01273 819919

Brighton Marina YC Peacehaven — 01273 818711

Brighton Marina Brighton — 01273 819919

Brighton Police — 01273 606744

Cantell and Son Ltd Newhaven — 01273 514118

Waypoint Guide Area 3 – South East England - Selsey Bill to North Foreland

1	**Nab Tower** - 0·5M NW of	....	50°40'·38N	00°57'·55W
96	**Cherbourg** - 0·5M N of W entrance	....	49°40'·95N	01°39'·35W
132	**Owers SCM** - 1·8M SE of	....	50°36'·80N	00°40'·60W
133	**Boulder Lt by** - 0·1M N of	....	50°41'·60N	00°49'·03W
134	**East Borough Hd Lt By** - 0·1M N of	....	50°41'·60N	00°39'·00W
135	**Littlehampton entrance** - 1M 165°of on leading Lts	....	50°47'·00N	00°32'·00W
136	**Shoreham entrance** - 1M S of on leading Lts	....	50°48'·50N	00°14'·65W
137	**Brighton entrance** - 1M S of	....	50°47'·50N	00°06'·30W
138	**Newhaven entrance** - 1M S of	....	50°45'·50N	00°03'·60E
139	**Beachy Hd** - 1·5M S of	....	50°42'·50N	00°14'·60W
140	**Eastbourne** - 1·2M SE of Langney Pt	....	50°46'·25N	00°21'·10E
141	**Rye** - 0·1M S of Rye Fairway By	....	50°53'·90N	00°48'·13E
142	**Dungeness** - 1M SE of	....	50°54'·00N	00°59'·65E
143	**Folkestone** - 0·5M SE of breakwater	....	51°04'·17N	01°12'·35E
144	**Dover** - 1·2M SE of Western entrance	....	51°05'·80N	01°21'·10E
145	**South Foreland** - 2M E of	....	51°08·70N	01°26'·25E
146	**South Goodwin Lt By** - 0·2M SE of	....	51°I 0'·43N	01°32'·59E
147	**East Goodwin Lt Float** - 0·8M W of	....	51°I 3'·23N	01°35'·20E
148	**East Goodwin Lt By** - 0·2M E of	....	51°I 6'·00N	01°35'·92E
149	**Goodwin Knoll** - 1M SE of	....	51°I 8'·84N	01°33'·43E
150	**Ramsgate** - 1M E of; and for Pegwell Bay	....	51°I 9'·47N	01°27'·13E
151	**North Foreland** - 1M E of	....	51°22'·50N	01°28'·70E
152	**Foreness Pt** - 1M NNE of	....	51°24'·46N	01°26'·36E
153	**Margate** - 0·7M N of	....	51°24'·10N	01°22'·50E
197	**Cap Gris-Nez** - 2·0 M NW of headland	....	50°53'·30N	01°32'·50E
198	**Boulogne** - 2·0 M WNW of entrance	....	50°45'·30N	01°31'·50E
199	**Étaples** - 3·0M W of Le Touquet point	....	50°32'·20N	01°30'·80E
200	**St Valéry-sur-Somme** - 5M WNW Le Hourdel Pt	....	50°15'·30N	01°27'·10E
	Dieppe - 1M NW of entrance	....	49°57'·00N	01°04'·00E
	Fécamp - 1M NW of entrance	....	49°46'·70N	00°20'·80E
	Le Havre - 0·5M NE of Le Havre LHA	....	49°32'·00N	00°09'·20W

Distance Table - South East England

Approximate distances in nautical miles are by the most direct route while avoiding dangers and allowing for Traffic Separation Schemes

		1	2	3	4	5	6	7	8	9	10	11	12	13	14	15	16	17	18
1.	**Portland Bill Lt**	**1**																	
2.	**Nab Tower**	60	**2**																
3.	**Boulder Lt Buoy**	65	5	**3**															
4.	**Owers Lt Buoy**	69	11	8	**4**														
5.	**Littlehampton**	78	19	13	12	**5**													
6.	**Shoreham**	90	32	24	21	13	**6**												
7.	**Brighton**	93	35	28	24	17	5	**7**											
8.	**Newhaven**	97	40	34	29	24	12	7	**8**										
9.	**Beachy Head Lt**	104	46	41	36	30	20	14	8	**9**									
10.	**Eastbourne**	111	51	45	40	34	24	19	12	7	**10**								
11.	**Rye**	129	72	67	62	56	46	41	34	25	23	**11**							
12.	**Dungeness Lt**	134	76	71	66	60	50	44	38	30	26	9	**12**						
13.	**Folkestone**	152	92	84	81	76	65	60	53	43	40	23	13	**13**					
14.	**Dover**	157	97	89	86	81	70	65	58	48	45	28	18	5	**14**				
15.	**Ramsgate**	172	112	104	101	96	85	80	73	63	60	43	33	20	15	**15**			
16.	**N Foreland Lt**	175	115	107	104	99	88	83	76	66	63	46	36	23	18	3	**16**		
17.	**Sheerness**	206	146	139	135	132	119	114	107	97	96	79	67	54	49	34	31	**17**	
18.	**London Bridge**	248	188	184	177	177	161	156	149	139	141	124	109	96	91	76	73	45	**18**

Area 3 - South East England

WAYCHART

Selsey Bill to North Foreland

Marinecall®
MACMILLAN REEDS

Weather Forecasts
by Fax & Telephone

Coastal/Inshore	48-hour by Fax	5-day by Tel
Mid Channel	09061 502 119	09066 526 241
Channel East	09061 502 118	09066 526 240
Anglia	09061 502 117	09066 526 239
National (3-5 day)	09061 502 109	09066 526 234

Offshore	2-5 day by Fax	2-5 day by Tel
English Channel	09061 502 161	09066 526 251
Southern North Sea	09061 502 160	09066 526 252

09066 calls cost 60p per min. 09061 calls cost £1.50 per min.

Symbols used:

- • Port
- ⊙ Waypoint
- — Track – between waypoints
- -- Track – close to possible dangers

ENGLAND

FRANCE

Calais **WP 196** 110° 18 Miles

Boulogne **WP 198** 162° 22 Miles

Boulogne **WP 198** 107° 35 Miles

Eastbourne **WP 140** 288° 45 Miles

Fécamp 195° 70 Miles

Dieppe 138° 68 Miles

Fécamp 165° 63 Miles

Cherbourg 222° 88 Miles

Le Havre LHA 156° 75 Miles

11 Miles

18 Miles

31 Miles

34 Miles

N. Foreland
Ramsgate
Margate
Isle of Sheppey
R. Medway
R. Swale
Whitstable
S. Foreland
Dover
Folkestone
Rye
Dungeness
Eastbourne
Beachy Hd
Newhaven
Brighton
Shoreham
Littlehampton
Chichester Harbour
Nab Tower

Boulogne
Cap d'Alprech
Le Touquet
Etaples

1°E
0°
51°N
30'

N

Miles

0 5 10 15 20 25

Not to be used for navigation

Important Note

Any waypoint being used for the first time must be checked by plotting on a suitable chart. The waypoints listed have been lifted from UK Admiralty charts prior to conversion to WGS 84 datum, so the appropriate datum should be selected in any GPS device being used.

These charts are for planning purposes only, and must not be used for navigation.

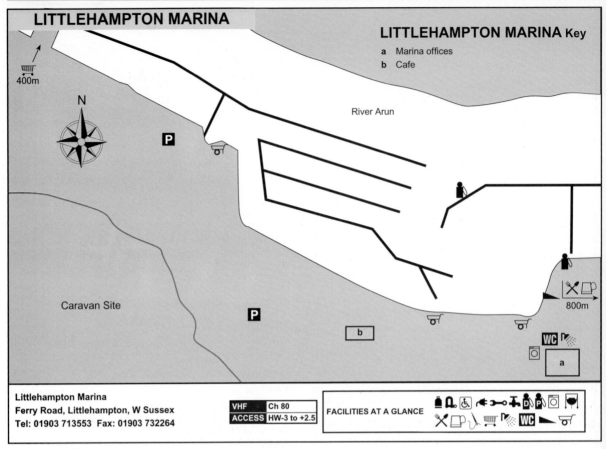

LITTLEHAMPTON MARINA

LITTLEHAMPTON MARINA Key

- **a** Marina offices
- **b** Cafe

400m

N

River Arun

P

Caravan Site

P

b

800m

WC

a

Littlehampton Marina
Ferry Road, Littlehampton, W Sussex
Tel: 01903 713553 Fax: 01903 732264

VHF	Ch 80
ACCESS	HW-3 to +2.5

FACILITIES AT A GLANCE

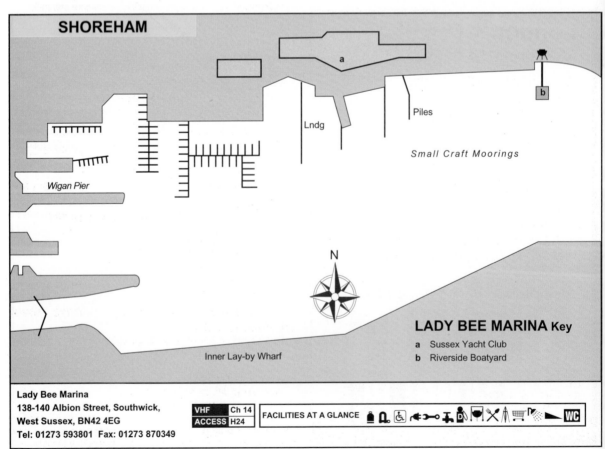

SHOREHAM

a

b

Piles

Lndg

Small Craft Moorings

Wigan Pier

N

Inner Lay-by Wharf

LADY BEE MARINA Key

- **a** Sussex Yacht Club
- **b** Riverside Boatyard

Lady Bee Marina
138-140 Albion Street, Southwick,
West Sussex, BN42 4EG
Tel: 01273 593801 Fax: 01273 870349

VHF	Ch 14
ACCESS	H24

FACILITIES AT A GLANCE

3

AREA

CREWSAVER
Mumby Road, Gosport, Hampshire PO12 1AQ
+44 (0)23 9252 8621
+44 (0)23 9251 090
e-mail: sales@crewsaver.co.uk
www.crewsaver.co.uk
Established manufacturer of lifejackets, lifesaving equipment, sailing clothing and accessories. Check out the latest range of products online at www.crewsaver.co.uk.

David Hillyard Littlehampton	01903 713327
Davis's Yacht Chandler Littlehampton	01903 722778
Dover HM	01304 240400 Ext 4520
Dover Marina Dover	01304 241663
Dover Police	01304 216084
Dover Police	01304 240055
Dover Yacht Co Dover	01304 201073
Eastbourne HM	01323 470099
Eastbourne Police	01323 722522
Fathom Diving (Chislehurst) Chislehurst	020 8289 8237
Folkestone HM	01303 715354
Folkestone Police	01303 850055
Folkestone Yacht and Motor BC Folkestone	01303 251574
GP Barnes Ltd Shoreham	01273 591705/596680

GRAHAM BOOTH MARINE SURVEYS
96 Canterbury Road, Birchington-on-Sea,
Kent CT7 9BB
Tel: (01843) 843793
Fax: (01843) 846860
e-mail: gbma@clare.net
Authorised for MCA Codes of Practice, most frequently on French and Italian Riviera - also for certification of Sail Training vessels and other commercial craft. Call UK office for further information. Other expert marine consultancy services also available.

Hastings and St Leonards YC Hastings	01424 420656

IRON WHARF BOATYARD
Abbeyfields, Faversham, Kent ME13 7BT
Tel: (01795) 537122
Fax: (01795) 532020
Moorings, storage, cranage, chandlery, brokerage and fuel.

Lady Bee Marina Brighton	01273 593801
Littlehampton HM	01903 721215
Littlehampton Marina Littlehampton	01903 713553
Littlehampton Police	01903 731733
Littlehampton Sailing and Motor Club Littlehampton	01903 715859
Newhaven & Seaford SC Seaford	01323 890077
Newhaven HM	01273 612868
Newhaven Marina Ltd Newhaven	01273 513881
Newhaven Police	01273 515801

NORWOOD MARINE
65 Royal Esplanade, Margate, Kent CT9 5ET
Tel: (01843) 835711
Fax: 01843 832044
e-mail: greenfieldgr@aol.com
Marine consultants and advisers. Specialists in collisions, groundings, pioltage, yachting and RYA examinations - Fellows of Nautical Institute and RIN.

Peter Leonard Marine Newhaven	01273 515987

ProProtector LTD
74 Abingdon Road, Maidstone, Kent ME16 9EE
Tel: (01622) 728738
Fax: (01622) 727973
e-mail: sails@prop-protector.co.uk
www.prop-protector.co.uk
Prevention is better than cure when it comes to fouled propellers. ProProtectors are now welcome and used worldwide as the most economical and simplest way to combat stray rope, netting, weed and plastic bags. Fit one before it is too late.

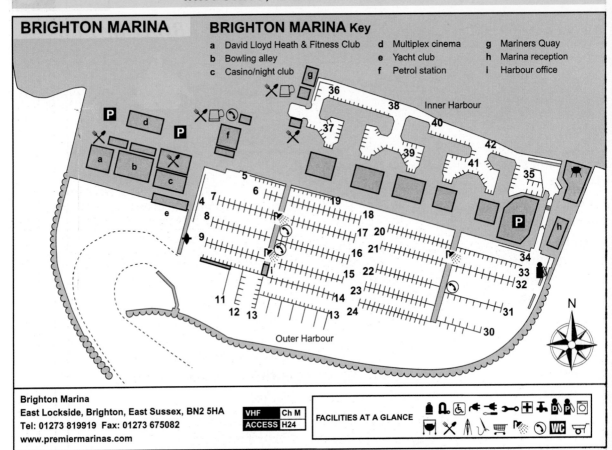

BRIGHTON MARINA

BRIGHTON MARINA Key

- **a** David Lloyd Heath & Fitness Club
- **b** Bowling alley
- **c** Casino/night club
- **d** Multiplex cinema
- **e** Yacht club
- **f** Petrol station
- **g** Mariners Quay
- **h** Marina reception
- **i** Harbour office

Brighton Marina
East Lockside, Brighton, East Sussex, BN2 5HA
Tel: 01273 819919 Fax: 01273 675082
www.premiermarinas.com

VHF Ch M
ACCESS H24

FACILITIES AT A GLANCE

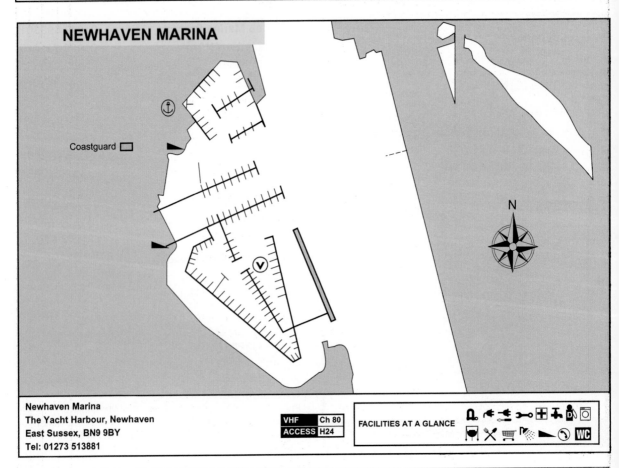

NEWHAVEN MARINA

Newhaven Marina
The Yacht Harbour, Newhaven
East Sussex, BN9 9BY
Tel: 01273 513881

VHF Ch 80
ACCESS H24

FACILITIES AT A GLANCE

BRIGHTON MARINA
East Lockside,
Brighton Marina, Brighton,
East Sussex BN2 5HA
Tel: (01273) 819919
Fax: (01273) 675082
e-mail: brighton@premiermarinas.com
www.premiermarinas.com

The UK's largest marina with 1300 pontoon berths, superb facilities, professional staff, a 24 hour manned reception and CCTV. The marina boasts extensive boatyard services, excellent on shore facilities and is accessible at all states of tide. There are numerous bars/restaurants, superstore, cinema, fitness centre and Bowlplex on site. This PREMIER MARINA is 5 minutes from the city centre.

Ramsgate HM	01843 572100	**Russell Simpson Marine Ltd**	
Ramsgate Police	01843 231055	Newhaven	01273 612612
Ramsgate Royal Harbour Marina		**Rye Harbour SC** Rye	01797 223136
Ramsgate	01843 592277	**Rye Police**	01797 222112
Riverside Yard Shoreham Beach	01273 592456	**Sandrock Marine** Rye	01797 222679
Royal Cinque Ports YC Dover	01304 206262	**Sea Cruisers of Rye** Rye	01797 222070
Royal Harbour Marina Ramsgate	01843 592277	**Sea Technical Services Ltd**	
Royal Temple YC Ramsgate	01843 591766	Denmead	023 92255200
Russell Simpson Marine Ltd		**Sea-Lift Ltd** Dover	01304 201112
Brighton	01273 681543	**Sharp & Enright** Dover	01304 206295
Russell Simpson Marine Ltd		**Shoreham HM**	01273 598100
Eastbourne	01323 470213	**Shoreham Police**	01273 454521
		Shoreham SC Henfield	01273 453078

SILLETTE SONIC LTD
182 Church Hill Road, North Cheam,
Sutton, Surrey SM3 8NF
Tel: (020) 8715 0100
Fax: (020) 8286 0742
Mobile: 0410 270107
e-mail: sales@sillette.co.uk
www.sillette.co.uk

Sillette manufactures a range of propulsion systems - stern drive, saledrives etc and stern gear. Markets Radice & Gori fixed and folding propellors. Acts as agents for Morse controls, Yanmar and Lombardini marine engines, and Fuji Robin generators.

EASTBOURNE

SOVEREIGN HARBOUR Key

a   The Waterfront, shops, restaurants, pubs and offices
b   Harbour office - weather information and visitors information
c   Cinema
d   Retail park - supermarket and post office
e   Restuarant
f   Toilets, showers, telephone, laundrette and disabled facilities
g   24 hr fuel pontoon (diesel, petrol, LPG, and holding tank pump out)
h   Recycling centre
i   Boatyard, boatpark, marine engineers, riggers and electricians

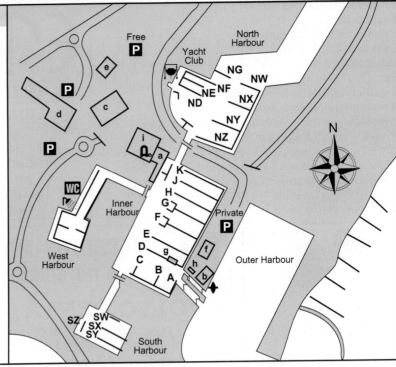

Sovereign Harbour Marina Ltd,
Pevensey Bay Road, Eastbourne,
East Sussex, BN23 6JH
Tel: 01323 470099 Fax: 01323 470077
www.sovereignharbour.co.uk

VHF	Ch17
ACCESS	H24

FACILITIES AT A GLANCE

Smith & Gibbs Eastbourne	01323 734656
Sovereign Harbour Marina Eastbourne	01323 470099
Sovereign Harbour YC Eastbourne	01323 470888
Strand Shipyard Rye	01797 222070
Surry Boatyard Shoreham-by-Sea	01273 461491
Sussex Marine Centre Shoreham	01273 454737
Sussex Marine St Leonards on Sea	01424 425882
Sussex YC Shoreham-by-Sea	01273 464868
UK Customs Nationwide	0845 0109000
Ursula Wilkinson Brighton	01273 677758
XM Yachting Ltd Polegate	01323 870092

DOVER MARINA

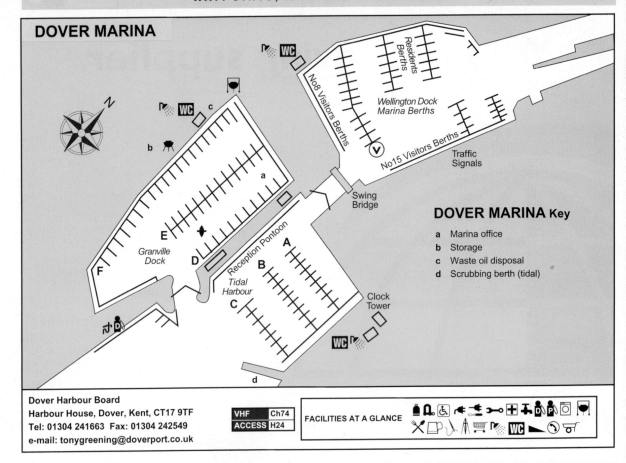

DOVER MARINA Key

a Marina office
b Storage
c Waste oil disposal
d Scrubbing berth (tidal)

Dover Harbour Board
Harbour House, Dover, Kent, CT17 9TF
Tel: 01304 241663 Fax: 01304 242549
e-mail: tonygreening@doverport.co.uk

| VHF | Ch74 |
| ACCESS | H24 |

FACILITIES AT A GLANCE

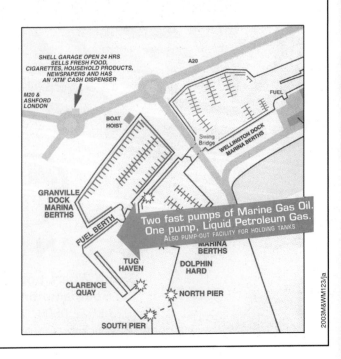

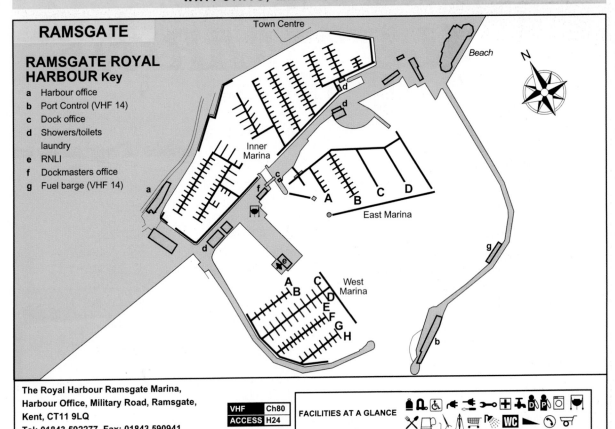

RAMSGATE

RAMSGATE ROYAL HARBOUR Key

a Harbour office
b Port Control (VHF 14)
c Dock office
d Showers/toilets laundry
e RNLI
f Dockmasters office
g Fuel barge (VHF 14)

The Royal Harbour Ramsgate Marina,
Harbour Office, Military Road, Ramsgate,
Kent, CT11 9LQ
Tel: 01843 592277 Fax: 01843 590941
www.ramsgatemarina.co.uk

VHF	Ch80
ACCESS	H24

FACILITIES AT A GLANCE

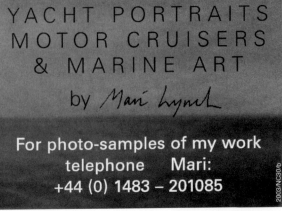

Planning a trip?

Make it plain sailing
– for your free copy
of the *2002 Marine Weather Services* booklet
call the Met Office Customer Centre
on **0845 300 0300** or go to
www.metoffice.com/leisuremarine/mwsbooklet.html

For a five-day inshore forecast
for The Wash – North Foreland,
dial **09060 100 455*** from your fax machine.

*09060 calls are charged at £1 per minute at all times.

Met Office

Key to Marina Plans symbols

♨	Calor Gas	P	Parking
Ⓠ	Chandler	✕	Pub/Restaurant
♿	Disabled facilities	♁	Pump out
🔌	Electrical supply		Rigging service
	Electrical repairs		Sail repairs
⊶	Engine repairs	✂	Shipwright
✚	First Aid	🛒	Shop/Supermarket
⊥	Fresh Water		Showers
Ⓓ	Fuel - Diesel		Slipway
Ⓟ	Fuel - Petrol	WC	Toilets
	Hardstanding/boatyard	Ⓢ	Telephone
⬚	Laundry facilities	⛟	Trolleys
	Lift-out facilities	Ⓥ	Visitors berths

Area 4 - East England

MARINAS

Telephone Numbers
VHF Channel
Access Times

Gallions Pt Marina
020 7476 7054
Ch 80 HW-2½ to+1½
South Dock Marina
020 7252 2244
Ch 80 HW-2½ to+1½
Poplar Dock Marina
020 7515 1046
Ch 13 HW±1
St Katherine Haven
020 7481 8350
Ch 80 HW-2 to+1½
Chelsea Harbour
020 7225 9108
Ch 80 HW+1½
Brentford Dock Marina
020 8232 8941
HW±2½
Penton Hook Marina
01932 568681
Ch 80 H24
Windsor Marina
01753 853911

Fox's Marina 01473 689111 **Ch 80** H24
Neptune Marina 01473 215204 **Ch 68** H24
Ipswich Haven Marina 01473 236644 **Ch 80** H24
Woolverstone Marina 01473 780206 **Ch 80** H24
Suffolk Yacht Hbr 01473 659240 **Ch M** H24

Burnham Yacht Harbour 01621 782150 **Ch M** H24
Essex Marina 01702 258531 **Ch M** H24
West Wick Marina 01621 741268 **Ch M** HW±5
Bridge Marsh Marina 01621 740414 **Ch 80** HW±4

Limehouse Basin
020 7308 9930
Ch 80 HW±3

Hoo Marina 01634 250311 **Ch 80** HW±3

Chatham Marina
01634 899200

Gillingham Marina
01634 280022
Ch 80 HW±4½

Gt Yarmouth
Lowestoft
Royal Norfolk & Suffolk YC
01520 566726
Ch 14, 80 H24
Southwold

Shotley Marina
01473 788982
Ch M H24
Orford
Ipswich
Harwich
Titchmarsh Marina
01255 672185 Walton Yacht Marina
Ch 80 HW±5 01255 675873

Bradwell Marina 01621 776235 **Ch 37, 80** HW±4½
Blackwater Marina 01621 740264 **Ch M** HW±2
Tollesbury Marina 01621 869202 **Ch 80** HW-2
Heybridge Basin 01621 853506 **Ch 80** HW±1

R Thames

N. Foreland

Ramsgate

N

A M Smith(Marine) Ltd London	020 8529 6988
Aldeburgh YC Aldeburgh	01728 452562
Alexandra YC	01702 340363
Allington Marina Maidstone	01622 752057
B & G Marine Maylandsea	01621 743546
Bedwell and Co Walton-on-the-Naze	01255 675873
Benfleet YC Canvey Island	01268 792278

BISHAM ABBEY SAILING & NAVIGATION SCHOOL
National Sports Centre, Bisham, Nr. Marlow, Bucks
SL7 1RT
Tel: (01628) 474960
www.bishamabbeysailing.co.uk

RYA recognised establishment. Dinghy Sailing for adults and children. Shore-based navigation, intensive and semi-intensive - Dayskipper, Yachtmaster, YMOcean. One day - 1st aid, VHF-SRC, Radar, Diesel Engine, Electronic Navigation, CEVNI, Boat handling, Powerboat, IWHC, ICC. Boat Safety Scheme.

Blackwater Marina Maylandsea	01621 740264
Blackwater SC Maldon	01621 853923
Boatacs Westcliffe on Sea	01702 475057
Bradwell CC	01621 892970
Bradwell Chandlery Bradwell-on-Sea	01621 776147
Bradwell Marina Bradwell-on-Sea	01621 776235
Bradwell Quay YC Wickford	01268 776539

Waypoint Guide Area 4 – East England - North Foreland to Great Yarmouth

149	**Goodwin Knoll** - 1M SE of	51°18'·83N	01°33'·40E
150	**Ramsgate** - 1M E Pegwell Bay	51°19'·47N	01°27'·13E
151	**North Foreland** - 1M E	51°22'·50N	01°28'·70E
152	**Foreness Pt** - 1M NNE of	51°24'·46N	01°26'·36E
153	**Margate** - 0·7M N of	51°24'·10N	01°22'·50E
154	**Fisherman's Gat** - SE turning waypoint	51°33'·30N	01°25'·00E
155	**Fisherman's Gat** - NW turning waypoint	51°36'·30N	01°20'·70E
156	**Black Deep/Sunk Sand** - turning waypoint	51°40'·94N	01°25'·00E
157	**Barrow No 2 Lt By** - 0·3M NE	51°42'·16N	01°23'·34E
158	**Barrow No 3 Lt By** - 0·3M N	51°42'·29N	01°20'·35E
159	**Whitaker channel** - for River Crouch (6M)	51°40'·40N	01°05'·30E
160	**Swin Spitway Lt By** - 0·1M SSW	51°41'·83N	01°08'·36E
161	**Spitway North** - turning waypt	51°43'·70N	01°07'·10E
162	**Colne,Blackwater** - 0·3M W Eagle Lt By	51°44'·10N	01°03'·43E
163	**NE Gunfleet Lt By** - 0·5M NW of	51°50'·25N	01°27'·35E
164	**Medusa Lt By** - 0·3M SW of	51°51'·00N	01°20'·00E
165	**Kentish Knock Lt By** - 0·2M E	51°38'·50N	01°40'·80E
166	**Trinity Lt By** - 0·6M N of	51°49'·65N	01°36'·45E
167	**Sunk Lt F** - 0·2M SW of	51°50'·87N	01°34'·80E
168	**Cork Lt By** - 1M E Harwich Yt ch ent	51°55'·35N	01°29'·00E
171	**Orfordness** - 1·5M ESE of	52°04'·20N	01°37'·00E
172	**Southwold** - 2M ESE of ent	52°18'·00N	01°43'·70E
173	**Lowestoft** - 2·8M E of ent	52°28'·30N	01°50'·10E
174	**Gt Yarmouth** - 0·5M WNW of S Corton SCM	52°32'·07N	01°49'·36E
175	**Gt Yarmouth** - 4·7M E of ent	52°34'·33N	01°52'·10E

Distance Table - East England

Approximate distances in nautical miles are by the most direct route while avoiding dangers and allowing for Traffic Separation Schemes

	1	2	3	4	5	6	7	8	9	10	11	12	13	14	15	16	17	18	19	20
1. **Ramsgate**	1																			
2. **Whitstable**	22	2																		
3. **Sheerness**	34	14	3																	
4. **Gravesend**	56	36	22	4																
5. **London Bridge**	76	55	45	23	5															
6. **Southend-on-Sea**	35	17	6	20	43	6														
7. **Havengore**	33	15	12	32	55	12	7													
8. **Burnham-on-Crouch**	44	36	34	53	76	33	30	8												
9. **West Mersea**	43	38	29	49	72	30	29	22	9											
10. **Brightlingsea**	41	36	28	47	71	28	26	22	8	10										
11. **Walton-on-the-Naze**	40	40	46	59	82	39	37	25	23	23	11									
12. **Harwich**	40	40	50	65	83	40	41	31	24	24	6	12								
13. **Ipswich**	49	49	59	74	92	49	50	40	33	33	15	9	13							
14. **River Deben (ent)**	45	45	55	71	89	46	46	35	38	38	10	6	15	14						
15. **River Ore (ent)**	47	47	60	75	93	50	51	38	43	43	14	10	19	4	15					
16. **Southwold**	62	67	80	95	113	70	71	58	63	63	33	30	39	23	20	16				
17. **Lowestoft**	72	77	90	105	123	80	81	68	73	73	43	40	49	33	30	10	17			
18. **Great Yarmouth**	79	84	97	112	130	87	88	76	81	80	51	52	61	41	38	18	7	18		
19. **Blakeney**	123	128	141	156	174	131	132	120	125	124	95	96	105	85	82	62	51	44	19	
20. **Bridlington**	207	198	224	226	244	201	215	204	205	204	181	175	184	169	165	145	135	114	79	20

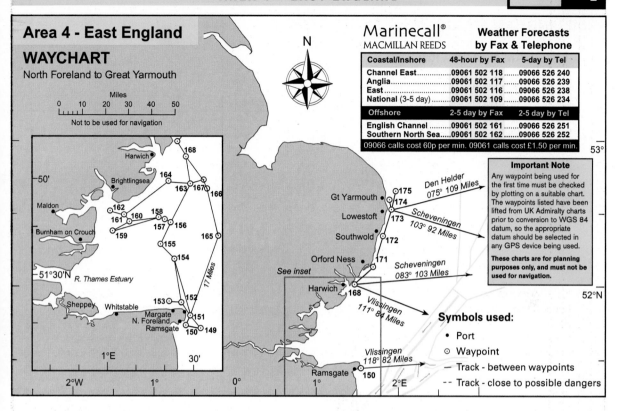

Area 4 - East England
WAYCHART
North Foreland to Great Yarmouth

Miles
0 10 20 30 40 50

Not to be used for navigation

Marinecall®
MACMILLAN REEDS

Weather Forecasts by Fax & Telephone

Coastal/Inshore	48-hour by Fax	5-day by Tel
Channel East	09061 502 118	09066 526 240
Anglia	09061 502 117	09066 526 239
East	09061 502 116	09066 526 238
National (3-5 day)	09061 502 109	09066 526 234

Offshore	2-5 day by Fax	2-5 day by Tel
English Channel	09061 502 161	09066 526 251
Southern North Sea	09061 502 162	09066 526 252

09066 calls cost 60p per min. 09061 calls cost £1.50 per min.

Important Note
Any waypoint being used for the first time must be checked by plotting on a suitable chart. The waypoints listed have been lifted from UK Admiralty charts prior to conversion to WGS 84 datum, so the appropriate datum should be selected in any GPS device being used.

These charts are for planning purposes only, and must not be used for navigation.

Symbols used:
• Port
⊙ Waypoint
— Track - between waypoints
-- Track - close to possible dangers

Brandy Hole YC Hullbridge 01702 230320

BRAY MARINA
Monkey Island Lane, Bray, Berkshire SL6 2EB
Tel: (01628) 623654
Fax: (01628) 773485
e-mail: bray@mdlmarinas.co.uk
www.marinas.co.uk
400 berths with fully serviced pontoons for boats up to 18 metres. 24 hour security. Shower and toilet facilities. Licensed restaurant. Chandlery, car park, fuel and Calor gas. Yacht brokerage, engineering and repair services. Boat lifting and hard standing area.

Brentford Dock Marina Brentford 020 8298 8941

Bridge Marsh Marina Althorpe 01621 740414

Brightlingsea Boatyard Brightlingsea 01206 302003/8

Brightlingsea SC Colchester 01206 303275

Bure Marine Ltd Great Yarmouth 01493 656996

Burnham Yacht Harbour Marina Ltd
Burnham-on-Crouch 01621 782150

Burnham-on-Crouch HM 01621 783602

Burnham-on-Crouch Police 01621 782121

Burnham-on-Crouch Police 01621 782121

Burnham-on-Crouch SC
Burnham-on-Crouch 01621 782812

Cabin Yacht Stores Rochester 01634 718020

Captain O M Watts London 020 7493 4633

Charity & Taylor Ltd Lowestoft 01502 581529

Chatham Maritime Marina Chatham 01634 899200

Chelsea Harbour Marina London 020 7225 9108

Chelsea Harbour Marina
Tel: 020 7225 9108 Fax: 020 7352 7868
Mobile: 07770 542783
A tranquil and intimate marina of 55 berths, close to the heart of the West End of London. 5-Star Hotel – Restaurants – Bars and Overnight River Pontoon with amenities. 24hr security patrols and CCTV.

Chiswick Quay Marina London 020 8994 8743

Colchester Police 01206 762212

Colne YC Brightlingsea 01206 302594

Creeksea SC Burnham-on-Crouch 01245 320578

Crouch YC Burnham-on-Sea 01278 782252

Cuxton Marina Ltd Rochester 01634 721941

D Purcell - Crouch Sailing School
Burnham 01621 784140/0585 33

Danson Marine Sidcup 0208 304 5678

Dauntless Co Canvey Island 01268 793782

DAVID M. CANNELL & ASSOCIATES
River House, Quay Street, Wivenhoe,
Essex CO7 9DD.
Tel: +44 (0) 1206 823 337
Fax: +44 (0) 1206 825 939
e-mail: enquiries@dmcmarine.com
www.dmcmarine.com
Design of yachts and commercial craft to 80m. Newbuilding and refit overseeing. condition surveys, valuations, MCA Code of Practice Compliance and Stability, Expert Witness. Members: Royal Institution of Naval Architects, Yacht Designers and Surveyors Association.

Deben YC Woodbridge 01394 385400

Dinghy Store Whitstable 01227 274168

GILLINGHAM MARINA

GILLINGHAM MARINA Key

a   Undercover storage
b   Workshop
c   Showers & toilets
d   Shop
e   Laundry
f   Play area
g   Reception & club
h   Showers & toilets
i   Tender storage
j   Lead in pontoon
k   Petrol, diesel & marine gas
l   Leisure centre

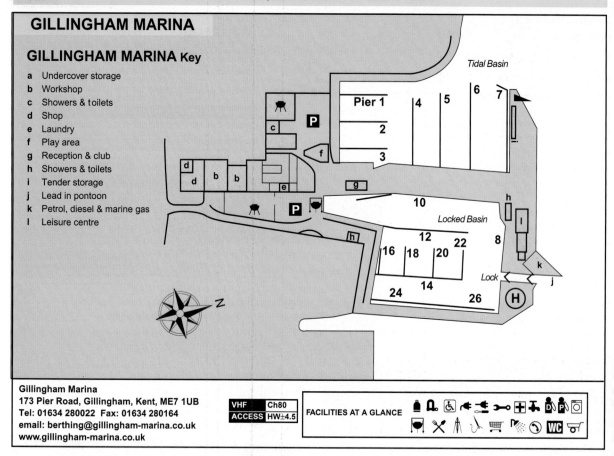

Gillingham Marina
173 Pier Road, Gillingham, Kent, ME7 1UB
Tel: 01634 280022 Fax: 01634 280164
email: berthing@gillingham-marina.co.uk
www.gillingham-marina.co.uk

VHF	Ch80
ACCESS	HW±4.5

FACILITIES AT A GLANCE

HOO MARINA

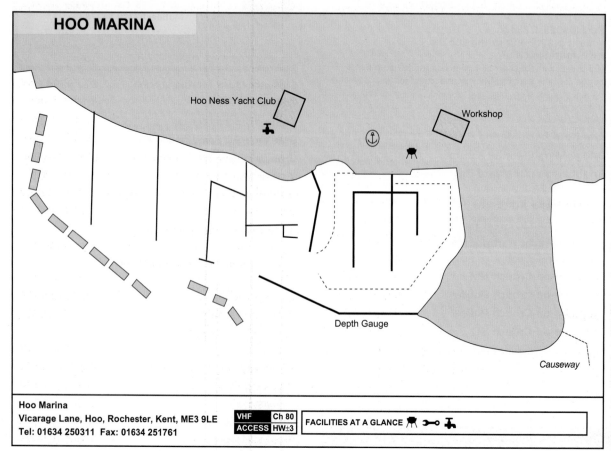

Hoo Marina
Vicarage Lane, Hoo, Rochester, Kent, ME3 9LE
Tel: 01634 250311 Fax: 01634 251761

VHF	Ch 80
ACCESS	HW±3

FACILITIES AT A GLANCE

Dolphin Sails Harwich	01255 243366
Dove Marina London	020 8748 9474
East Anglian Sea School Ipswich	01473 659992
East Coast Sails Walton-on-the-Naze	01255 678353
Elmhaven Marina Halling	01634 240489
ER Birch Boatbuilders	01268 696094
Essex Marina Rochford	01702 258531
Essex YC Southend	01702 478404
Eyott SC Mayland	01245 320703
Fairways Chandlery Burnham-on-Crouch	01621 782659
Fairways Marine Engineers Maldon	01621 852866
Felixarc Marine Ltd Felixstowe	01394 676497
Felixstowe Ferry Boatyard Felixstowe	01394 282173
Felixstowe Ferry SC Felixstowe	01394 283785
Fox's Marina Ipswich Ltd Ipswich	01473 689111
Frank Halls & Son Walton on the Naze	01255 675596

French Marine Motors Ltd Brightlingsea	01206 302133
Gallions Point Marina London	020 7476 7054
Gibbs Chandlery Shepperton	01932 242977
Gillingham Marina Gillingham	01634 280022
Goldfinch Sails Whitstable	01227 272295
Goodchild Marine Services Great Yarmouth	01493 782301
Gorleston Marine Ltd Great Yarmouth	01493 661883
Gowen Sails Nr Colchester	01206 382922
Gravesend SC Gravesend	01474 533974
Great Yarmouth HM	01493 335501
Great Yarmouth Police	01493 336200
Great Yarmouth Police	01493 336200
Greenwich YC London	020 8858 7339
Halcon Marine Ltd Canvey Island	01268 511611
Halfway YC	01702 582025
Hampton Pier YC Herne Bay	01227 364749
Harbour Marine Services Ltd (HMS) Southwold	01502 724721
Harbour Marine Services Ltd Southwold	01502 724721
Harwich Town SC Harwich	01255 503200
Haven Ports YC Woodbridge	01394 659658
Herne Bay SC Herne Bay	01227 375650
Heron Marine Whitstable	01227 361255
Heybridge Basin Maldon	01621 853506
Hoo Marina Rochester	01634 250311
Hoo Ness YC Sidcup	01634 250052
Hullbridge YC	01702 231797
Hurlingham YC London	020 8788 5547
Hyde Sails (Benfleet) Benfleet	01268 756254
Ipswich Haven Marina Ipswich	01473 236644
Iron Wharf Boatyard Faversham	01795 536296
Island YC Canvey Island	01268 510360
J Lawrence Sailmakers Brightlingsea	01206 302863
Jeckells and Son Ltd Lowestoft	01502 565007
Jim Spencer Sailing Services Brightlingsea	01206 302911
John Hawkins Marine Shipstores Rochester	01634 840812
Kew Marina London	020 8940 8364
Leigh-on-Sea SC	01702 476788
LH Morgan & Sons Marine Brightlingsea	01206 302003
Limehouse Basin Marina London	020 7537 2828
Lowestoft CC Lowestoft	01502 574376
Lowestoft HM	01502 572286
Lowestoft Police	01986 855321
Lowestoft Police	01986 855321

CHATHAM MARITIME MARINA

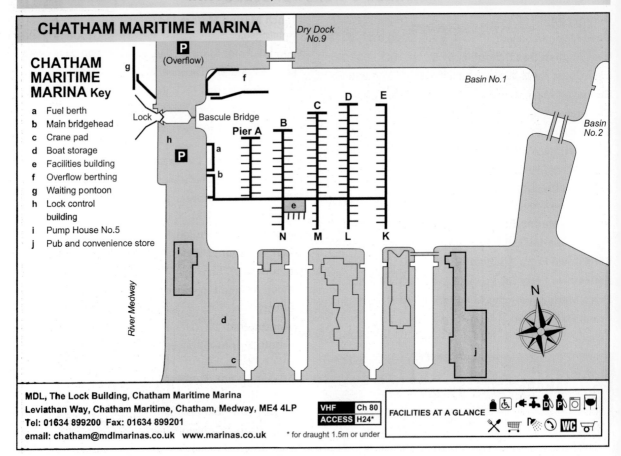

CHATHAM MARITIME MARINA Key

a Fuel berth
b Main bridgehead
c Crane pad
d Boat storage
e Facilities building
f Overflow berthing
g Waiting pontoon
h Lock control building
i Pump House No.5
j Pub and convenience store

MDL, The Lock Building, Chatham Maritime Marina
Leviathan Way, Chatham Maritime, Chatham, Medway, ME4 4LP
Tel: 01634 899200 Fax: 01634 899201
email: chatham@mdlmarinas.co.uk   www.marinas.co.uk

VHF	Ch 80
ACCESS	H24*

* for draught 1.5m or under

FACILITIES AT A GLANCE

GALLIONS POINT MARINA

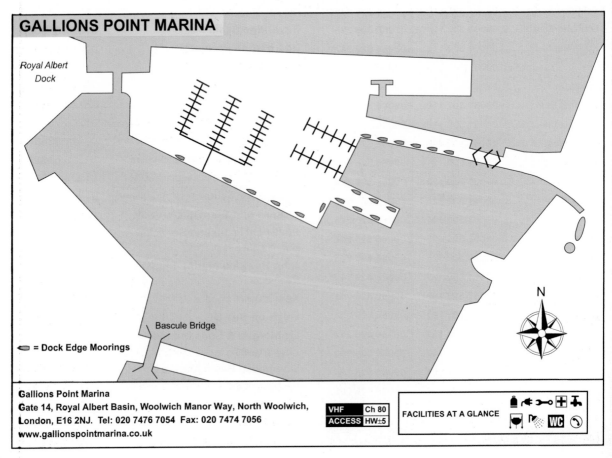

◖ = Dock Edge Moorings

Gallions Point Marina
Gate 14, Royal Albert Basin, Woolwich Manor Way, North Woolwich,
London, E16 2NJ. Tel: 020 7476 7054 Fax: 020 7474 7056
www.gallionspointmarina.co.uk

VHF	Ch 80
ACCESS	HW±5

FACILITIES AT A GLANCE

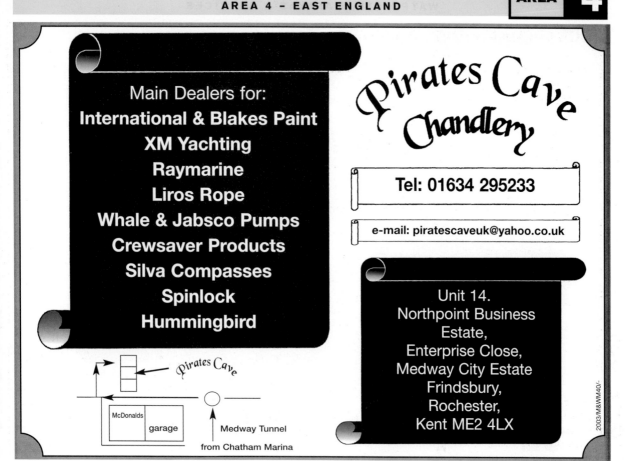

CHATHAM MARITIME MARINA
The Lock Building, Leviathan Way, Chatham Maritime, Chatham, Medway ME4 4LP
Tel: (01634) 899200
Fax: (01634) 899201
e-mail: chatham@mdlmarinas.co.uk
www.marinas.co.uk
New marina on the River Medway in Kent. Accessible from the river at all states of the tide through a lock entrance (restrictions may apply). 300 berth capacity with fully serviced pontoons for boats up to 24 metres. Shower, toilet and laundry facilities. Diesel and petrol fuel. Boat lifting and hard standing area with 20 ton crane.

Maldon Little Ship Club	01621 854139
Margate YC Margate	01227 292602
Marine Force Burnham-on-Crouch	01621 782890
Marine Force London	020 7247 0521
Marine Force London	020 7247 2047
Marine Force London	020 7480 6630
Marine Force Southend-on-Sea	01702 444444
Marine Store Maldon	01621 854280
Marine Store Walton on the Naze	01255 679028
Mariners Farm Boatyard Gillingham	01634 233179
Martello Yacht Services Canvey Island	01268 681970
McKillop Sails (Sail Locker) Ipswich	01473 780007
Medway Bridge Marina Rochester	01634 843576

Medway Diving Contractors Ltd Gillingham	01634 851902
Medway Pier Marina Gillingham	01634 851113
Medway Police	01634 811281
Medway Police	01634 811281
Medway YC Rochester	01634 718399

MICHAEL SHANLY INVESTMENTS LTD
Sorbon, Aylesbury End, Beaconsfield, Bucks HP27 9LB
Tel: (01494) 671331
Fax: (01494) 683912
Saxon moorings Old Windsor - Moorings available.

NEPTUNE MARINA LTD
Neptune Quay, Ipswich, Suffolk IP4 1AX
Tel: (01473) 215204
Fax: (01473) 215206
e-mail: enquiries@neptune-marina.com
www.neptune-marina.com
Accessible through continuously operating lockgates (VHF Channel 68) Neptune Marina (VHF Channels 80 or 37) is located on the north side of Ipswich wet dock immediately adjacent to the town centre and integrated into the rapidly regenerating northern quays.

Norfolk Marine Chandlery Shop Norwich	01603 783150
Norfolk Marine Great Yarmouth	01692 670272
North Fambridge Yacht Centre	01621 740370
North Sea Sails Tollesbury	01621 869367
Ocean Leisure Ltd London	020 7930 5050

SOUTH DOCK MARINA

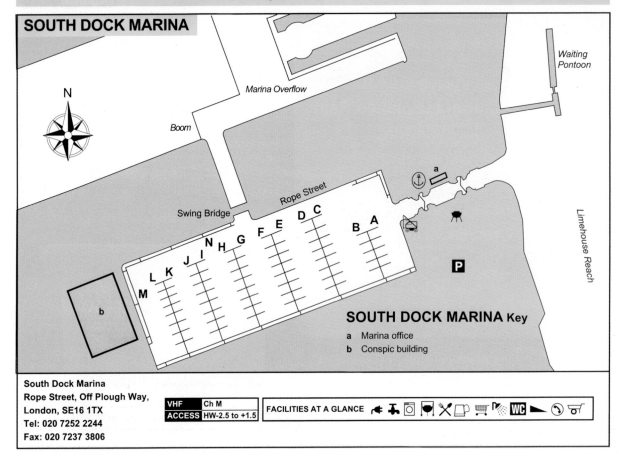

SOUTH DOCK MARINA Key

a Marina office
b Conspic building

South Dock Marina
**Rope Street, Off Plough Way,
London, SE16 1TX
Tel: 020 7252 2244
Fax: 020 7237 3806**

VHF	Ch M
ACCESS	HW-2.5 to +1.5

FACILITIES AT A GLANCE

POPLAR DOCK MARINA

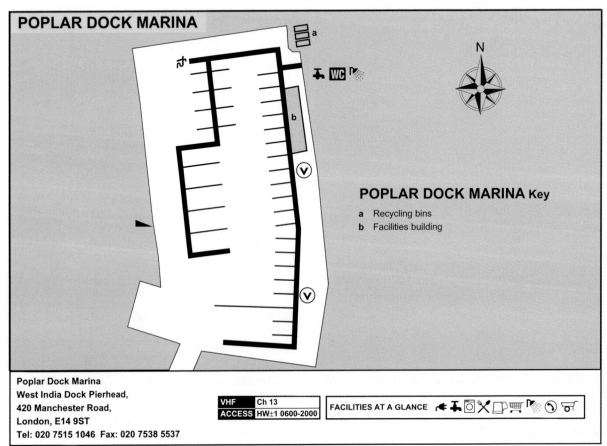

POPLAR DOCK MARINA Key

a Recycling bins
b Facilities building

**Poplar Dock Marina
West India Dock Pierhead,
420 Manchester Road,
London, E14 9ST
Tel: 020 7515 1046 Fax: 020 7538 5537**

VHF	Ch 13
ACCESS	HW±1 0600-2000

FACILITIES AT A GLANCE

LIMEHOUSE BASIN

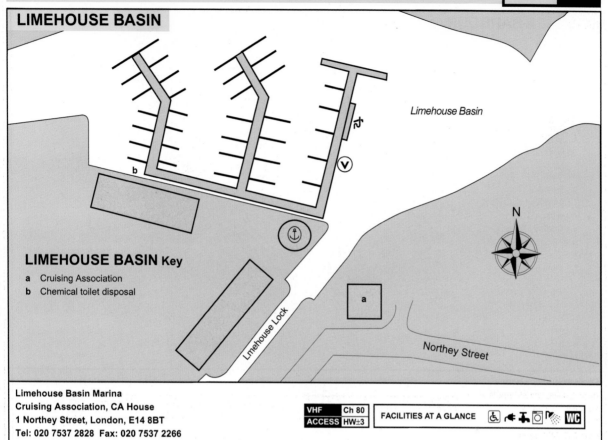

Limehouse Basin

LIMEHOUSE BASIN Key

a Cruising Association
b Chemical toilet disposal

Limehouse Lock

Northey Street

Limehouse Basin Marina
Cruising Association, CA House
1 Northey Street, London, E14 8BT
Tel: 020 7537 2828 Fax: 020 7537 2266

VHF	Ch 80
ACCESS	HW±3

FACILITIES AT A GLANCE

ST KATHARINE HAVEN

ST KATHARINE HAVEN Key

a Ivory House
b Dickens Inn
c Haven office
d Tower Hotel

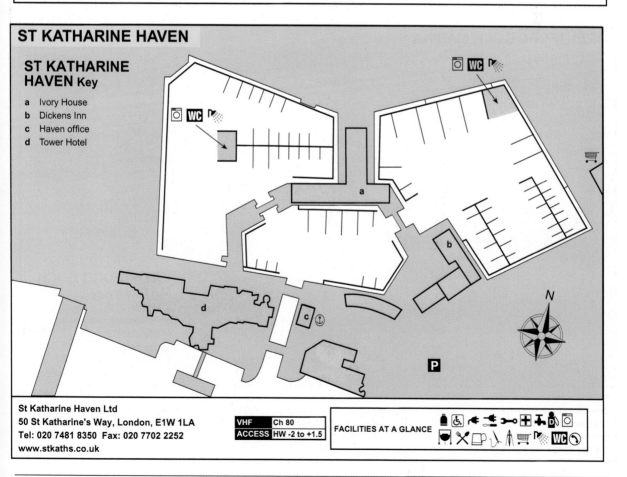

St Katharine Haven Ltd
50 St Katharine's Way, London, E1W 1LA
Tel: 020 7481 8350 Fax: 020 7702 2252
www.stkaths.co.uk

VHF	Ch 80
ACCESS	HW -2 to +1.5

FACILITIES AT A GLANCE

CHELSEA HARBOUR MARINA

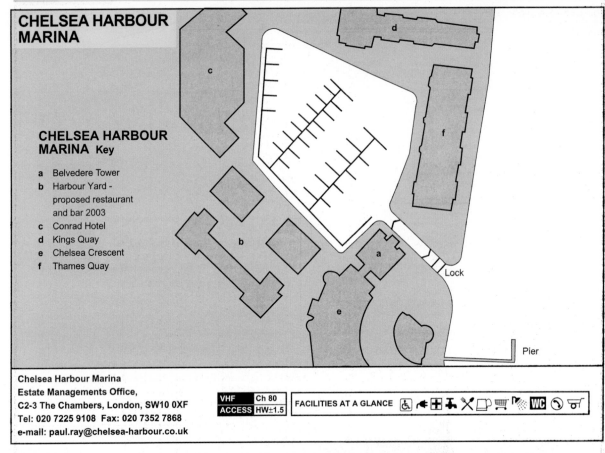

CHELSEA HARBOUR MARINA Key

a Belvedere Tower
b Harbour Yard -
   proposed restaurant
   and bar 2003
c Conrad Hotel
d Kings Quay
e Chelsea Crescent
f Thames Quay

Lock

Pier

Chelsea Harbour Marina
Estate Managements Office,
C2-3 The Chambers, London, SW10 0XF
Tel: 020 7225 9108 Fax: 020 7352 7868
e-mail: paul.ray@chelsea-harbour.co.uk

VHF	Ch 80
ACCESS	HW±1.5

FACILITIES AT A GLANCE

BRENTFORD DOCK MARINA

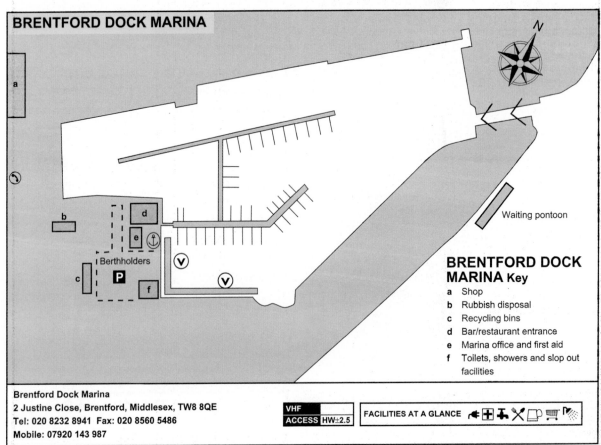

Waiting pontoon

Berthholders

P

BRENTFORD DOCK MARINA Key

a Shop
b Rubbish disposal
c Recycling bins
d Bar/restaurant entrance
e Marina office and first aid
f Toilets, showers and slop out
   facilities

Brentford Dock Marina
2 Justine Close, Brentford, Middlesex, TW8 8QE
Tel: 020 8232 8941 Fax: 020 8560 5486
Mobile: 07920 143 987

VHF	
ACCESS	HW±2.5

FACILITIES AT A GLANCE

One Stop Chandlery Chelmsford	01245 380680
Orford SC Woodbridge	01394 450444
Orwell YC Ipswich	01473 602288
Oulton Broad Yacht Station	01502 574946
Parker & Kay Sailmakers - East Ipswich	01473 659878
Penton Hook Chertsey	01932 568681
Pin Mill SC Woodbridge	01394 780271

PIRATES CAVE LTD
Unit 14, Northpoint Business Estate,
Enterprise Close, Medway City Estate, Frindsbury,
Rochester ME2 4LX
Tel: (01634) 295233
Fax: (01634) 722326
e-mail: piratescaveuk@yahoo.co.uk
We hold a very large stock of general chandlery as well as being main dealers for XM, Silva, Raymarine, Whale, Jabsco, Barton, Spincock and ECS products. Staffed by people with boating experience.

Poplar Dock Marina London	020 7515 1046

Port Medway Marina Rochester	01634 720033
Port of London Authority Gravesend	01474 560311

PREMIUM LIFERAFT SERVICES COLCHESTER
Tel: (01206) 579245
e-mail: info@liferafts.com
www.liferafts.com
Hire and sales of DoT and RORC approved liferafts and safety equipment.

PREMIUM LIFERAFT SERVICES LEVINGTON
Tel: (01473) 659465
Freephone: 0800 243673
e-mail: info@liferafts.com
www.liferafts.com
Hire and sales of DoT and RORC approved liferafts and safety equipment.

PREMIUM LIFERAFT SERVICES LONDON
Tel: 020 8519 2227
Freephone: 0800 243673
e-mail: info@liferafts.com
www.liferafts.com
Hire and sales of DoT and RORC approved liferafts and safety equipment.

PREMIUM LIFERAFT SERVICES WEST MERSEA
Tel: (01206) 382545
Freephone: 0800 243673
e-mail: info@liferafts.com
www.liferafts.com
Hire and sales of DoT and RORC approved liferafts and safety equipment.

Queenborough Harbour

Queenborough Isle of Sheppey	01795 662051
Queenborough HM	01795 662051
Queenborough Police	01795 477055
Queenborough Police	01795 477055
Queenborough YC Queenborough	01795 663955
RF Upson and Co Aldeburgh	01728 453047
Rice and Cole Ltd Burnham-on-Crouch	01621 782063
River Blackwater HM	01621 856487
River Colne (Brightlingsea) HM	01206 302200
River Colne Police	01255 221312
River Colne Police	01255 221312
River Deben HM	01394 270106
River Deben Police	01394 383377
River Medway HM	01795 596593
River Orwell HM	01473 231010
River Orwell Police	01473 233000
River Roach HM	01621 783602
River Stour HM	01255 243000
River Stour Police	01255 241312
Rivers Alde & Ore HM	01473 450481
Rivers Alde and Ore Police	01394 613500
RJ Prior (Burnham) Ltd Burnham-on-Crouch	01621 782160
Robertsons Boatyard Woodbridge	01394 382305

PENTON HOOK MARINA

PENTON HOOK MARINA Key

a Information point
b Dock manager's office

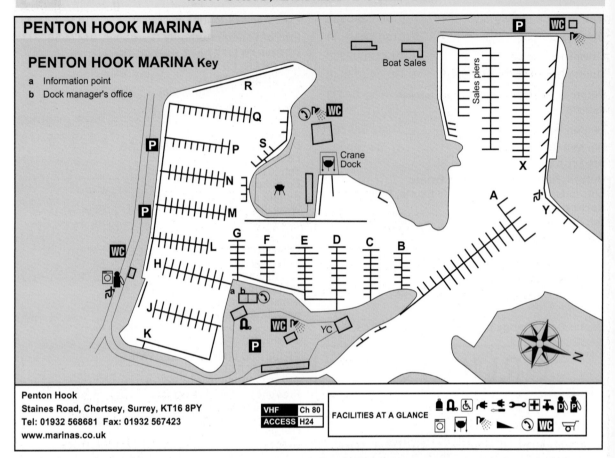

Penton Hook
Staines Road, Chertsey, Surrey, KT16 8PY
Tel: 01932 568681 Fax: 01932 567423
www.marinas.co.uk

| VHF | Ch 80 |
| ACCESS | H24 |

FACILITIES AT A GLANCE

WINDSOR MARINA

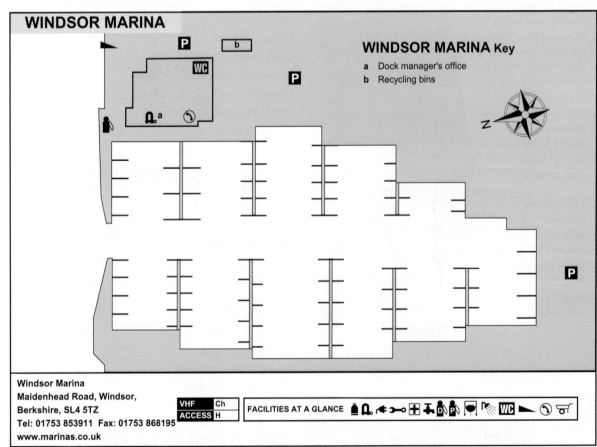

WINDSOR MARINA Key

a Dock manager's office
b Recycling bins

Windsor Marina
Maidenhead Road, Windsor,
Berkshire, SL4 5TZ
Tel: 01753 853911 Fax: 01753 868195
www.marinas.co.uk

| VHF | Ch |
| ACCESS | H |

FACILITIES AT A GLANCE

PENTON HOOK MARINA
Staines Road, Chertsey, Surrey KT16 8PY
Tel: (01932) 568681
Fax: (01932) 567423
e-mail: pentonhook@mdlmarinas.co.uk
www.marinas.co.uk

Britain's largest inland marina. 610 berth marina with fully serviced pontoons for boats up to 30 metres. 24 hour security. Shower, toilet and laundry facilities. Yacht club. Chandlery, car park, fuel and Calor gas. Engineering and repairs. Boat lifting and hard standing area. Refuse and chemical toilet disposal. Trailer boat storage and yacht brokerage.

WINDSOR MARINA
Maidenhead Road, Windsor, Berkshire SL4 5TZ
Tel: (01753) 853911
Fax: (01753) 868195
e-mail: windsor@mdlmarinas.co.uk
www.marinas.co.uk

200 berth marina with fully serviced pontoons for boats up to 15 metres. 24 hour security. Showers and toilet facilities. Private yacht club. Chandlery, yacht brokerage, car park, petrol, diesel and Calor gas. Engineering and repair services. Refuse and chemical toilet disposal and pump-out. Boat lifting and hard standing area with mobile crane. Slipway, trailer boat storage.

AREA **4**

BURNHAM YACHT HARBOUR

BURNHAM YACHT HARBOUR
Key

a Workshop
b Yacht sales
c Marina office
d Chandlery
e Shower block
f The Swallowtail
g RNLI shore station
h Country park

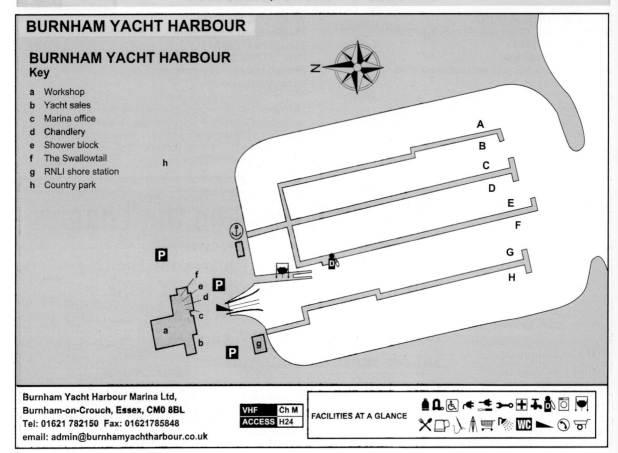

Burnham Yacht Harbour Marina Ltd,
Burnham-on-Crouch, Essex, CM0 8BL
Tel: 01621 782150 Fax: 01621785848
email: admin@burnhamyachtharbour.co.uk

VHF	Ch M
ACCESS	H24

FACILITIES AT A GLANCE

ESSEX MARINA

Small Craft Moorings

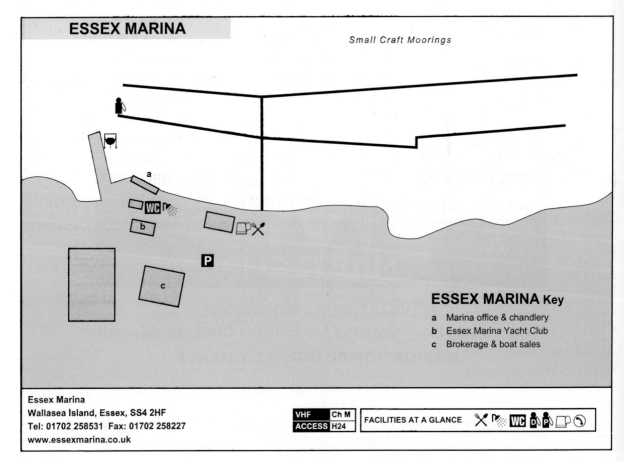

ESSEX MARINA Key

a Marina office & chandlery
b Essex Marina Yacht Club
c Brokerage & boat sales

Essex Marina
Wallasea Island, Essex, SS4 2HF
Tel: 01702 258531 Fax: 01702 258227
www.essexmarina.co.uk

VHF	Ch M
ACCESS	H24

FACILITIES AT A GLANCE

WEST WICK MARINA

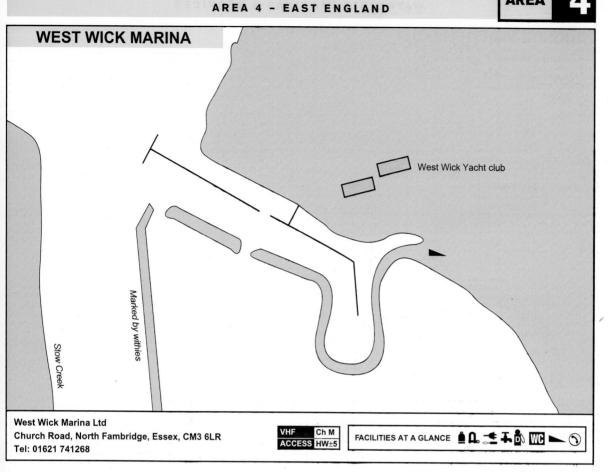

Marked by withies

Stow Creek

West Wick Yacht club

West Wick Marina Ltd
Church Road, North Fambridge, Essex, CM3 6LR
Tel: 01621 741268

VHF	Ch M
ACCESS	HW±5

FACILITIES AT A GLANCE

AREA 4

PREMIUM LIFERAFT SERVICES
Head Office: Liferaft House,
Burnham Business Park,
Burnham-on-Crouch, Essex CM0 8TE.
Freephone: 0800 243673
Fax: (01621) 785934 e-mail: info@liferafts.com
Hire, servicing and sales of DoT and RORC approved liferafts and other safety equipment. Long and short-term hire from 26 depots nationwide – see Area by Area section for regional units.

Rochester CC Rochester	01634 841350
Royal Burnham YC Burnham-on-Crouch	01621 782044
Royal Corinthian YC (Burnham-on-Crouch) Burnham-on-Crouch	01621 782105

Royal Harwich YC Ipswich   01473 780319
ROYAL INSTITUTE OF NAVIGATION
1 Kensington Gore,
London SW7 2AT
Tel: (020) 7591 3130
Fax: (020) 7591 3131
e-mail: info@rin.org.uk
www.rin.org.uk
Forum for all interested in navigation - Air: Sea: Land: Space.

Royal Norfolk & Suffolk YC
Lowestoft   01502 566726

Royal Norfolk and Suffolk Yacht Club
Lowestoft   01502 566726

BRIDGE MARSH MARINA

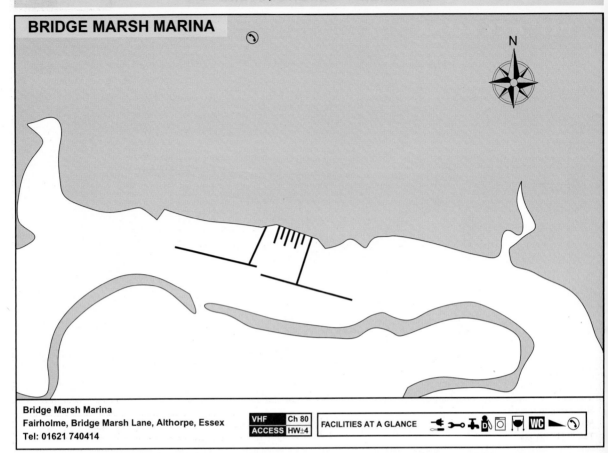

Bridge Marsh Marina
Fairholme, Bridge Marsh Lane, Althorpe, Essex
Tel: 01621 740414

VHF	Ch 80
ACCESS	HW±4

FACILITIES AT A GLANCE

BRADWELL MARINA

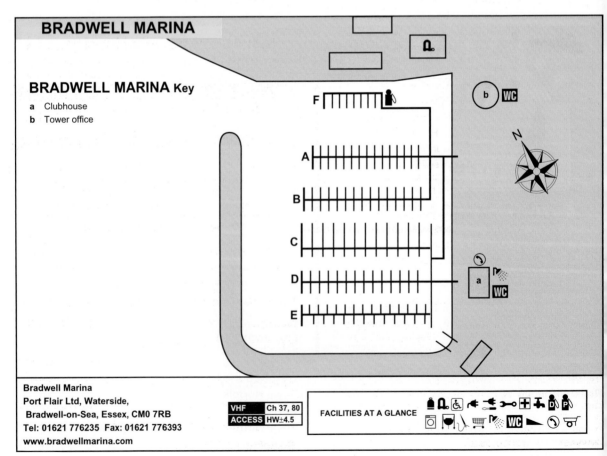

BRADWELL MARINA Key

a Clubhouse
b Tower office

Bradwell Marina
Port Flair Ltd, Waterside,
Bradwell-on-Sea, Essex, CM0 7RB
Tel: 01621 776235 Fax: 01621 776393
www.bradwellmarina.com

VHF	Ch 37, 80
ACCESS	HW±4.5

FACILITIES AT A GLANCE

BLACKWATER MARINA

BLACKWATER MARINA Key

a   Maylandsea Bay YC
b   Harlow (Blackwater) Sailing Club

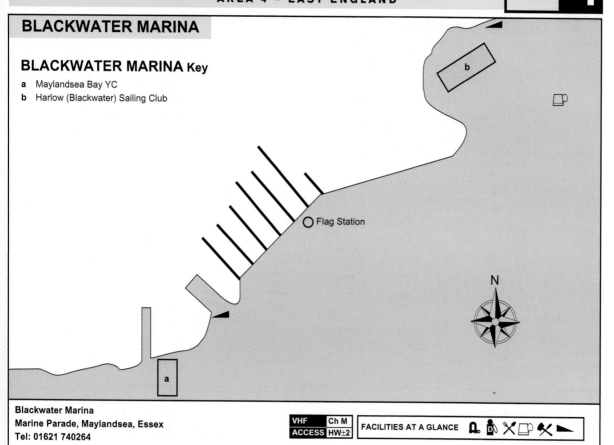

Flag Station

N

Blackwater Marina
Marine Parade, Maylandsea, Essex
Tel: 01621 740264

VHF	Ch M
ACCESS	HW±2

FACILITIES AT A GLANCE

TOLLESBURY MARINA

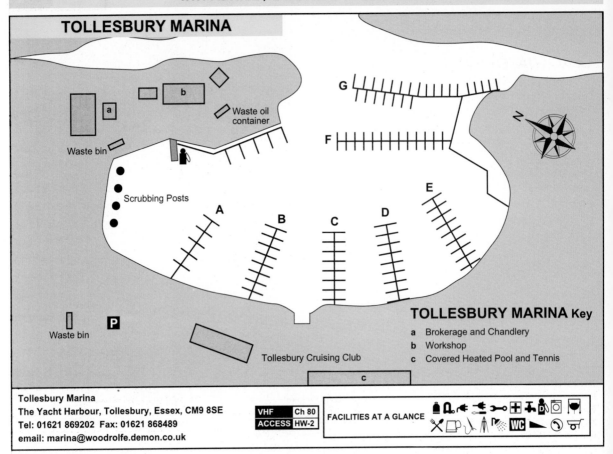

TOLLESBURY MARINA Key

a   Brokerage and Chandlery
b   Workshop
c   Covered Heated Pool and Tennis

Tollesbury Marina
The Yacht Harbour, Tollesbury, Essex, CM9 8SE
Tel: 01621 869202 Fax: 01621 868489
email: marina@woodrolfe.demon.co.uk

VHF   Ch 80
ACCESS   HW-2

FACILITIES AT A GLANCE

HEYBRIDGE BASIN

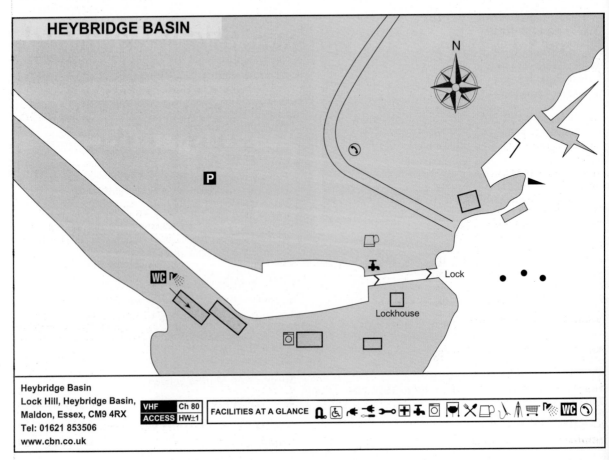

Heybridge Basin
Lock Hill, Heybridge Basin,
Maldon, Essex, CM9 4RX
Tel: 01621 853506
www.cbn.co.uk

VHF   Ch 80
ACCESS   HW±1

FACILITIES AT A GLANCE

TITCHMARSH MARINA

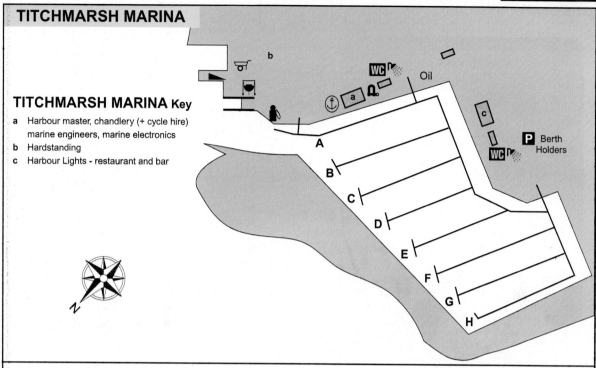

TITCHMARSH MARINA Key

a   Harbour master, chandlery (+ cycle hire) marine engineers, marine electronics
b   Hardstanding
c   Harbour Lights - restaurant and bar

Titchmarsh Marina Ltd
Coles Lane, Walton on the Naze,
Essex, CO14 8SL
Tel: 01255 672185 Fax: 01255 851901
www.titchmarshmarina.co.uk email: office@titchmarshmarina.co.uk

VHF	Ch80
ACCESS	HW±5

FACILITIES AT A GLANCE

HARBOUR LIGHTS RESTAURANT
(Walton-on-the-Naze) Ltd
**Titchmarsh Marina, Coles Lane,
Walton-on-the-Naze, Essex CO14 8SL
Tel: (01255) 851887
Fax: (01255) 677300
www.titchmarshmarina.com**

Open 7 days a week the Harbour Lights provides fine views overlooking the marina and a warm welcome. English/continental breakfasts and extensive bar meals are served daily. Summer evening barbecues and a la carte restaurant with traditional English fayre.

TITCHMARSH MARINA
**Coles Lane, Walton-on-the-Naze,
Essex CO14 8SL
Tel: (01255) 672185
Fax: (01255) 851901
www:titchmarshmarina.com**

Friendly service in the peaceful backwaters. Visiting yachtsmen welcome. Sheltered marina berths. Full marina facilities: Travel-lift, cranage, 16-amp electricity, diesel. Winter storage. Brokerage. Restaurant and bar (see Harbour Lights Restaurant.)

Small Craft Deliveries Ltd	
Woodbridge	01394 382655
Smith AM (Marine) Ltd London	020 8529 6988
South Dock Marina London	020 7252 2244
South Woodham Ferrers YC	
Chelmsford	01245 325391
Southend-on-Sea HM	01702 611889
Southend-on-Sea Police	01702 341212

Southwold HM	01502 724712
Southwold Police	01986 855321
Southwold SC	01502 716776
St Katharine Haven London	020 7481 8350
Stanford's International Map Centre	
London	020 7836 1321

SHOTLEY MARINA

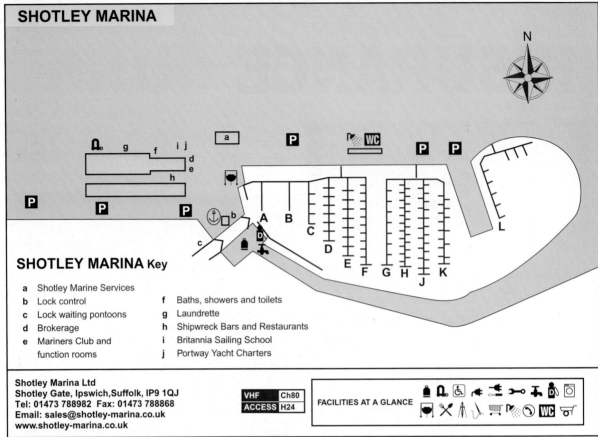

SHOTLEY MARINA Key

a Shotley Marine Services
b Lock control
c Lock waiting pontoons
d Brokerage
e Mariners Club and
  function rooms
f Baths, showers and toilets
g Laundrette
h Shipwreck Bars and Restaurants
i Britannia Sailing School
j Portway Yacht Charters

Shotley Marina Ltd
Shotley Gate, Ipswich, Suffolk, IP9 1QJ
Tel: 01473 788982 Fax: 01473 788868
Email: sales@shotley-marina.co.uk
www.shotley-marina.co.uk

VHF	Ch80
ACCESS	H24

FACILITIES AT A GLANCE

WALTON YACHT BASIN

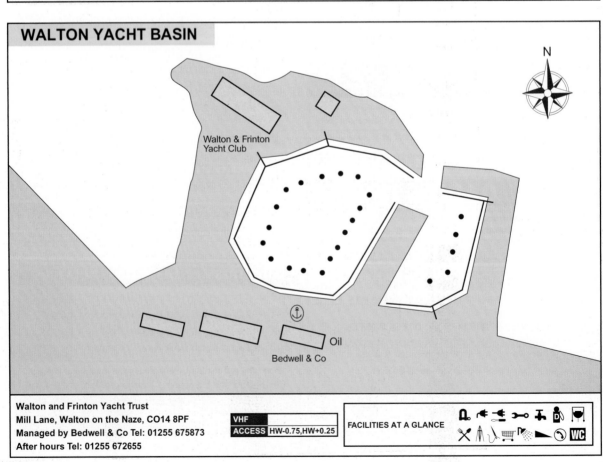

Walton & Frinton Yacht Club

Oil

Bedwell & Co

Walton and Frinton Yacht Trust
Mill Lane, Walton on the Naze, CO14 8PF
Managed by Bedwell & Co Tel: 01255 675873
After hours Tel: 01255 672655

VHF	
ACCESS	HW-0.75, HW+0.25

FACILITIES AT A GLANCE

FOX'S MARINA

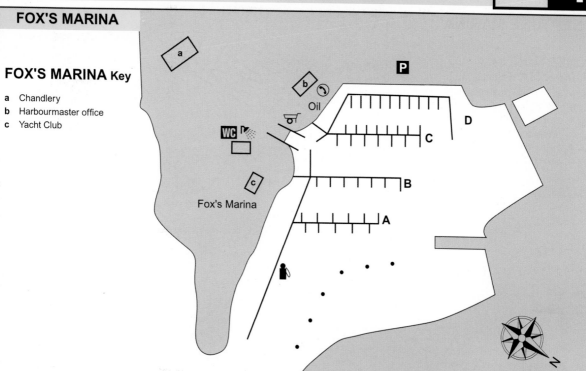

FOX'S MARINA Key

a Chandlery
b Harbourmaster office
c Yacht Club

Fox's Marina

Fox's Marina Ltd
The Strand, Wherstead, Ipswich, Suffolk, IP2 8SA
Tel: 01473 689111 Fax: 01473 601737

VHF	Ch80
ACCESS	H24

FACILITIES AT A GLANCE

AREA **4**

FOX's MARINA IPSWICH LTD
The Strand, Ipswich, Suffolk IP2 8SA
Tel: (01473) 689111
Fax: (01473) 601737

Comprehensive boatyard. New 100ft workshop. Specialists in osmosis and spray painting. Marina access 24hrs. Diesel dock, travel hoists to 70 tons, 10 ton crane. Full electronics, rigging, engineering, stainless steel services. Extensive chandlery.

SHOTLEY MARINA LTD
Shotley Gate, Ipswich,
Suffolk IP9 1QJ.
Tel: (01473) 788982
Fax: (01473) 788868
e-mail: sales@shotley-marina.co.uk
www.shotley-marina.co.uk

A modern state of the art marina with 350 berths offering all the services expected. Open 24-hours with full security. Access all states of tide, ideal cruising base. Well stocked chandlery and general store, repair facilities, laundry and ironing centre, showers/baths and toilets. Restaurants, bar, children's room, TV/video and function rooms with dance floor and bar. Disabled facilities.

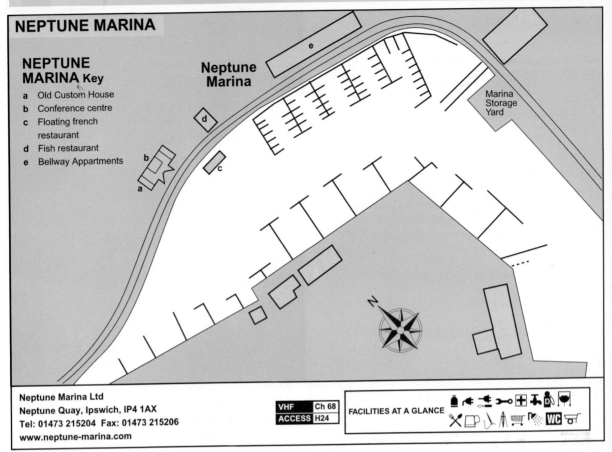

NEPTUNE MARINA

NEPTUNE MARINA Key

a Old Custom House
b Conference centre
c Floating french restaurant
d Fish restaurant
e Bellway Appartments

Neptune Marina

Marina Storage Yard

Neptune Marina Ltd
Neptune Quay, Ipswich, IP4 1AX
Tel: 01473 215204 Fax: 01473 215206
www.neptune-marina.com

VHF Ch 68
ACCESS H24

FACILITIES AT A GLANCE

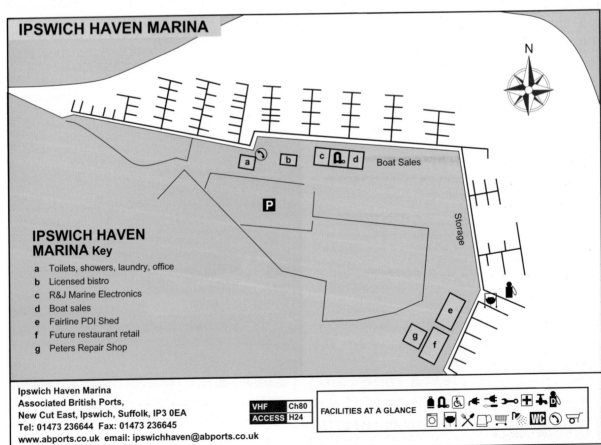

IPSWICH HAVEN MARINA

Boat Sales

Storage

P

IPSWICH HAVEN MARINA Key

a Toilets, showers, laundry, office
b Licensed bistro
c R&J Marine Electronics
d Boat sales
e Fairline PDI Shed
f Future restaurant retail
g Peters Repair Shop

Ipswich Haven Marina
Associated British Ports,
New Cut East, Ipswich, Suffolk, IP3 0EA
Tel: 01473 236644 Fax: 01473 236645
www.abports.co.uk email: ipswichhaven@abports.co.uk

VHF Ch80
ACCESS H24

FACILITIES AT A GLANCE

IPSWICH HAVEN MARINA
New Cut East, Ipswich, Suffolk IP3 0EA
Tel: (01473) 236644
Fax: (01473) 236644
e-mail: ipswichhaven@abports.co.uk
5 gold anchor marina, access through lock manned 24 hours, 70 tonne boat hoist, storage ashore, licenced club house, chronology, new and used boat sales, 5 mins walk from Ipswich town centre, 10 mins to station.

Stoke SC Ipswich	01473 780815
Stour SC	01206 393924
Strood YC Aylesford	01634 718261
Suffolk Sails Woodbridge	01394 386323
Suffolk Yacht Harbour Ltd Ipswich	01473 659240
Swale HM	01795 561234
Swale Marina Ltd Teynham	01795 521562
T C S Chandlery Grays	01375 374702
Thames Estuary HM	01474 562200
Thames Estuary Police	020 7275 4421

Marinecall REEDS
MACMILLAN
WEATHER FORECASTS BY FAX & TELEPHONE

Coastal/Inshore	2-day by Fax	5-day by Phone
National (3-5 day)	09061 502 109	09066 526 234
Scotland North	09061 502 110	09066 526 235
Scotland East	09061 502 114	09066 526 236
North East	09061 502 115	09066 526 237
East	09061 502 116	09066 526 238
Anglia	09061 502 117	09066 526 239
Channel East	09061 502 118	09066 526 240
Mid Channel	09061 502 119	09066 526 241
South West	09061 502 120	09066 526 242
Bristol	09061 502 121	09066 526 243
Wales	09061 502 122	09066 526 244
North West	09061 502 123	09066 526 245
Clyde	09061 502 124	09066 526 246
Caledonia	09061 502 125	09066 526 247
Minch	09061 502 126	09066 526 248
Northern Ireland	09061 502 127	09066 526 249
Mid Channel	09061 502 119	09066 526 241
English Channel	09061 502 161	09066 526 251
S North Sea	09061 502 162	09066 526 252
Irish Sea	09061 502 163	09066 526 253
Biscay	09061 502 164	09066 526 254
NW Scotland	09061 502 165	09066 526 255
N North Sea	09061 502 166	09066 526 2569

09066 CALLS COST 60P PER MIN. 09061 CALLS COST £1.50 PER MIN.

Thames Estuary YC	01702 345967

THE DINGHY STORE
The Sea Wall, Whitstable, Kent CT5 1BX
Tel: (01227) 274168
Fax: (01227) 772750
e-mail: sales@thedinghystore.co.uk
www.thedinghystore.co.uk
One of the largest marine chandlers in Kent. 1st floor: Harken, Holt, RWO, Marlow, International Paints, charts, books. 2nd floor: Musto, Henri Lloyd, Gill, Crewsaver, Chatham, Icom radios. Open seven days a week in summer months.

The Swale Police	01795 536639
Thorpe Bay YC	01702 587563
Thurrock YC Grays	01375 373720
Tide Mill Yacht Harbour Woodbridge	01394 385745
Titchmarsh Marina Walton-on-the-Naze	01255 672185
Tollesbury CC Tollesbury	01621 869561
Tollesbury Marina Tollesbury	01621 869202
UK Customs Nationwide	0845 0109000
Up River YC Hullbridge	01702 231654
Upnor SC Upnor	01634 718043
Wakering YC Rochford	01702 530926
Waldringfield SC Wickham Market	01728 736633
Walton & Frinton YC Walton-on-the-Naze	01255 675526
Walton and Frinton Yacht Trust Walton on the Naze	01255 675873
Walton Backwaters Police	01255 241312
Walton Backwaters Police	01255 241312
Walton-on-the-Naze HM	01255 851899
West Mersea Police	01206 382930
West Mersea Police	01206 382930
West Mersea YC Colchester	01206 382947
West Wick Marina Ltd Nr Chelmsford	01245 741268
Whitstable HM	01227 274086

WHITSTABLE MARINE
The Sea Wall, Whitstable, Kent CT5 1BX
Tel: (01227) 262525
Fax: (01227) 772750
e-mail: sales@thedinghystore.co.uk
www.thedinghystore.co.uk
Main Mercury outboard dealer. Sales & service. Quicksilver GRP boats and new inflatables. O'Brien waterskiing equipment. Quicksilver oils and lubes.

Whitstable Police	01227 770055
Whitstable YC Whitstable	01227 272343
Wilkinson Sails Teynham	01795 521503
Windsor Marina Windsor	01753 853911
Wivenhoe SC Colchester	01206 822132
Woodbridge CC Woodbridge	01394 386737
Woodrolfe Boatyard Maldon	01621 869202
Woolverstone Marina Ipswich	01473 780206
Wyatts Chandlery Ltd Colchester	01206 384745
Yare Boatique Norwich	01603 715289

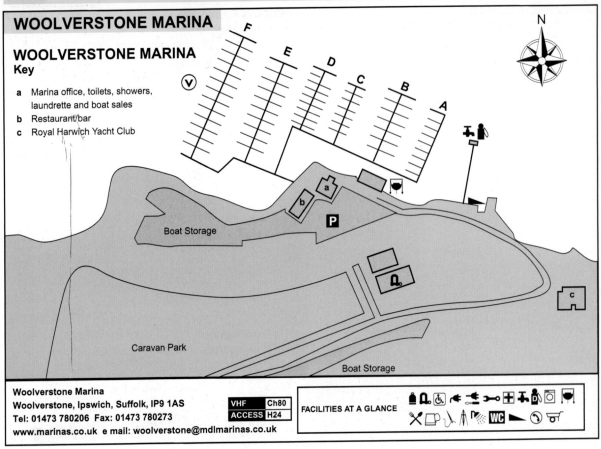

WOOLVERSTONE MARINA

WOOLVERSTONE MARINA
Key

a Marina office, toilets, showers, laundrette and boat sales
b Restaurant/bar
c Royal Harwich Yacht Club

Boat Storage

Caravan Park

Boat Storage

Woolverstone Marina
Woolverstone, Ipswich, Suffolk, IP9 1AS
Tel: 01473 780206 Fax: 01473 780273
www.marinas.co.uk e mail: woolverstone@mdlmarinas.co.uk

VHF Ch80
ACCESS H24

FACILITIES AT A GLANCE

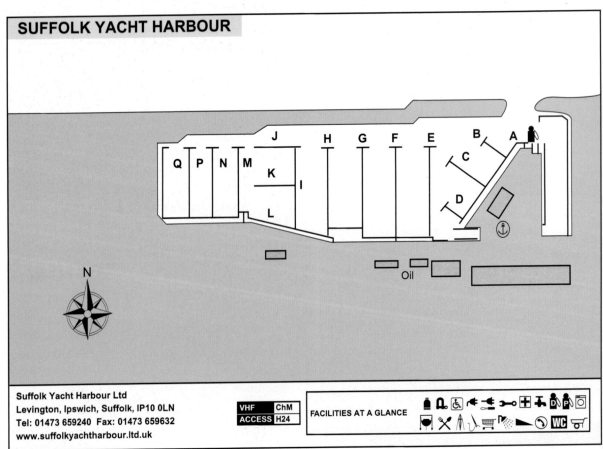

SUFFOLK YACHT HARBOUR

Oil

Suffolk Yacht Harbour Ltd
Levington, Ipswich, Suffolk, IP10 0LN
Tel: 01473 659240 Fax: 01473 659632
www.suffolkyachtharbour.ltd.uk

VHF ChM
ACCESS H24

FACILITIES AT A GLANCE

BLUE BAKER YACHTS
Charter & Brokerage Management.
Woolverstone Marina,
Woolverstone, Ipswich, Suffolk IP9 1AS
Tel: (01473) 780111 / 780008
Fax: (01473) 780911
e-mail:
brokerage@bluebakeryachts.com
www.bluebakeryachts.com
Blue Baker Yacht Management, East Coast Brokerage and Charter Management for bareboat, skippered and corporate yacht charters. Sales of new and used yachts.

QUANTUM-PARKER & KAY SAILMAKERS - EAST
Suffolk Yacht Harbour,
Levington, Ipswich,
Suffolk IP10 0LN
Tel: (01473) 659878
Fax: (01473) 659197
e-mail: jparker@quantumsails.com
www.quantumsails.com
A complete sail making service, from small repairs to the construction of custom designed sails for racing or cruising yachts. Covers constructed for sail and powercraft, plus the supply of all forms of sail handling hardware.

WOOLVERSTONE MARINA
Woolverstone, Ipswich,
Suffolk IP9 1AS
Tel: (01473) 780206
Fax: (01473) 780273
e-mail:
woolverstone@mdlmarinas.co.uk
www.marinas.co.uk
210 berth marina with fully serviced pontoons for boats up to 24 metres. 120 swining moorings with water taxi service. 24 hour security. Shower, toilet and laundry facilities. Chandlery, foodstore, restaurant and bar. Car park, diesel fuel and Calor gas. Boat lifting and hard standing area with 20 ton mobile crane. Repair yard. Storage sheds. Yacht brokerage, sailing school and caravan park.

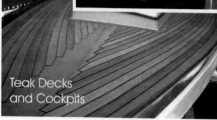

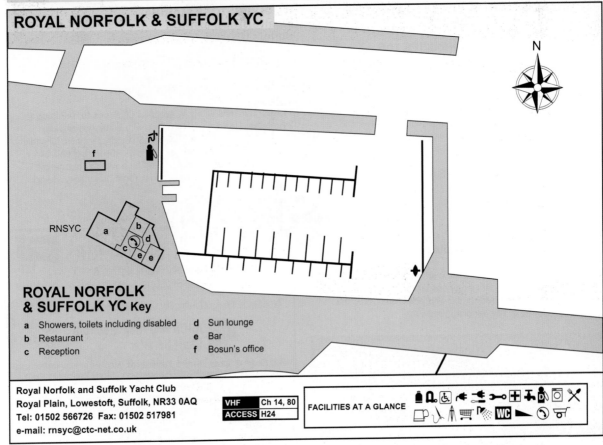

ROYAL NORFOLK & SUFFOLK YC

RNSYC

ROYAL NORFOLK & SUFFOLK YC Key

a Showers, toilets including disabled
b Restaurant
c Reception
d Sun lounge
e Bar
f Bosun's office

Royal Norfolk and Suffolk Yacht Club
Royal Plain, Lowestoft, Suffolk, NR33 0AQ
Tel: 01502 566726 Fax: 01502 517981
e-mail: rnsyc@ctc-net.co.uk

VHF	Ch 14, 80
ACCESS	H24

FACILITIES AT A GLANCE

Planning a trip?

Make it plain sailing – for your free copy of the *2002 Marine Weather Services* booklet call the Met Office Customer Centre on **0845 300 0300** or go to www.metoffice.com/leisuremarine/mwsbooklet.html

For a five-day inshore forecast for the Wash – North Foreland, dial **09060 100 455*** from your fax machine.
For Whitby – the Wash, dial **09060 100 454.***
For Berwick – Whitby dial **09060 100 453.***

*09060 calls are charged at £1 per minute at all times.

Key to Marina Plans symbols

Calor Gas		P	Parking
Chandler			Pub/Restaurant
Disabled facilities			Pump out
Electrical supply			Rigging service
Electrical repairs			Sail repairs
Engine repairs			Shipwright
First Aid			Shop/Supermarket
Fresh Water			Showers
Fuel - Diesel			Slipway
Fuel - Petrol		WC	Toilets
Hardstanding/boatyard			Telephone
Laundry facilities			Trolleys
Lift-out facilities		V	Visitors berths

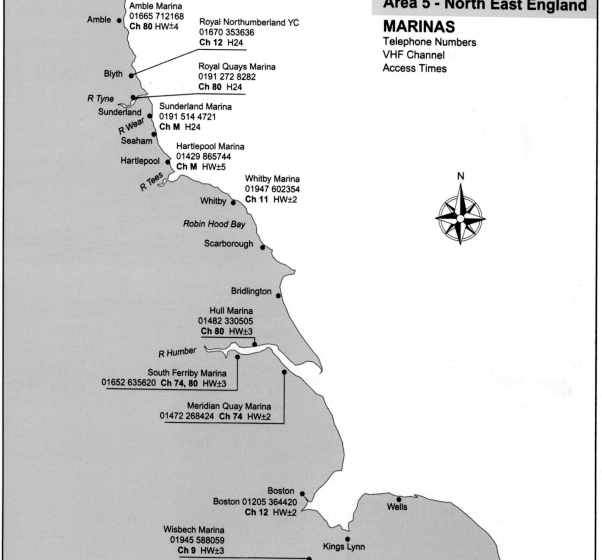

Area 5 - North East England

MARINAS
Telephone Numbers
VHF Channel
Access Times

Amble

Amble Marina
01665 712168
Ch 80 HW±4

Royal Northumberland YC
01670 353636
Ch 12 H24

Blyth

Royal Quays Marina
0191 272 8282
Ch 80 H24

R Tyne
Sunderland

Sunderland Marina
0191 514 4721
Ch M H24

R Wear
Seaham

Hartlepool

Hartlepool Marina
01429 865744
Ch M HW±5

R Tees

Whitby Marina
01947 602354
Ch 11 HW±2

Whitby

Robin Hood Bay

Scarborough

Bridlington

Hull Marina
01482 330505
Ch 80 HW±3

R Humber

South Ferriby Marina
01652 635620 **Ch 74, 80** HW±3

Meridian Quay Marina
01472 268424 **Ch 74** HW±2

Boston
Boston 01205 364420
Ch 12 HW±2

Wells

Wisbech Marina
01945 588059
Ch 9 HW±3

Kings Lynn

Waypoint Guide Area 5 – North East England - Great Yarmouth to Berwick-upon-Tweed

174	Gt Yarmouth - 0·5M WNW of S Corton SCM	52°32'·07N	01°49'·36E
175	Gt Yarmouth - 4·7M E of ent	52°34'·33N	01°52'·10E
176	Winterton - 0·5M NE Cockle ECM	52°44'·40N	01°44'·20E
177	Winterton - 5·2M NE of	52°46'·90N	01°48'·50E
178	Cromer - 3·0M NNE of Lt	52°58'·15N	01°21'·20E
179	North Well Lt By - 0·5M NE	53°03'·35N	00°28'·60E
180	Inner Dowsing Lt By - 0·5M NE of	53°20'·10N	00°34'·50E
181	Spurn Head - 2·6M Eof Spurn Lightship	53°34'·80N	00°17'·70E
182	Flamborough Head - 2·0 M E	54°07'·10N	00°01'·10W
183	Scarborough - 1·0M E of ent	54°16'·87N	00°21'·56W
184	Robin Hood's Bay - 2·6M NE	54°26'·40N	00°27'·30W
185	Whitby - 1·6M N of ent	54°31'·10N	00°36'·60W
186	River Tees - Fairway Buoy	54°40'·93N	01°06'·38W
187	Seaham - 0·9M E of ent	54°50'·40N	01°17'·70W
188	Sunderland - 1·7M E of ent	54°55'·25N	01°18'·10W
189	R Tyne - 1·7 M E by N of ent	55°01'·15N	01°21'·10W
190	Blyth - 1·5M E of entrance	55°07'·00N	01°26'·50W
191	Amble - 2·5M NE of ent	55°21'·85N	01°30'·70W
192	Farne Island - 2·0 M NE of Longstone Lt	55°40'·00N	01°33'·95W
193	Holy Island - 1·0M NE of Emmanuel Hd	55°41'·95N	01°45'·50W
194	Berwick-upon-Tweed - 1·5M E of Breakwater	55°45'·90N	01°56'·30W

Amble Boat Co Ltd Amble	01665 710267
Amble HM	01665 710306
Amble Marina Amble	01665 712168
B Cooke & Son Ltd Hull	01482 223454
Berwick-upon-Tweed HM	01289 307404
Berwick-upon-Tweed Police	01289 307111
Blyth HM	01670 352678
Blyth Marina Blyth	01679 353636
Blyth Police	01661 872555
Boston HM	01205 362328
Boston Marina Boston	01205 364420
Boston Police	01205 366222
Brancaster Sailing and Sailboard Centre Kings Lynn	01485 210236
Brancaster Staithe SC	01485 210249
Bridlington HM	01262 670148/9
Bridlington Police	01262 672222

BURGH CASTLE MARINA
Butt Lane, Burgh Castle, Norfolk NR31 9PZ
Tel: (01493) 780331
Fax: (01493) 780163
e-mail: burghcastlemarina@aol.com
Safe pontoon moorings with full tidal access on river Waveney and Bellamy Goldaways Holiday Park. One hour sail from sea. Central for Broadland cruising. Amenities include pub-restaurant, pool, showers, laundery & exhibition centre.

Breathtakingly Beautiful Burgh
Cruise centre for Broadland and the Norfolk Coast
Our peaceful location at the confluence
of the Yare and Waveney Rivers and the
Head of Breydon Water is ideal for day cruising
inland or at sea
Tel: 01493 780331 Fax: 01493 780163
Email: burghcastlemarin@aol.com

Burnham Overy Staithe SC	01328 730961
C & J Marine Services Newcastle Upon Tyne	0191 295 0072
C & M Marine Bridlington	01262 672212
Castlegate Marine Club Stockton on Tees	01642 583299
Clapson & Son (Shipbuilders) Ltd Barton-on-Humber	01652 635620
Cliff Reynolds Hartlepool	01429 272049
Coastal Marine Boatbuilders (Berwick upon Tweed) Eyemouth	01890 750328

COATES MARINE LTD
Northern Spars & rigging Services, The Marina Boatyard, Whitby, North Yorkshire YO21 1EU
Tel: (01947) 604486
Fax: (01947) 600580
Boat storage and repairs, full rigging services, repairs, clothing, chandlery.

Coquet YC	01665 711179
Divesafe Sunderland	0191 567 8423
Divetech UK King's Lynn	01485 572323
Eccles Marine Co Middlesbrough	01642 230123
Farrow & Chambers Yacht Builders Humberston	01472 632424
Fishermans Mutual Asssociation (Eyemouth) Ltd Eyemouth	01890 750373
George Hewitt Binham	01328 830078
Gibbons Ship Chandlers Ltd Sunderland	0191 567 2101
Grimsby and Cleethorpes YC Grimsby	01472 356678
Hartlepool Marina Hartlepool	01429 865744

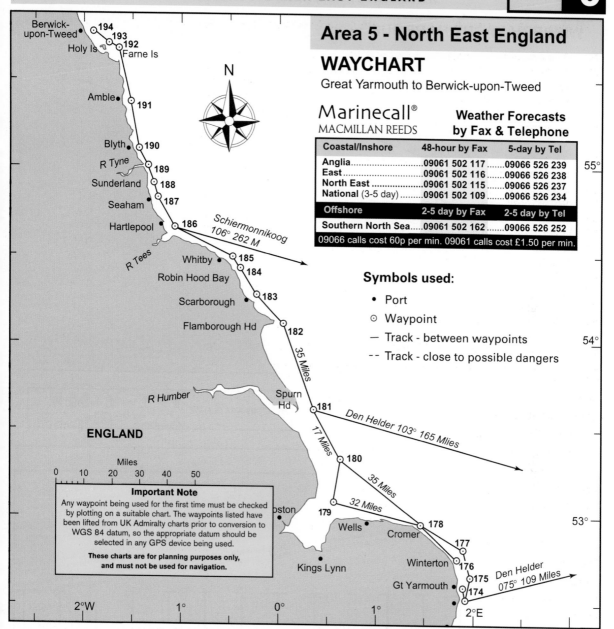

Area 5 - North East England

WAYCHART
Great Yarmouth to Berwick-upon-Tweed

Marinecall®
MACMILLAN REEDS

Weather Forecasts
by Fax & Telephone

Coastal/Inshore	48-hour by Fax	5-day by Tel
Anglia	09061 502 117	09066 526 239
East	09061 502 116	09066 526 238
North East	09061 502 115	09066 526 237
National (3-5 day)	09061 502 109	09066 526 234
Offshore	2-5 day by Fax	2-5 day by Tel
Southern North Sea	09061 502 162	09066 526 252

09066 calls cost 60p per min. 09061 calls cost £1.50 per min.

Symbols used:

- • Port
- ⊙ Waypoint
- — Track - between waypoints
- -- Track - close to possible dangers

Important Note

Any waypoint being used for the first time must be checked by plotting on a suitable chart. The waypoints listed have been lifted from UK Admiralty charts prior to conversion to WGS 84 datum, so the appropriate datum should be selected in any GPS device being used.

These charts are for planning purposes only, and must not be used for navigation.

Distance Table - North East England

Approximate distances in nautical miles are by the most direct route while avoiding dangers and allowing for Traffic Separation Schemes

	1	2	3	4	5	6	7	8	9	10	11	12	13	14	15	16	17	18	19	20
1. Great Yarmouth	1																			
2. Blakeney	44	2																		
3. King's Lynn	85	42	3																	
4. Boston	83	39	34	4																
5. Humber Lt Buoy	82	45	55	54	5															
6. Grimsby	99	54	61	58	17	6														
7. Hull	113	68	75	72	31	14	7													
8. Bridlington	114	79	87	83	35	44	58	8												
9. Scarborough	130	96	105	98	50	59	81	20	9											
10. Whitby	143	101	121	114	66	75	88	35	16	10										
11. River Tees (ent)	166	122	138	135	87	96	118	56	37	21	11									
12. Hartlepool	169	126	140	137	89	98	122	58	39	24	4	12								
13. Seaham	175	137	151	145	100	106	133	66	47	33	15	11	13							
14. Sunderland	180	142	156	149	105	110	138	70	51	36	20	16	5	14						
15. Tynemouth	183	149	163	154	112	115	145	75	56	41	27	23	12	7	15					
16. Blyth	190	156	171	162	120	123	153	83	64	49	35	31	20	15	8	16				
17. Amble	203	170	185	176	126	143	157	102	81	65	46	42	32	27	21	14	17			
18. Holy Island	225	191	196	198	148	166	180	126	104	88	68	65	54	50	44	37	22	18		
19. Berwick-on-Tweed	232	200	205	205	157	166	189	126	107	91	82	78	67	61	55	47	31	9	19	
20. Eyemouth	240	208	213	213	165	174	197	134	115	99	90	86	75	69	63	55	39	17	8	20

WISBECH YACHT HARBOUR

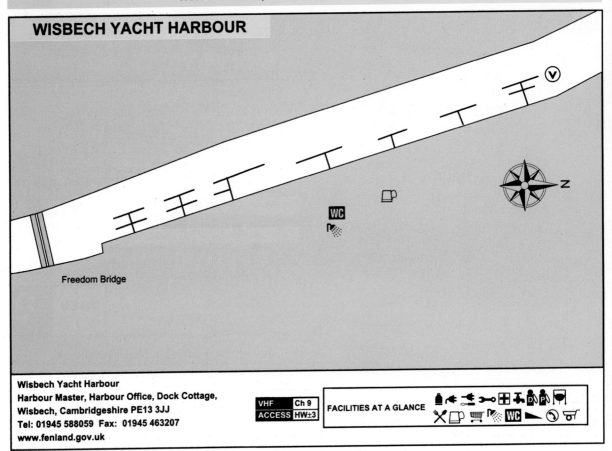

Freedom Bridge

Wisbech Yacht Harbour
Harbour Master, Harbour Office, Dock Cottage,
Wisbech, Cambridgeshire PE13 3JJ
Tel: 01945 588059 Fax: 01945 463207
www.fenland.gov.uk

VHF	Ch 9
ACCESS	HW±3

FACILITIES AT A GLANCE

BOSTON MARINA

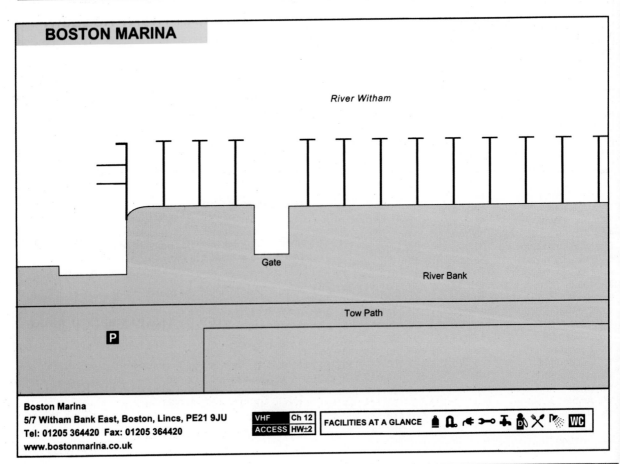

River Witham

Gate

River Bank

Tow Path

P

Boston Marina
5/7 Witham Bank East, Boston, Lincs, PE21 9JU
Tel: 01205 364420 Fax: 01205 364420
www.bostonmarina.co.uk

VHF	Ch 12
ACCESS	HW±2

FACILITIES AT A GLANCE

MERIDIAN QUAY MARINA

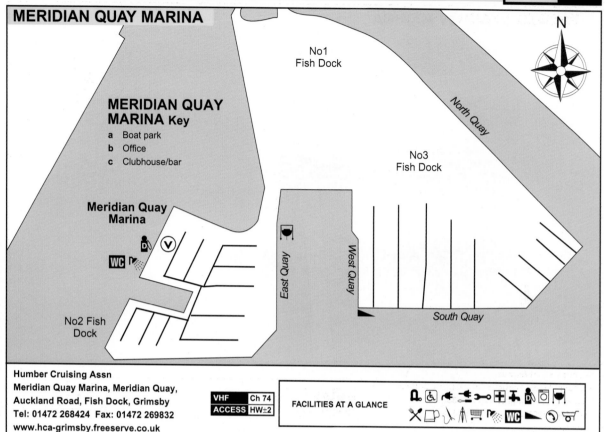

No1
Fish Dock

North Quay

No3
Fish Dock

**MERIDIAN QUAY
MARINA Key**

a   Boat park
b   Office
c   Clubhouse/bar

**Meridian Quay
Marina**

East Quay

West Quay

South Quay

No2 Fish
Dock

Humber Cruising Assn
Meridian Quay Marina, Meridian Quay,
Auckland Road, Fish Dock, Grimsby
Tel: 01472 268424 Fax: 01472 269832
www.hca-grimsby.freeserve.co.uk

VHF	Ch 74
ACCESS	HW±2

FACILITIES AT A GLANCE

WISBECH YACHT HARBOUR
Dock Cottage, Crab Marsh, Wisbech, Cambs
PE13 3JJ
Tel: 01945 588059
Fax: 01945 463207
e-mail: torbeau@btclick.com
www.fenland.gov.uk/harbour
The finest moorings between the Humber and Lowestoft! 102 all
afloat, fully serviced pontoon moorings in heart of historic,
Georgian Wisbech. Max. 40m LOA. Unbeatable rates. Visitors
welcome. Pilot guide and brochure available.

Hartlepool Marine Engineering Hartlepool	01429 867883
Hartlepool Marine Supplies Hartlepool	01429 862932
Hartlepool Police	01429 221151
Hartlepool YC Hartlepool	01429 233423
Holy Island HM	01289 389217
Hull Marina Hull	01482 330505
Humber Cruising Association Marina Grimsby	01472 268424
Humber Yawl Club	01724 733458
Imray Laurie Norie and Wilson Ltd Huntingdon	01480 462114
Jeckells and Son Ltd (Wroxham) Wroxham	01603 782223
John Lilley & Gillie Ltd North Shields	0191 257 2217
John Lilley and Gillie Ltd North Shields	0191 258 3519
Kildale Marine Hull	01482 227464
Meridian Quay Marina Grimsby	01472 268424
Naburn Marina	01904 621021
North Sunderland Marine Club Sunderland	01665 721231
Northern Divers (Engineering) Ltd Hull	01482 227276

SOUTH FERRIBY MARINA

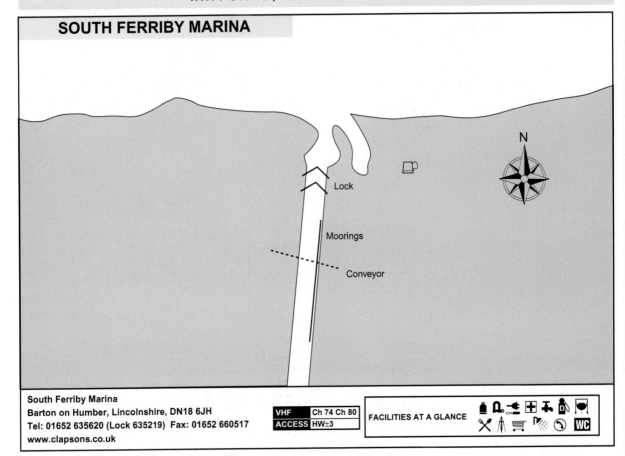

Lock

Moorings

Conveyor

N

South Ferriby Marina
Barton on Humber, Lincolnshire, DN18 6JH
Tel: 01652 635620 (Lock 635219) Fax: 01652 660517
www.clapsons.co.uk

VHF	Ch 74 Ch 80
ACCESS	HW±3

FACILITIES AT A GLANCE

HULL MARINA

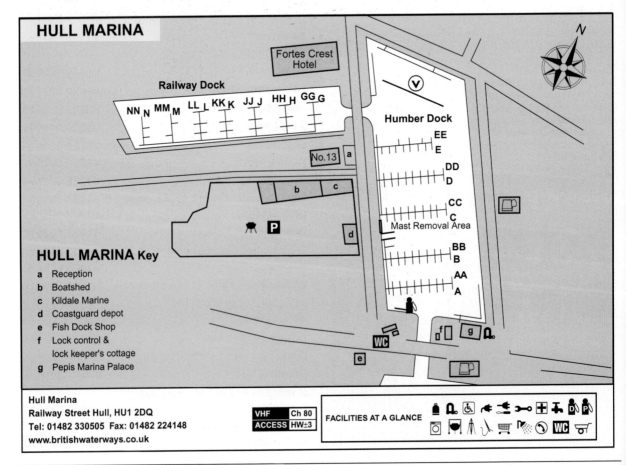

Fortes Crest Hotel

Railway Dock

NN N MM M LL L KK K JJ J HH H GG G

Humber Dock

EE
E

DD
D

CC
C

Mast Removal Area

BB
B

AA
A

No.13 a

b   c

P

d

WC

f g

e

HULL MARINA Key

a Reception
b Boatshed
c Kildale Marine
d Coastguard depot
e Fish Dock Shop
f Lock control &
   lock keeper's cottage
g Pepis Marina Palace

Hull Marina
Railway Street Hull, HU1 2DQ
Tel: 01482 330505 Fax: 01482 224148
www.britishwaterways.co.uk

VHF	Ch 80
ACCESS	HW±3

FACILITIES AT A GLANCE

NORTHSHORE
The Boat Yard, Brancaster Staithe, King's Lynn, Norfolk PE31 8BP
Tel: (01485) 210236
e-mail: info@northshoresport.co.uk
www.sailcraft.co.uk
Northshore - situated at the head of Brancaster Staithe harbour - is Norfolk's premier chandlery. Stockists of Barton - Harken etc. Suppliers of Musto - Gill & Henri Lloyd. Plus Sailcraft Sea School - dinghy & powerboat & shore based yachtmaster training.

Ouse Amateur SC Kings Lynn	01553 772239
PA Lynch Ltd Morpeth	01670 512291
Parker Yachts and Dinghys Ltd Nr Boston	01205 722697

PREMIUM LIFERAFT SERVICES MORPETH
Tel: (01670) 512291
Freephone: 0800 243673
e-mail: info@liferafts.com
www.liferafts.com
Hire and sales of DoT and RORC approved liferafts and safety equipment.

PREMIUM LIFERAFT SERVICES SCARBOROUGH
Tel: (01723) 859480
Freephone: 0800 243673
e-mail: info@liferafts.com
www.liferafts.com
Hire and sales of DoT and RORC approved liferafts and safety equipment.

R Donnelly South Shields	07973119455
River Humber (Grimsby) HM	01472 327171
River Humber Police	01482 359171
River Tyne Police	0191 232 3451
River Tyne/North Shields HM	0191 257 2080
Royal Northumberland YC Blyth	01670 353636
Royal Quays Marina North Shields	0191 272 8282
Royal Yorkshire YC Bridlington	01262 672041
S Cook Boatbuilders and Repairers Whitby	01947 820521
Scarborough HM	01723 373530
Scarborough Marine Engineering Ltd Scarborough	01723 375199
Scarborough Police	01723 500300
Scarborough YC Scarborough	01723 373821
Seaham HM	0191 581 3246
Seaham Police	0191 581 2255
Shipshape Marine King's Lynn	01553 764058
South Bank Marine (Charts) Ltd Grimsby	01472 361137
South Bank Marine (Charts) Ltd Immingham	01469 576757
South Dock (Seaham Harbour Dock Co) Seaham	0191 581 3877
South Ferriby Marina Barton on Humber	01652 635620

WHITBY MARINA

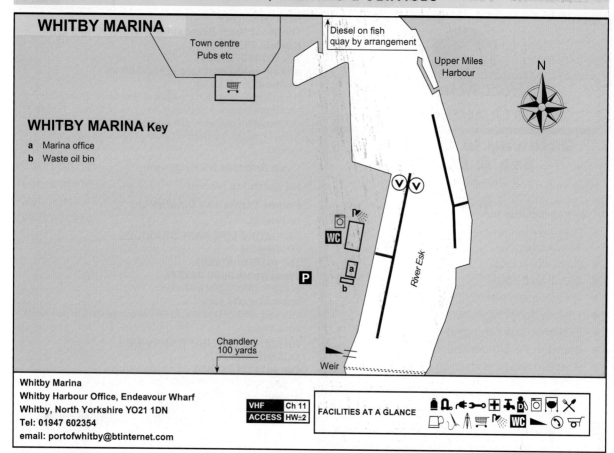

Town centre
Pubs etc

Diesel on fish
quay by arrangement

Upper Miles
Harbour

N

WHITBY MARINA Key

a Marina office
b Waste oil bin

WC

a
b

P

River Esk

Chandlery
100 yards

Weir

Whitby Marina
Whitby Harbour Office, Endeavour Wharf
Whitby, North Yorkshire YO21 1DN
Tel: 01947 602354
email: portofwhitby@btinternet.com

VHF	Ch 11
ACCESS	HW±2

FACILITIES AT A GLANCE

South Gare Marine Club - Sail Section	
Middlesbrough	01642 453031
South Shields SC South Shields	0191 456 5821
St Peter's Marina Newcastle upon Tyne	0191 265 4472
Standard House Boatyard	
Wells-next-the-Sea	01328 710593
Standard House Chandlery	
Wells-next-the-Sea	01328 710593
Storrar Marine Store	
Newcastle upon Tyne	0191 266 1037
Sub Aqua Services North Ormesby	01642 230209
Sunderland HM	0191 567 2626
Sunderland Marina Sunderland	0191 5144721
Sunderland Police	0191 4547555
Sunderland YC Sunderland	0191 567 5133
Tees & Hartlepool Port Authority	01429 277205
Tees & Hartlepool YC	01429 233423

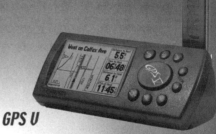

HARTLEPOOL MARINA

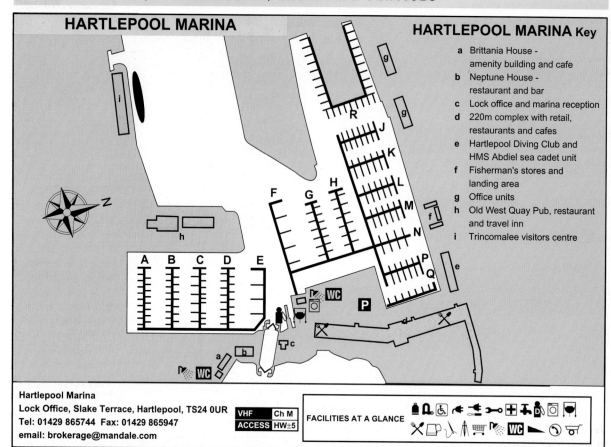

HARTLEPOOL MARINA Key

a Brittania House -
amenity building and cafe

b Neptune House -
restaurant and bar

c Lock office and marina reception

d 220m complex with retail,
restaurants and cafes

e Hartlepool Diving Club and
HMS Abdiel sea cadet unit

f Fisherman's stores and
landing area

g Office units

h Old West Quay Pub, restaurant
and travel inn

i Trincomalee visitors centre

Hartlepool Marina
Lock Office, Slake Terrace, Hartlepool, TS24 0UR
Tel: 01429 865744 Fax: 01429 865947
email: brokerage@mandale.com

| VHF | Ch M |
| ACCESS | HW±5 |

FACILITIES AT A GLANCE

PREMIUM LIFERAFT SERVICES
HARTLEPOOL
Tel: (01429) 862932
Freephone: 0800 243673
e-mail: info@liferafts.com
www.liferafts.com
Hire and sales of DoT and RORC approved liferafts and safety equipment.

Tees SC Aycliffe Village		01429 265400
Trident Sails Gateshead		0191 490 1736
Trident UK North Shields		0191 259 6797
Tynemouth SC Newcastle upon Tyne		0191 2572167
UK Customs Nationwide		0845 0109000
VJ Pratt and Sons King's Lynn		01553 764058

WARD & McKENZIE
(NORTH EAST)
11 Sherbuttage Drive, Pocklington, East Yorkshire YO42 2ED
Tel: (01759) 304322
Fax: (01759) 303194
E-mail: surveyor@proworks.co.uk
Professional yacht & powerboat surveyors, services include damage, pre purchase, insurance condition surveys & technical advice. Competitive rates, fast reliable 24 hour service.
Members of the International Institute of Marine Surveyors.

Wear Boating Association	0191 567 5313
Wells SC Wells-next-the-sea	01328 711190
Wells-next-the-Sea HM	01328 711646
Wells-next-the-Sea Police	01493 336200
Whitby HM	01947 602354
Whitby Marina Whitby	01947 602354
Whitby Police	01947 603443
Whitby YC Whitby	01947 603623
William Leith Berwick on Tweed	01289 307264
William Woolford Bridlington	01262 671710
Wisbech Yacht Harbour Wisbech	01945 588059
Witham SC Boston	01205 363598

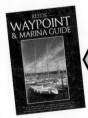

When replying to adverts please mention the Waypoint & Marina Guide

SUNDERLAND MARINA

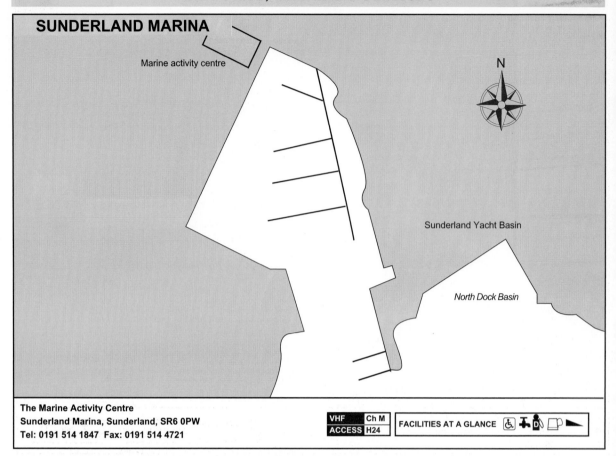

Marine activity centre

Sunderland Yacht Basin

North Dock Basin

N

The Marine Activity Centre
Sunderland Marina, Sunderland, SR6 0PW
Tel: 0191 514 1847 Fax: 0191 514 4721

VHF	Ch M
ACCESS	H24

FACILITIES AT A GLANCE

ROYAL QUAYS MARINA

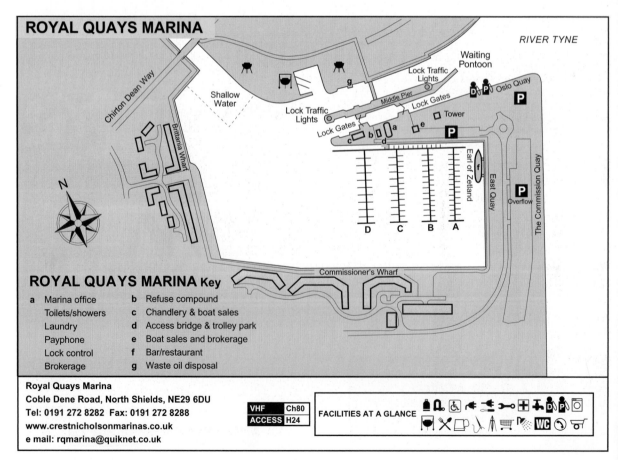

RIVER TYNE

Chirton Dean Way

Shallow Water

Britania Wharf

N

Lock Traffic Lights

Middle Pier

Lock Gates

Lock Traffic Lights

Lock Gates

Waiting Pontoon

Oslo Quay

Tower

g

c   b   a
d

e

P

P

Earl of Zetland

East Quay

The Commission Quay

P

Overflow

f

D   C   B   A

Commissioner's Wharf

ROYAL QUAYS MARINA Key

a	Marina office	**b**	Refuse compound
	Toilets/showers	**c**	Chandlery & boat sales
	Laundry	**d**	Access bridge & trolley park
	Payphone	**e**	Boat sales and brokerage
	Lock control	**f**	Bar/restaurant
	Brokerage	**g**	Waste oil disposal

Royal Quays Marina
Coble Dene Road, North Shields, NE29 6DU
Tel: 0191 272 8282 Fax: 0191 272 8288
www.crestnicholsonmarinas.co.uk
e mail: rqmarina@quiknet.co.uk

VHF	Ch80
ACCESS	H24

FACILITIES AT A GLANCE

BLYTH MARINA

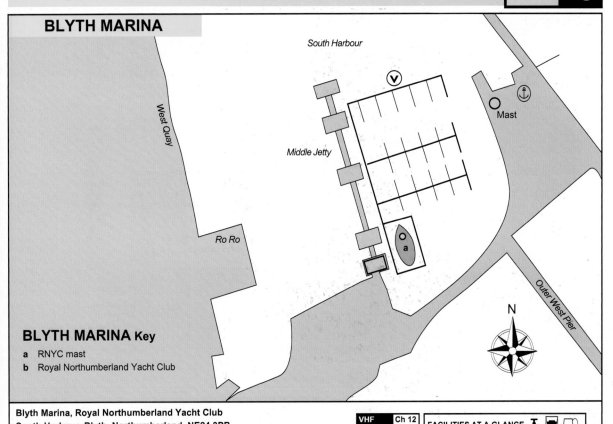

South Harbour

West Quay

Middle Jetty

Ro Ro

Mast

Outer West Pier

N

BLYTH MARINA Key

a RNYC mast
b Royal Northumberland Yacht Club

Blyth Marina, Royal Northumberland Yacht Club
South Harbour, Blyth, Northumberland, NE24 3PB
Tel: 01679 353636

VHF	Ch 12
ACCESS	H24

FACILITIES AT A GLANCE

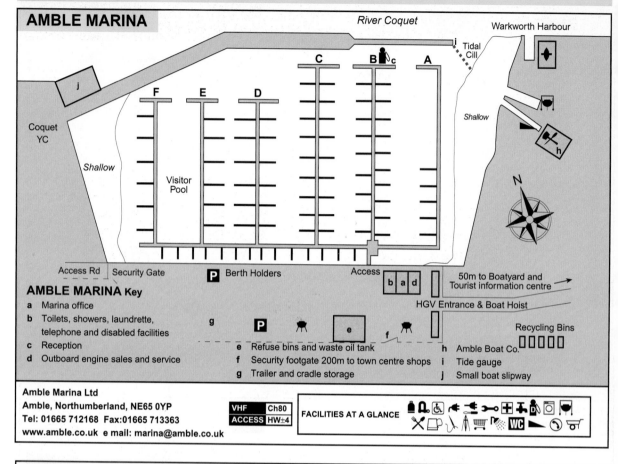

AMBLE MARINA

River Coquet

Warkworth Harbour

Tidal Cill

Coquet YC

Shallow

Shallow

Visitor Pool

C   B   c   A

N

Access Rd | Security Gate   **P** Berth Holders   Access   b a d   50m to Boatyard and Tourist information centre →

HGV Entrance & Boat Hoist

AMBLE MARINA Key

a   Marina office
b   Toilets, showers, laundrette, telephone and disabled facilities
c   Reception
d   Outboard engine sales and service

g   **P**   e

e   Refuse bins and waste oil tank
f   Security footgate 200m to town centre shops
g   Trailer and cradle storage

h   Amble Boat Co.
i   Tide gauge
j   Small boat slipway

Recycling Bins

Amble Marina Ltd
Amble, Northumberland, NE65 0YP
Tel: 01665 712168 Fax:01665 713363
www.amble.co.uk e mail: marina@amble.co.uk

VHF	Ch80
ACCESS	HW±4

FACILITIES AT A GLANCE

Planning a trip?

Make it plain sailing
– for your free copy
of the *2002 Marine Weather Services* booklet
call the Met Office Customer Centre
on **0845 300 0300** or go to
www.metoffice.com/leisuremarine/mwsbooklet.html

For a five-day inshore forecast
for Rattray Head – Berwick,
dial **09060 100 452*** from your fax machine.

*09060 calls are charged at £1 per minute at all times.

Met Office

Key to Marina Plans symbols

Calor Gas		P	Parking
Chandler		✗	Pub/Restaurant
Disabled facilities		↗	Pump out
Electrical supply		⚓	Rigging service
Electrical repairs			Sail repairs
Engine repairs		✗	Shipwright
First Aid		🛒	Shop/Supermarket
Fresh Water			Showers
Fuel - Diesel			Slipway
Fuel - Petrol		WC	Toilets
Hardstanding/boatyard		🔍	Telephone
Laundry facilities			Trolleys
Lift-out facilities		V	Visitors berths

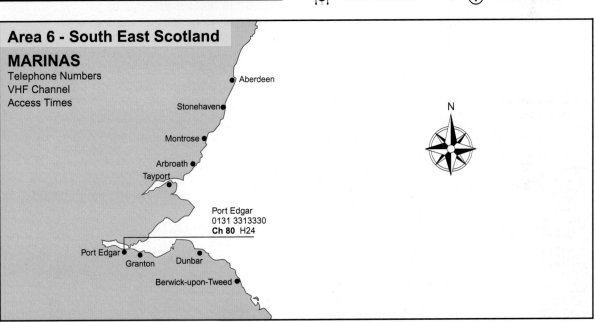

Area 6 - South East Scotland

MARINAS
Telephone Numbers
VHF Channel
Access Times

Aberdeen
Stonehaven
Montrose
Arbroath
Tayport

Port Edgar
0131 3313330
Ch 80 H24

Port Edgar
Granton   Dunbar
Berwick-upon-Tweed

N

AREA 6

Aberdeen and Stonehaven SC	
Nr Inverurie	01569 764006
Aberdeen HM	01224 597000
Aberdeen Police	01224 386000
Aberdour BC	01383 860632
Anstruther HM	01333 310836
Anstruther Police	01333 592100
Arbroath Fishermens Association	
Arbroath	01241 873132
Arbroath HM	01241 872166
Arbroath Police	01241 872222
Argonaut Marine Aberdeen	01224 706526
Bissett and Ross Aberdeen	01224 580659
Brown Son & Ferguson Ltd Glasgow	0141 429 1234

Chattan Shipping Services Ltd	
Edinburgh	0131 555 3155
Coastal Marine Boatbuilders Ltd	
(Dunbar) Eyemouth	01890 750328
Coastcraft Ltd Cockenzie	01875 812150
Cosalt International Ltd Aberdeen	01224 588327
Crail HM	01333 450820
Cramond BC	0131 336 1356
Dunbar HM	01368 863206
Dunbar Police	01368 862718
Dunbar SC Cockburnspath	01368 86287
Dundee HM	01382 224121
East Lothian YC	01620 892698
Elie HM	01333 330051
Eyemouth HM	01890 750223

Waypoint Guide Area 6 – South East Scotland - Eyemouth to Rattray Head

No.	Name	Latitude	Longitude
194	Berwick-upon - Tweed - 1·5M E	55°45'·90N	01°56'·30W
399	Cape Wrath - 2M NW of	58°38'·90N	05°02'·80W
400	Whiten Head - 4·4M N of	58°39'·20N	04°34'·90W
401	Scrabster - 1·4M NE of Holborn Hd	58°38'·60N	03°30'·70W
402	Dunnet Head Lt - 1·7M NW of	58°41'·60N	03°24'·30W
403	Pentl'd Firth - 1·5M NE by N Stroma	58°43'·00N	03°05'·40W
404	Duncansby Head - 2M NE of	58°39'·80N	02°58'·40W
405	Stromness - 2·8M NW Graemsay Lt.	58°57'·10N	03°23'·70W
406	Stronsay - 0·8M NW Ness Lt.	59°10'·00N	02°35'·80W
407	Kirkwall - 1·5M NW of Mull Hd.	58°59'·40N	02°40'·40W
408	Copinsay Lt - 2·5M E of	58°54'·10N	02°35'·10W
409	Lerwick - 1·1M SW of Bressay Lt	60°06'·60N	01°08'·60W
410	Wick - 1·6M E of South Hd	58°25'·80N	03°01'·00W
411	Scarlet Hd - 2M E by S	58°21'·90N	03°02'·50W
412	Helmsdale - 1·8M SE of ent	58°05'·50N	03°36'·80W
413	Tarbat Ness Lt - 2M E of	57°51'·80N	03°42'·70W
414	Inverness - 0·5 NE of Frwy By	57°40'·30N	03°53'·30W
415	Findhorn - 2·2M NW of bay	57°41'·45N	03°40'·00W
416	Lossiemouth - 1·7M N	57°45'·20N	03°16'·70W
417	Buckie - 2·0M WNW	57°41'·70N	03°00'·90W
418	Scar Nose - 1·6M N	57°44'·00N	02°50'·90W
419	Banff - 1·3M N of Meavie Pt	57°41'·60N	02°31'·40W
420	Troup Head - 1·8M N	57°43'·50N	02°17'·70W
421	Kinnairds Head - 1·6M N	57°43'·50N	02°00'·20W
422	Cairnbulg Point Lt - 1·9M NE	57°42'·20N	01°53'·70W
423	Rattray Head Lt - 1·8M ENE	57°37'·40N	01°45'·90W

Distance Table - South East Scotland

Approximate distances in nautical miles are by the most direct route while avoiding dangers and allowing for Traffic Separation Schemes

	1	2	3	4	5	6	7	8	9	10	11	12	13	14	15	16	17	18	19	20
1. Great Yarmouth	1																			
2. Berwick-on-Tweed	232	2																		
3. Eyemouth	240	10	3																	
4. Dunbar	257	26	17	4																
5. North Berwick	266	35	25	9	5															
6. Granton	285	54	44	27	19	6														
7. Port Edgar	290	58	50	34	26	7	7													
8. Burntisland	283	53	43	26	18	5	8	8												
9. Methil	276	45	36	20	13	14	20	12	9											
10. Anstruther	269	38	29	14	10	23	29	22	11	10										
11. Fife Ness	269	38	29	17	14	28	34	27	16	5	11									
12. Bell Rock	276	43	36	27	25	40	47	39	28	17	12	12								
13. Dundee	289	58	49	37	34	48	54	47	36	25	20	20	13							
14. Arbroath	284	51	44	34	31	45	51	44	33	22	17	10	15	14						
15. Montrose	291	59	51	43	41	55	61	54	43	32	27	17	27	12	15					
16. Stonehaven	300	72	66	60	58	72	78	71	60	49	44	32	45	30	20	16				
17. Aberdeen	308	82	78	73	70	84	90	83	72	61	56	44	57	42	32	13	17			
18. Peterhead	318	105	98	93	95	106	108	105	94	83	78	68	80	64	54	35	25	18		
19. Fraserburgh	334	121	114	109	108	122	128	121	110	99	94	83	96	79	68	51	39	16	19	
20. Wick	391	178	171	166	165	179	185	178	167	156	151	140	153	136	125	108	96	72	57	20

Area 6 - South East Scotland

WAYCHART

Eyemouth to Rattray Head

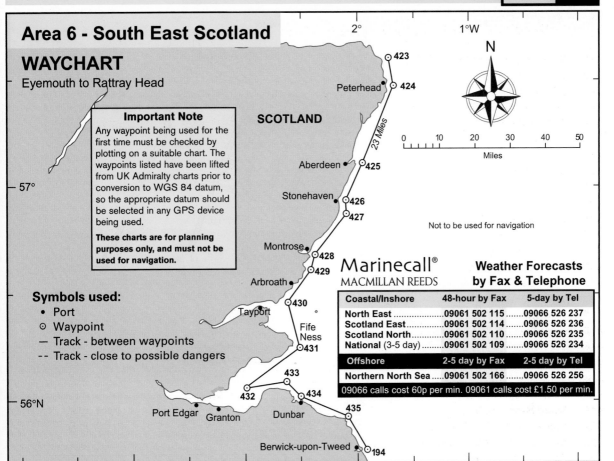

Important Note

Any waypoint being used for the first time must be checked by plotting on a suitable chart. The waypoints listed have been lifted from UK Admiralty charts prior to conversion to WGS 84 datum, so the appropriate datum should be selected in any GPS device being used.

These charts are for planning purposes only, and must not be used for navigation.

Symbols used:

- • Port
- ⊙ Waypoint
- — Track - between waypoints
- -- Track - close to possible dangers

Not to be used for navigation

Marinecall®
MACMILLAN REEDS

Weather Forecasts by Fax & Telephone

Coastal/Inshore	48-hour by Fax	5-day by Tel
North East	09061 502 115	...... 09066 526 237
Scotland East	09061 502 114	...... 09066 526 236
Scotland North	09061 502 110	...... 09066 526 235
National (3-5 day)	09061 502 109	...... 09066 526 234

Offshore	2-5 day by Fax	2-5 day by Tel
Northern North Sea	09061 502 166	...... 09066 526 256

09066 calls cost 60p per min. 09061 calls cost £1.50 per min.

Eyemouth Police	01890 750217	
Ferry Marine South Queensferry	0131 331 1233	
Fisherrow HM	0131 665 5900	
Forth Corinthian YC Haddington	0131 552 5939	
Forth YCs Association Edinburgh	0131 552 3006	
Gourdon HM	01569 762741	
J Buchan & Son Ltd Peterhead	01779 475395	
JNW Services Peterhead	01779 477346	
Johnshaven HM	01561 362262	
Methil HM	01333 462725	
Methil Police	01592 418888	
Montrose HM	01674 672302	
Montrose Police	01674 672222	
Montrose SC Montrose	01674 672554	
Peterhead Bay Marina Peterhead	01779 474020	
Peterhead HM	01779 483630	
Peterhead Police	01779 472571	

Peterhead SC Ellon	01779 75527	
Peterhead Watersports Centre Peterhead	01779 480888	
Pittenweem HM	01333 312591	
Port Edgar Marina & Sailing School South Queensferry	0131 331 3330	
Port Edgar YC Penicuik	01968 674210	
Royal Forth YC Edinburgh	0131 552 3006	
Royal Tay YC Dundee	01382 477516	
S. Queensferry Police	0131 331 1798	
Sea & Shore Ship Chandler Dundee	01382 202666	
Sea Span Edinburgh	0131 552 2224	
St Monans HM	01333 350055	
Stonehaven HM	01569 762741	
Stonehaven Police	01569 762963	
Tay Corinthian BC Dundee	01382 553534	
Tay YCs Association	01738 621860	
Tayport Harbour	01382 553679	
The Bosuns Locker South Queensferry	0131 331 3875/4496	
Thomas Gunn Navigation Services Aberdeen	01224 595045	
UK Customs Nationwide	0845 0109000	
Wormit BC	01382 553878	

PORT EDGAR MARINA

PORT EDGAR MARINA Key

a Changing rooms and toilets
b Landing and trolleys
c Port Edgar Yacht Club
d Sail loft
e Cafe
f Marina office
g Ferry Marine
h Blue V
i Bosuns Locker

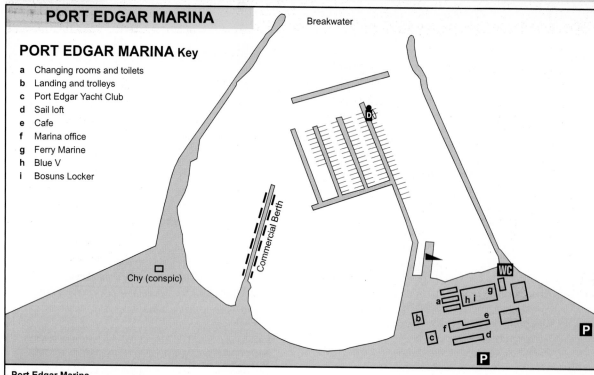

Breakwater

Commercial Berth

Chy (conspic)

WC

P

Port Edgar Marina
Shore Road, South Queensferry,
West Lothian, EH3 9SX
Tel: 0131 331 3330 Fax: 0131 331 4878
www.portedgar.co.uk

| VHF | Ch 80 |
| ACCESS | H24 |

FACILITIES AT A GLANCE

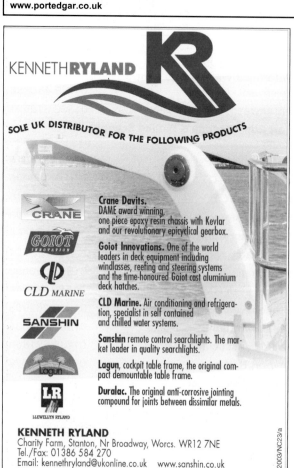

Planning a trip?

Met Office

Make it plain sailing
– for your free copy
of the *2002 Marine Weather Services* booklet
call the Met Office Customer Centre
on **0845 300 0300** or go to
www.metoffice.com/leisuremarine/mwsbooklet.html

For a five-day inshore forecast
for Cape Wrath – Rattray Head inc. Orkney,
dial **09060 100 451*** from your fax machine.

*09060 calls are charged at £1 per minute at all times.

Key to Marina Plans symbols

Calor Gas	P	Parking
Chandler		Pub/Restaurant
Disabled facilities		Pump out
Electrical supply		Rigging service
Electrical repairs		Sail repairs
Engine repairs		Shipwright
First Aid		Shop/Supermarket
Fresh Water		Showers
Fuel - Diesel		Slipway
Fuel - Petrol	WC	Toilets
Hardstanding/boatyard		Telephone
Laundry facilities		Trolleys
Lift-out facilities	V	Visitors berths

Area 7 - North East Scotland

MARINAS
Telephone Numbers
VHF Channel
Access Times

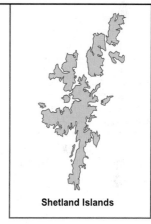

Shetland Islands

Kirkwall Marina
01856 872292
Ch 12 H24

Stromness Marina
01856 850744
Ch 12 H24

Orkney Islands

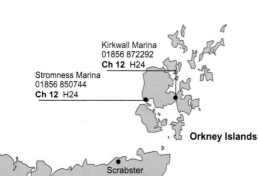

Scrabster

Wick

Helmsdale

Ullapool

Lossiemouth 01343 813066
Ch 12 HW±4

Inverness

Nairn

Buckie

Macduff

Banff

Peterhead

Peterhead Bay Marina
01779 474020
Ch 14 H24

Caley Marina
01463 236539
Ch 74 H24
Seaport Marina
01463 233140
Ch 16, 74 HW±4½

Findhorn

Burghead

Lossiemouth

Hopeman

Mallaig

Aberdeen

N

Waypoint Guide Area 7 – North East Scotland - Rattray Head to Cape Wrath

399	**Cape Wrath** - 2M NW of	58°38'·90N	05°02'·80W
400	**Whiten Head** - 4·4M N of	58°39'·20N	04°34'·90W
401	**Scrabster** - 1·4M NE of Holborn Hd	58°38'·60N	03°30'·70W
402	**Dunnet Head Lt** - 1·7M NW of	58°41'·60N	03°24'·30W
403	**Pentl'd Firth** - 1·5M NE by N Stroma	58°43'·00N	03°05'·40W
404	**Duncansby Head** - 2M NE of	58°39'·80N	02°58'·40W
405	**Stromness** - 2·8M NW Graemsay Lt.	58°57'·10N	03°23'·70W
406	**Stronsay** - 0·8M NW Ness Lt.	59°10'·00N	02°35'·80W
407	**Kirkwall** - 1·5M NW of Mull Hd.	58°59'·40N	02°40'·40W
408	**Copinsay Lt** - 2·5M E of	58°54'·10N	02°35'·10W
409	**Lerwick** - 1·1M SW of Bressay Lt	60°06'·60N	01°08'·60W
410	**Wick** - 1·6M E of South Hd	58°25'·80N	03°01'·00W
411	**Scarlet Hd** - 2M E by S	58°21'·90N	03°02'·50W
412	**Helmsdale** - 1·8M SE of ent	58°05'·50N	03°36'·80W
413	**Tarbat Ness Lt** - 2M E of	57°51'·80N	03°42'·70W
414	**Inverness** - 0·5 NE of Frwy By	57°40'·30N	03°53'·30W
415	**Findhorn** - 2·2M NW of bay	57°41'·45N	03°40'·00W
416	**Lossiemouth** - 1·7M N	57°45'·20N	03°16'·70W
417	**Buckie** - 2·0M WNW	57°41'·70N	03°00'·90W
418	**Scar Nose** - 1·6M N	57°44'·00N	02°50'·90W
419	**Banff** - 1·3M N of Meavie Pt	57°41'·60N	02°31'·40W
420	**Troup Head** - 1·8M N	57°43'·50N	02°17'·70W
421	**Kinnairds Head** - 1·6M N	57°43'·50N	02°00'·20W
422	**Cairnbulg Point Lt** - 1·9M NE	57°42'·20N	01°53'·70W
423	**Rattray Head Lt** - 1·8M ENE	57°37'·40N	01°45'·90W
424	**Peterhead** - 2·1M ESE	57°29'·30N	01°42'·60W
425	**Aberdeen** - 2M E by N Girdle Ness	57°08'·80N	01°59'·00W
426	**Stonehaven** - 2M E	56°57'·60N	02°08'·20W
427	**Todhead Point Lt** - 2·5M E	56°53'·10N	02°08'·30W
428	**Montrose** - 2·1M E Scurdie Ness Lt	56°42'·10N	02°22'·40W
429	**Red Head** - 1·8M E of	56°37'·40N	02°25'·30W
430	**Tayport** - 0·5M E Fairway By	56°29'·25N	02°37'·24W
431	**Fife Ness** - 2·8M ESE	56°15'·95N	02°30'·30W
432	**Granton** - 0·5M N Inchkeith By	56°04'·00N	03°00'·00W
433	**Bass Rock Lt** - 1·5M N	56°06'·10N	02°38'·40W
434	**Dunbar** - 1·5M NNE	56°01'·76N	02°30'·20W
435	**St Abb's Head Lt** - 1·5M NE	55°56'·10N	02°06'·40W
	Hoek van Holland - 1·2M WNW	51°59'·90N	04°01'·00E

Distance Table - North East Scotland

Approximate distances in nautical miles are by the most direct route while avoiding dangers and allowing for Traffic Separation Schemes

		1	2	3	4	5	6	7	8	9	10	11	12	13	14	15	16	17	18	19	20
1.	**Peterhead**	1																			
2.	**Fraserburgh**	16	2																		
3.	**Banff/Macduff**	33	18	3																	
4.	**Buckie**	46	31	15	4																
5.	**Lossiemouth**	56	41	25	11	5															
6.	**Findhorn**	69	54	38	24	13	6														
7.	**Nairn**	79	64	48	34	23	10	7													
8.	**Inverness**	90	75	59	45	34	23	13	8												
9.	**Tarbat Ness**	72	57	41	27	18	14	17	27	9											
10.	**Helmsdale**	74	59	44	33	26	28	32	43	16	10										
11.	**Wick**	72	57	50	46	44	51	58	69	42	29	11									
12.	**Duncansby Head**	82	67	62	58	57	64	71	81	54	41	13	12								
13.	**Scrabster**	100	85	80	76	75	82	89	99	72	59	31	18	13							
14.	**Kirkwall**	115	100	95	91	90	97	104	114	87	74	46	34	50	14						
15.	**Stromness**	104	89	84	80	79	85	92	103	76	63	35	22	25	32	15					
16.	**Fair Isle**	122	111	116	118	120	130	137	148	121	108	79	68	85	55	77	16				
17.	**Lerwick**	160	150	156	160	162	172	170	190	162	148	120	109	124	95	110	42	17			
18.	**Loch Eriboll (ent)**	137	122	117	113	112	119	126	136	109	96	68	55	37	80	50	110	150	18		
19.	**Cape Wrath**	145	130	125	121	120	127	126	144	117	104	76	63	47	79	58	120	155	13	19	
20.	**Ullapool**	198	183	178	174	173	180	179	197	170	157	129	116	100	132	111	173	208	66	53	20

Area 7 - North East Scotland

WAYCHART
Rattray Head to Cape Wrath
including Orkney & Shetland Isles

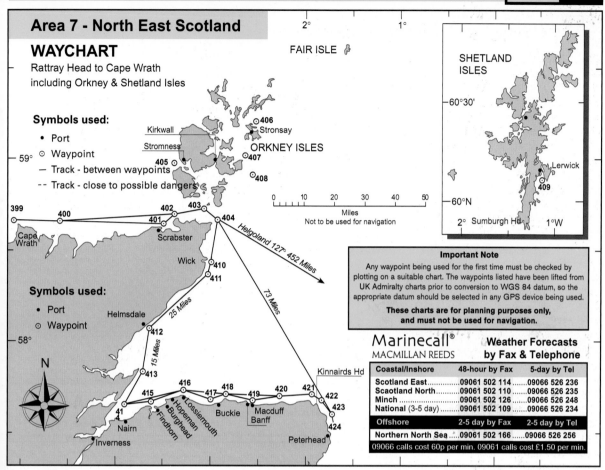

Symbols used:
- • Port
- ⊙ Waypoint
- — Track - between waypoints
- -- Track - close to possible dangers

Symbols used:
- • Port
- ⊙ Waypoint

Important Note

Any waypoint being used for the first time must be checked by plotting on a suitable chart. The waypoints listed have been lifted from UK Admiralty charts prior to conversion to WGS 84 datum, so the appropriate datum should be selected in any GPS device being used.

These charts are for planning purposes only, and must not be used for navigation.

Marinecall®
MACMILLAN REEDS

Weather Forecasts by Fax & Telephone

Coastal/Inshore	48-hour by Fax	5-day by Tel
Scotland East	09061 502 114	09066 526 236
Scaotland North	09061 502 110	09066 526 235
Minch	09061 502 126	09066 526 248
National (3-5 day)	09061 502 109	09066 526 234

Offshore	2-5 day by Fax	2-5 day by Tel
Northern North Sea	09061 502 166	09066 526 256

09066 calls cost 60p per min. 09061 calls cost £1.50 per min.

Banff HM	01261 815544	**Fraserburgh HM**	01346 515858
Banff SC Cults	01261 815296	**Fraserburgh Police**	01346 513121
Brown Son & Ferguson Ltd Glasgow	0141 429 1234	**Grampian Diving Services** New Deer	01771 644206
Buckie HM	01542 831700	**Helmsdale HM**	01431 821692
Buckie Police	01542 832222	**Helmsdale Police**	01431 821222
Buckie Shipyard Ltd Buckie	01542 831245	**Hopeman HM**	01343 835337
Burghead Boat Centre Findhorn	01309 690099	**Hopeman Police**	01343 830222
Burghead HM	01343 835337	**Ian Richardson Boatbuilders** Stromness	01856 850321
Caley Marina Inverness	01463 236328	**Invergordon BC**	01349 877612
Canal Office (Inverness) HM	01463 233140	**Inverness Boat Centre** North Kessock	01463 731383
Chanonry SC Fortrose	01463 221415	**Inverness HM**	01463 715715
Chattan Shipping Services Ltd Edinburgh	0131 555 3155	**Inverness Police**	01463 715555
Cromarty Firth HM	01381 600479	**J McCaughty (Boatbuilders)** Wick	01955 602858
Cullen HM	01261 842477	**JS Duncan Ltd** Wick	01955 602689
D MacDonald Nairn	01667 455661	**Kettletoft Bay HM**	01857 600227
Denholm Fishselling Scrabster	01847 896968	**Kirkwall HM**	01856 872292
Fathoms Ltd Wick	01955 605956	**Kirkwall Marina** Kirkwall	01856 872292
Findhorn Boatyard Findhorn	01309 690099	**Kirkwall Police**	01856 872241
Findhorn Police	01309 672224	**Leask Marine** Kirkwall	01856 874725
Findhorn YC Findhorn	01309 690247	**Lerwick BC** Lerwick	01595 696954
Findochty HM	01542 831466	**Lerwick HM**	01595 692991
Flotta HM	01856 701411	**Lerwick Police**	01595 692110

PETERHEAD BAY MARINA

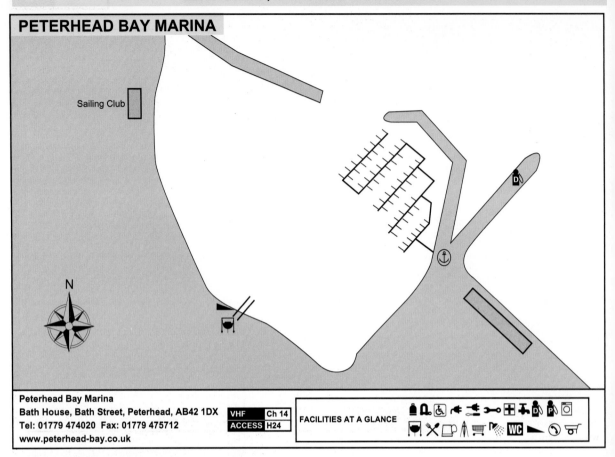

Peterhead Bay Marina
Bath House, Bath Street, Peterhead, AB42 1DX
Tel: 01779 474020 Fax: 01779 475712
www.peterhead-bay.co.uk

VHF	Ch 14
ACCESS	H24

FACILITIES AT A GLANCE

LOSSIEMOUTH MARINA

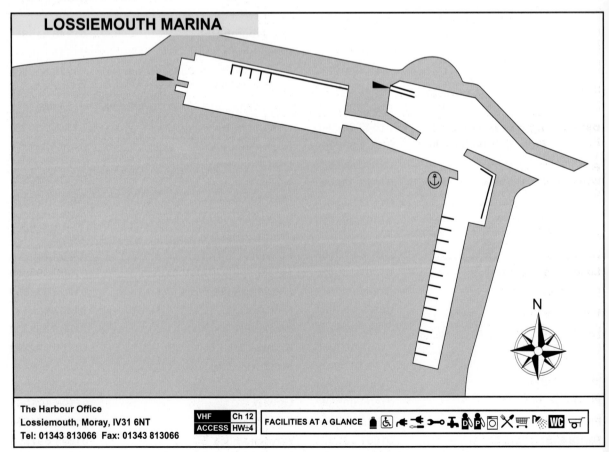

The Harbour Office
Lossiemouth, Moray, IV31 6NT
Tel: 01343 813066 Fax: 01343 813066

VHF	Ch 12
ACCESS	HW±4

FACILITIES AT A GLANCE

CALEY MARINA

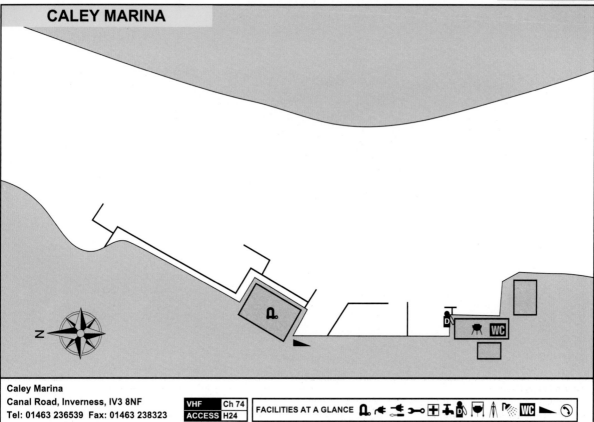

Caley Marina
Canal Road, Inverness, IV3 8NF
Tel: 01463 236539 Fax: 01463 238323
www.caleycruisers.com

| VHF | Ch 74 |
| ACCESS | H24 |

FACILITIES AT A GLANCE

AREA 7

PETERHEAD BAY AUTHORITY
Bath House, Bath Street, Peterhead AB42 1DX
Tel: (01779) 474020
Fax: (01779) 475712
www.peterhead-bay.co.uk
Contact Ken Bennions. Peterhead Bay Marina offers fully
serviced pontoon berthing for local and visiting boat owners.
Local companies provide a comprehensive range of supporting
services. Ideal stopover for vesels heading to/from Scandinavia
or the Caledonian Canal.

Longmans Yacht Haven Inverness	01463 715715	**Malakoff and Moore** Lerwick	01595 695544
Lossiemouth CC Fochabers	01348 812121	**Margaret Crawford** Kirkwall	01856 875692
Lossiemouth HM	01343 813066	**Montrose Rope and Sails** Montrose	01674 672657
Lossiemouth Marina Lossiemouth	01343 813066	**Nairn Police**	01667 452222
Lossiemouth Police	01343 812022	**Nairn SC** Nairn	01667 453897
Lyness HM	01856 791387	**North of England Yachting Association** Kirkwall	01856 872331
Macduff and Banff Police	01261 812555	**Orkney SC** Kirkwall	01856 872331
Macduff HM	01261 832236	**Paterson A** Macduff	01261 832784
Macduff Shipyard Ltd Macduff	01261 832234	**Pentland Firth YC** Thurso	01847 891803

SEAPORT MARINA

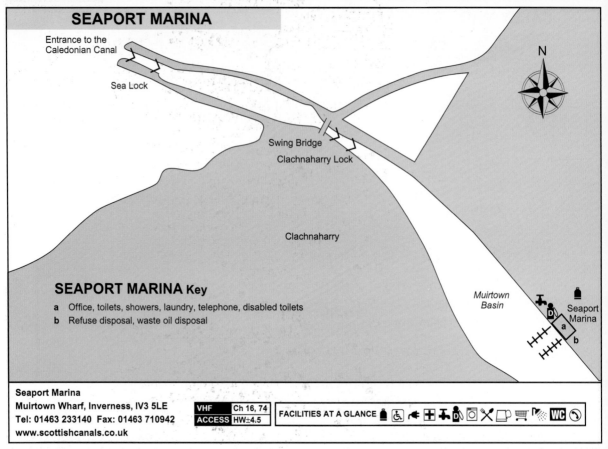

Entrance to the
Caledonian Canal

Sea Lock

Swing Bridge

Clachnaharry Lock

Clachnaharry

Muirtown
Basin

Seaport
Marina

SEAPORT MARINA Key

a   Office, toilets, showers, laundry, telephone, disabled toilets
b   Refuse disposal, waste oil disposal

Seaport Marina
Muirtown Wharf, Inverness, IV3 5LE
Tel: 01463 233140 Fax: 01463 710942
www.scottishcanals.co.uk

VHF	Ch 16, 74
ACCESS	HW±4.5

FACILITIES AT A GLANCE

KIRKWALL MARINA

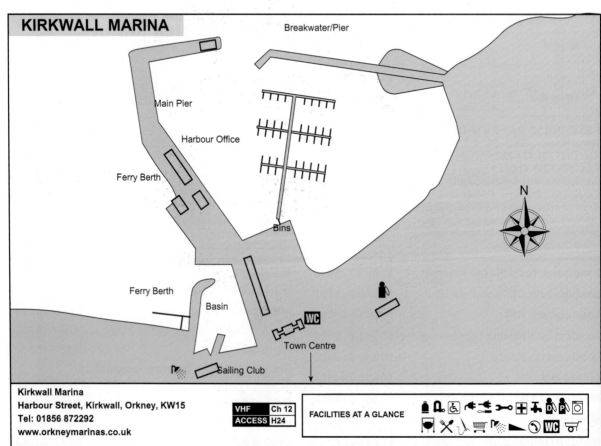

Breakwater/Pier

Main Pier

Harbour Office

Ferry Berth

Bins

Ferry Berth

Basin

Town Centre

Sailing Club

Kirkwall Marina
Harbour Street, Kirkwall, Orkney, KW15
Tel: 01856 872292
www.orkneymarinas.co.uk

VHF	Ch 12
ACCESS	H24

FACILITIES AT A GLANCE

Cruise the Orkney Islands
using our secure, serviced pontoon berthing in Kirkwall, Stromness and Westray

This beautiful archipelago of around 70 islands provides some of the finest sailing grounds in Northern Europe. An ancient maritime crossroads dating from the Vikings through the Hudson's Bay Company, and fleet anchorage for the Royal Navy in both world wars. Orkney has everything; history, hospitality, and superb cruising

Kirkwall Marina Piermaster 01856 872292 VHF 12/16

A brand new marina within the harbour and just yards from the attractions of this ancient port. Accessible at all states of tide, all year facility, excellent shelter. All facilities available. Opening Summer 2003.

Great food and drink	Golf
Repairs and chandlery	Leisure centre
Ferry and air links	Cathedral of St Magnus
Archaeological tours	Museums

2003/M&WM68/bh

Point your browser at **www.orkneymarinas.co.uk** for updates and to book your berth on-line.

ORKNEY MARINAS LIMITED
Scotts Road, Hatston, Kirkwall, Orkney KW15 1GR
www.orkneymarinas.co.uk
Cruise the Okney Islands using our secure, serviced pontoon. Berthing for visitors in three new marinas at Kirkwall, Stromness and Westray for Summer 2003.

MACMILLAN
REEDS
EASTERN ALMANAC 2003

Nautical Data Limited
tel: +44 (0)1243 389352 web: www.nauticaldata.com

Peter Georgeson Marina - Vaila Sound (Walls) Lerwick	01595 809273
Pierowall HM	01857 677216
Portknockie HM	01542 840833
Scalloway BC Lerwick	01595 880409
Scalloway HM	01595 880574
Scrabster HM	01847 892779
Scrabster Police	01847 893222
Seaport Marina Inverness	01463 233140
Seaway Marine Macduff	01261 832877
St Margaret's Hope HM	01856 831454
Stromness HM	01856 850744
Stromness Marina Stromness	01856 850744
Stromness Police	01856 850222
Stronsay HM	01857 616317
Stronsay Police	01857 872241
Sullom Voe HM	01806 242551
UK Customs Nationwide	0845 0109000
Walls Regatta Club Lerwick	01595 809273
Whitehills HM	01261 861291
Wick HM	01955 602030
Wick Police	01955 603551

AREA 7

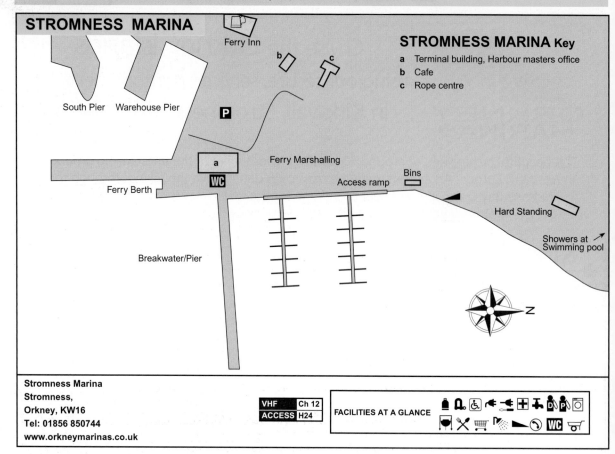

STROMNESS MARINA

STROMNESS MARINA Key

a   Terminal building, Harbour masters office
b   Cafe
c   Rope centre

South Pier   Warehouse Pier

Ferry Inn

P

a
WC

Ferry Berth

Ferry Marshalling

Access ramp   Bins

Hard Standing

Showers at Swimming pool

Breakwater/Pier

N

Stromness Marina
Stromness,
Orkney, KW16
Tel: 01856 850744
www.orkneymarinas.co.uk

| VHF | Ch 12 |
| ACCESS | H24 |

FACILITIES AT A GLANCE

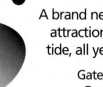

Planning a trip?

Met Office

Make it plain sailing
– for your free copy
of the *2002 Marine Weather Services* booklet
call the Met Office Customer Centre
on **0845 300 0300** or go to
www.metoffice.com/leisuremarine/mwsbooklet.html

For a five-day inshore forecast
for Ardnamurchan – Cape Wrath,
and the Western Isles,
dial **09060 100 464*** from your fax machine.

*09060 calls are charged at £1 per minute at all times.

Key to Marina Plans symbols

Calor Gas		P	Parking
Chandler			Pub/Restaurant
Disabled facilities			Pump out
Electrical supply			Rigging service
Electrical repairs			Sail repairs
Engine repairs			Shipwright
First Aid			Shop/Supermarket
Fresh Water			Showers
Fuel - Diesel			Slipway
Fuel - Petrol		WC	Toilets
Hardstanding/boatyard			Telephone
Laundry facilities			Trolleys
Lift-out facilities		V	Visitors berths

Area 8 - North West Scotland

MARINAS
Telephone Numbers
VHF Channel
Access Times

N

Stornoway

Ullapool

Portree

Mallaig

Corpach

Salen

Dunstaffnage Marina
01631 566555 **Ch M** H24

Tobermory

Melfort Pier
01852 200333
Ch 80 H24

Oban

Craobh Haven Marina
01852 500222
Ch 80 H24

Ardfern Yacht Centre
01852 500247
Ch 80 H24

Waypoint Guide Area 8 – North West Scotland - Cape Wrath to Crinan Canal

348	**Skerryvore Lt** - 6·8M W by N of	56°20'·80N	07°18'·80W
370	**Sound of Insh** - 1M SSW of Insh Island	56°17'·60N	05°41'·00W
371	**Kerrera Sound** - 0·7M SSW of Rubha Seanach	56°21'·70N	05°33'·90W
372	**Oban** - 0·5M WNW of Maiden Isle	56°26'·00N	05°30'·30W
373	**Between Lady's Rock and Eilean Musdile**	56°27'·20N	05°36'·70W
374	**Sound of Mull** - 1·6M SE of Ardtornish Pt	56°30'·15N	05°42'·75W
375	**Loch Aline** - 0·7M S by W of entrance	56°31'·30N	05°46'·80W
376	**Sound of Mull** - 1·8M N of Salen	56°33'·00N	05°56'·30W
377	**Tobermory** - 0·9M NE of harbour entrance	56°38'·40N	06°02'·40W
378	**Ardmore Point (Mull)** - 0·7M N of	56°40'·00N	06°07'·60W
379	**Point of Ardnamurchan** - 2·8M S of	56°40'·90N	06°13'·30W
380	**Point of Ardnamurchan** - 1·3M W of	56°43'·60N	06°15'·90W
381	**Mallaig** - 1·5 miles WNW of harbour entrance	57°01'·00N	05°52'·10W
382	**Neist Point Lt** - 4·0M W of	57°25'·45N	06°54'·50W
383	**Sound of Shiant** - 2·2M E of Eilean Glas Lt Ho	57°51'·20N	06°34'·40W
384	**Sound of Shiant** - 0·3M NW of Shiants Lt By	57°54'·80N	06°26'·00W
385	**Kebock Head** - 2·3M E of	58°02'·40N	06°17'·00W
386	**Stornoway** - 1·2M SE of harbour entrance	58°10'·30N	06°20'·60W
387	**Chicken Head** - 1·2M S of	58°09'·80N	06°15'·10W
388	**Sandaig Islands Lt** - 0·6M W by N of	57°10'·25N	05°43'·20W
389	**Kyle Rhea (S appr)** - 0·6M W of Glenelg	57°12'·75N	05°38'·80W
390	**Loch Alsh (W appr)** - 1·0M NW of entrance	57°17'·20N	05°46'·10W
391	**Crowlin Islands** - 1·5 M W of	57°20'·70N	05°53'·80W
392	**Inner Sound** - 1·7M E Rubha Ard Ghlaisen	57°29'·55N	05°55'·50W
393	**Portree** - 1·8M E of town	57°25'·00N	06°08'·00W
394	**Sd of Raasay** - 3·1M SE of Rubha nam Brathairean	57°33'·30N	06°03'·80W
395	**Rubha Reidh** - 3·0M W of	57°51'·60N	05°54'·40W
396	**Greenstone Point** - 1·6M NW of	57°56'·60N	05°39'·20W
397	**Ullapool** - 1·7M NE of Cailleach Head Lt	57°56'·90N	05°21'·80W
398	**Stoerhead Lt** - 2M NW of	58°15'·80N	05°26'·80W
399	**Cape Wrath** - 2M NW of	58°38'·90N	05°02'·80W
400	**Whiten Head** - 4·4M N of	58°39'·20N	04°34'·90W

Distance Table - North West Scotland

Approximate distances in nautical miles are by the most direct route while avoiding dangers and allowing for Traffic Separation Schemes

		1	2	3	4	5	6	7	8	9	10	11	12	13	14	15	16	17	18	19	20
1.	Cape Wrath	1																			
2.	Ullapool	54	2																		
3.	Stornoway	53	45	3																	
4.	East Loch Tarbert	75	56	33	4																
5.	Portree	83	57	53	42	5															
6.	Loch Harport	110	82	65	45	66	6														
7.	Kyle of Lochalsh	91	63	62	63	21	53	7													
8.	Mallaig	112	82	83	84	42	33	21	8												
9.	Eigg	123	98	97	75	54	34	35	14	9											
10.	Castlebay (Barra)	133	105	92	69	97	43	76	59	46	10										
11.	Tobermory	144	114	115	87	74	52	53	32	20	53	11									
12.	Loch Aline	157	127	128	100	87	65	66	45	33	66	13	12								
13.	Fort William	198	161	162	134	121	99	98	75	63	96	43	34	13							
14.	Oban	169	138	139	111	100	76	77	56	44	77	24	13	29	14						
15.	Loch Lathaich	160	130	124	98	91	62	67	49	35	56	31	53	77	48	15					
16.	Loch Melfort	184	154	155	117	114	92	93	69	61	92	40	27	45	18	45	16				
17.	Craobh Haven	184	155	155	117	114	93	92	70	60	93	40	27	50	21	43	5	17			
18.	Loch Craignish	188	158	159	131	118	95	96	76	64	98	44	31	55	26	46	17	14	18		
19.	Crinan	187	157	158	129	112	95	95	74	63	97	42	30	54	25	45	14	9	6	19	
20.	Mull of Kintyre	232	203	189	175	159	133	143	121	105	120	89	87	98	72	78	62	57	54	51	20

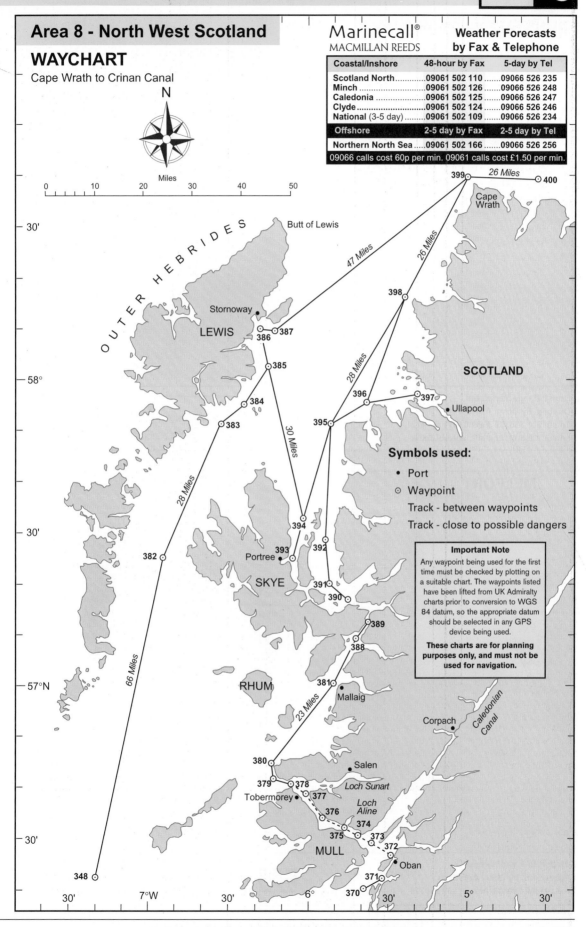

Area 8 - North West Scotland

WAYCHART

Cape Wrath to Crinan Canal

N

Miles

0 10 20 30 40 50

Marinecall®
MACMILLAN REEDS

Weather Forecasts by Fax & Telephone

Coastal/Inshore	48-hour by Fax	5-day by Tel
Scotland North............	09061 502 110	09066 526 235
Minch	09061 502 126	09066 526 248
Caledonia	09061 502 125	09066 526 247
Clyde	09061 502 124	09066 526 246
National (3-5 day)	09061 502 109	09066 526 234
Offshore	**2-5 day by Fax**	**2-5 day by Tel**
Northern North Sea	09061 502 166	09066 526 256

09066 calls cost 60p per min. 09061 calls cost £1.50 per min.

Symbols used:
- • Port
- ⊙ Waypoint
- —— Track - between waypoints
- ‑ ‑ ‑ Track - close to possible dangers

Important Note

Any waypoint being used for the first time must be checked by plotting on a suitable chart. The waypoints listed have been lifted from UK Admiralty charts prior to conversion to WGS 84 datum, so the appropriate datum should be selected in any GPS device being used.

These charts are for planning purposes only, and must not be used for navigation.

OUTER HEBRIDES

Butt of Lewis

Stornoway

LEWIS

SCOTLAND

Ullapool

SKYE

Portree

RHUM

Mallaig

Corpach

Caledonian Canal

Cape Wrath

26 Miles

47 Miles

26 Miles

28 Miles

30 Miles

28 Miles

66 Miles

23 Miles

399 400
398
387 386
385
384
383
396 397
395
394
393 392
391
390
389
388
382
381
380
379 378
377
376
374
375 373
372
371 370
348
Salen
Loch Sunart
Tobermorey
Loch Aline
MULL
Oban

DUNSTAFFNAGE MARINA

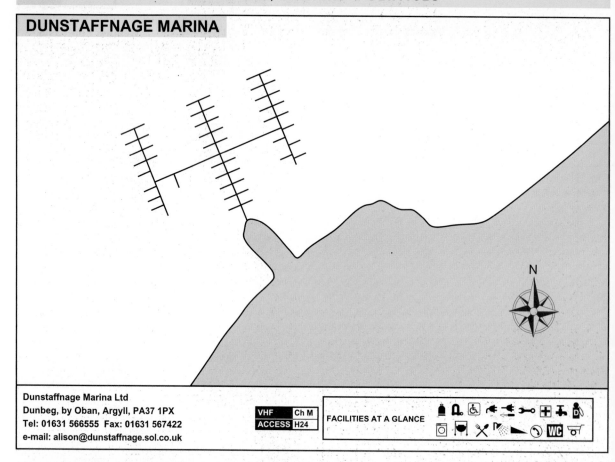

Dunstaffnage Marina Ltd
Dunbeg, by Oban, Argyll, PA37 1PX
Tel: 01631 566555 Fax: 01631 567422
e-mail: alison@dunstaffnage.sol.co.uk

VHF	Ch M
ACCESS	H24

FACILITIES AT A GLANCE

MELFORT

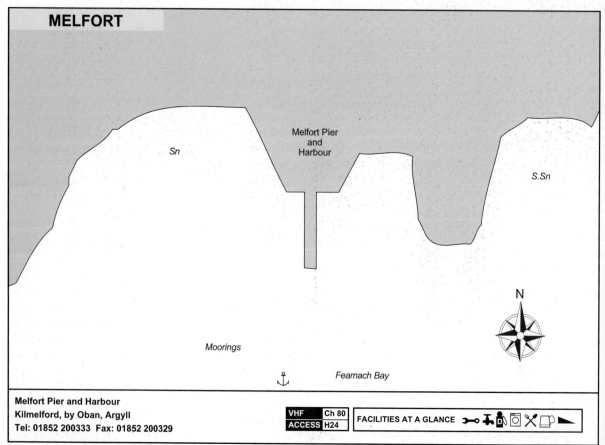

Melfort Pier and Harbour
Kilmelford, by Oban, Argyll
Tel: 01852 200333 Fax: 01852 200329

VHF	Ch 80
ACCESS	H24

FACILITIES AT A GLANCE

CRAOBH HAVEN MARINA

CRAOBH HAVEN MARINA Key

a Holiday cottages
b Village store
c Bar
d Gift shop

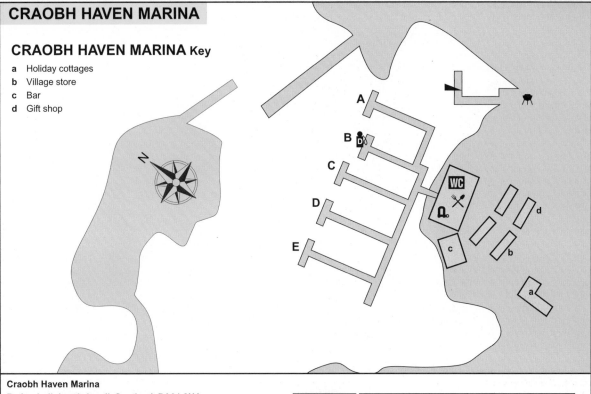

Craobh Haven Marina
By Lochgilphead, Argyll, Scotland, PA31 8UA
Tel: 01852 50022 Fax: 01852 500252
www.kipmarina.co.uk/pages/craobhcontent.html

VHF	Ch 80
ACCESS	H24

FACILITIES AT A GLANCE

Brown Son & Ferguson Ltd Glasgow	0141 429 1234
C I Diving Services Ltd Invergordon	01349 852500
Chattan Shipping Services Ltd Edinburgh	0131 555 3155
Corpach Boatbuilding Company Fort William	01397 772861
Corpach Canal Sea Lock HM	01397 772249
Corpach Police	01397 702361
Craobh Haven HM	01852 502222

Dunstaffnage Marina Ltd By Oban	01631 566555
Eigg Harbour HM	01687 482428
J Fleming Engineering	01851 703488
Johnston Brothers Mallaig	01687 462215
Kinlochbervie HM	01971 521235
Kinlochbervie Police	01971 521222
Loch Gairloch HM	01445 712140
Loch Inver HM	01571 844265
Loch Melfort Police	01852 562213
Lochaber YC Fort William	01397 772361
MacDougalls Marine Services	01681 700294
Mallaig Boat Building and Engineering Mallaig	01687 462304
Mallaig Police	01687 462177
Melfort Pier & Harbour Kilmelford	01852 200333
Nancy Black Oban	01631 562550
Norman Thorpe Portree	01478 612274
North Pier Oban	01631 562892
Oban HM	01631 562892
Oban Police	01631 562213
Oban SC Ledaig by Oban	01631 563999
Oban Yachts and Marine Services By Oban	01631 565333
Owen Sails By Oban	01631 720485
Plockton HM	01599 534589
Portree HM	01478 612926

ARDFERN YACHT CENTRE

ARDFERN YACHT CENTRE Key

a Workshop
b Showers, toilets and laundrette
c Chandlery and office

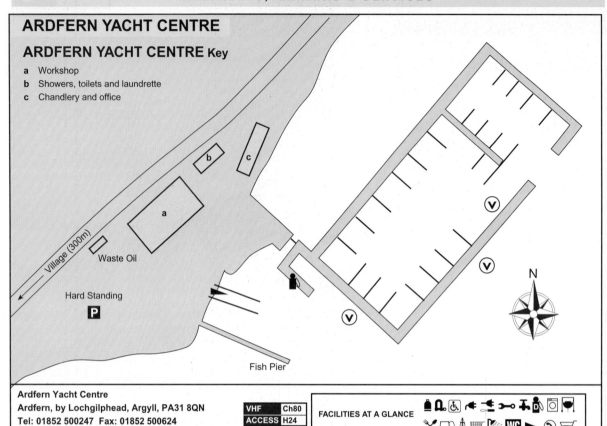

Ardfern Yacht Centre
Ardfern, by Lochgilphead, Argyll, PA31 8QN
Tel: 01852 500247 Fax: 01852 500624
www.ardfernyacht.co.uk

VHF	Ch80
ACCESS	H24

FACILITIES AT A GLANCE

Portree Police	01478 612888

PREMIUM LIFERAFT SERVICES
KYLE OF LOCHALSH
Tel: (01599) 534541
Freephone: 0800 243673
e-mail: info@liferafts.com
www.liferafts.com
Hire and sales of DoT and RORC approved liferafts and safety equipment.

PREMIUM LIFERAFT SERVICES OBAN
Tel: (01631) 562849
Freephone: 0800 243673
e-mail: info@liferafts.com
www.liferafts.com
Hire and sales of DoT and RORC approved liferafts and safety equipment.

Royal Highland YC Connel	01546 510261
Sandy Morrison Engineering Uig	01470 542300
Seafare Tobermory	01688 302277

SILVERS MARINA LTD
Silverhills, Rosneath, Helensburgh G84 0RW
Tel: (01436) 831222
Fax: (01436) 831879
Yacht storage, repairs, riggins, osmosis treatment, spray painting, engineering.

SLEAT MARINE SERVICES
Ardvasar, Isle of Skye IV45 8RS
Tel: (01471) 844216
Fax: (01471) 844387
e-mail: services@sleatmarineservices
www.sleatmarineservices.co.uk
Yacht Charter - we offer a choice of yachts in the 10-12 metre size range. Services to visiting yachts include: 15 ton hoist, general repairs, diesel, water, mooring and showers. We look forward to seeing you.

Stealaway Diving Oban	01631 566349
Stornoway Fishermen's Co-op Stornoway	01851 702563
Stornoway HM	01851 702688
Stornoway Police	01851 702222
Stornoway SC Stornoway	01851 705412
Tobermory Police	01688 302016
Tobermory Port Manager HM	01688 302017
UK Customs Nationwide	0845 0109000
Ullapool HM	01854 612091
Ullapool Police	01854 612017
WB Leitch and Son Tarbert	01880 820287
Western Isles YC	01688 302371

Planning a trip?

Make it plain sailing
– for your free copy
of the *2002 Marine Weather Services* booklet
call the Met Office Customer Centre
on **0845 300 0300** or go to
www.metoffice.com/leisuremarine/mwsbooklet.html

For a five-day inshore forecast for Mull of Kintyre –
Ardnamurchan, dial **09060 100 463*** from your
fax machine. For Mull of Gallway – Mull of Kintyre
and North Channel, dial **09060 100 462.***

*09060 calls are charged at £1 per minute at all times.

Met Office

Key to Marina Plans symbols

Calor Gas		Parking
Chandler		Pub/Restaurant
Disabled facilities		Pump out
Electrical supply		Rigging service
Electrical repairs		Sail repairs
Engine repairs		Shipwright
First Aid		Shop/Supermarket
Fresh Water		Showers
Fuel - Diesel		Slipway
Fuel - Petrol		Toilets
Hardstanding/boatyard		Telephone
Laundry facilities		Trolleys
Lift-out facilities		Visitors berths

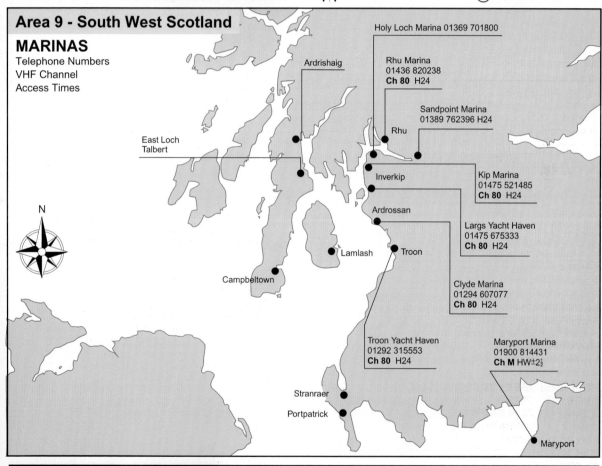

Area 9 - South West Scotland

MARINAS
Telephone Numbers
VHF Channel
Access Times

Holy Loch Marina 01369 701800

Ardrishaig

Rhu Marina
01436 820238
Ch 80 H24

Sandpoint Marina
01389 762396 H24

Rhu

East Loch
Talbert

Inverkip

Kip Marina
01475 521485
Ch 80 H24

Ardrossan

Largs Yacht Haven
01475 675333
Ch 80 H24

Lamlash   Troon

Clyde Marina
01294 607077
Ch 80 H24

Campbeltown

Troon Yacht Haven
01292 315553
Ch 80 H24

Maryport Marina
01900 814431
Ch M HW±2½

Stranraer

Portpatrick

Maryport

AREA 9

Waypoint Guide Area 9 – South West Scotland - Crinan Canal to Mull of Galloway

269	**Kirkcudbright** - 1·5M S Little Ross Lt	54°44'·50N	04°05'·00W
341	**South Rock Lt V** - 1·1M E of	54°24'·30N	05°20'·00W
342	**Burrow Head** - 2·0 M S of	54°38'·70N	04°23'·00W
343	**Mull of Galloway Lt** - 1·7M S of	54°36'·40N	04°51'·50W
344	**Crammag Head Lt** - 1·8M SW of	54°38'·60N	05°00'·00W
345	**Mull of Kintyre Lt** - 2·5M SW of	55°16'·90N	05°51'·30W
346	**Mull of Kintyre Lt** - 10·3M NW of	55°25'·50N	06°01'·50W
347	**Rhinns of Islay Lt** - 2·2M SW of	55°38'·85N	06°33'·50W
348	**Skerryvore Lt** - 6·8M W by N of	56°20'·80N	07°18'·80W
349	**Killantringan Lt** - 4·2M NW of	54°54'·20N	05°14'·70W
350	**Corsewall Pt Lt** - 1·8M WNW of	55°01'·20N	05°12'·20W
351	**Stranraer** - 1·0M NNW ent to Loch Ryan	55°02'·40N	05°05'·10W
352	**Bennane Head** - 1·5M NW of	55°09'·25N	05°01'·80W
353	**Troon** - 2·1M W of harbour ent	55°33'·10N	04°44'·70W
354	**Little Cumbrae Island Lt** - 0·8M SW of	55°42'·75N	04°59'·00W
355	**Rothesay** - Ent to Rothesay Sound	55°50'·90N	04°59'·60W
356	**Firth of Clyde, Cloch Point Lt** - 1·3M WSW of	55°55'·95N	04°54'·75W
357	**R. Clyde, Kempock Point** - 0·9M WNW of	55°58'·10N	04°50'·50W
358	**Lamlash** - 1·0M SE of S ent	55°29'·80N	05°03'·60W
359	**Lamlash** - 1·0M E of N ent	55°32'·90N	05°03'·00W
360	**Isle of Arran** - 2·0M NNE of Sannox Bay	55°41'·60N	05°08'·00W
361	**West Kyle** - 1·0M E Lamont Shelf IDM	55°48'·35N	05°11'·80W
362	**East Loch Tarbert** - 1·0 E of Loch	55°52'·20N	05°22'·00W
363	**Ardrishaig** - 1·3 SSE of hbr ent	55°59'·50N	05°25'·60W
364	**Campbeltown** - 1·0 NE of Loch ent	55°26'·40N	05°31'·00W
365	**Gigha Island** - 1·5M W of Cath Sgeir WCM	55°39'·70N	05°50'·00W
366	**Sound of Jura** - 2·5M NW of Island of Danna	55°58'·80N	05°45'·50W
367	**Loch Crinan** - 0·6M NW of Ardnoe Point	56°06'·00N	05°35'·40W
368	**Sound of Jura** - 2·0M SSW Reisa an t-Sruith I. Lt	56°06'·00N	05°39'·90W
369	**Sound of Luing** - 0·5M WSW of Ardluing SHM By	56°11'·00N	05°39'·40W
370	**Sound of Insh** - 1M SSW of Insh Island	56°17'·60N	05°41'·00W
371	**Kerrera Sound** - 0·7M SSW of Rubha Seanach	56°21'·70N	05°33'·90W

Distance Table - South West Scotland

Approximate distances in nautical miles are by the most direct route while avoiding dangers and allowing for Traffic Separation Schemes

	1	2	3	4	5	6	7	8	9	10	11	12	13	14	15	16	17	18	19	20
1. Loch Craignish	**1**																			
2. Port Ellen (Islay)	42	**2**																		
3. Crinan	5	39	**3**																	
4. Ardrishaig	14	48	9	**4**																
5. East Loch Tarbert	24	58	19	10	**5**															
6. Campbeltown	55	47	50	39	31	**6**														
7. Mull of Kintyre	56	27	51	54	45	20	**7**													
8. Lamlash	48	61	43	34	25	24	34	**8**												
9. Largs	48	94	43	34	24	39	47	17	**9**											
10. Rothesay	49	95	44	35	25	43	48	23	9	**10**										
11. Kip Marina	53	85	48	39	28	50	58	25	10	8	**11**									
12. Greenock	59	90	54	45	36	53	63	31	16	14	6	**12**								
13. Rhu (Helensburgh)	62	94	57	48	37	59	67	33	19	17	9	4	**13**							
14. Troon	54	71	49	40	33	33	44	16	20	25	29	34	38	**14**						
15. Girvan	67	58	62	53	43	29	31	20	33	40	46	49	51	21	**15**					
16. Stranraer	89	62	84	75	65	34	35	39	56	63	69	65	74	44	23	**16**				
17. Portpatrick	88	63	83	74	66	39	36	44	61	67	68	77	77	49	28	23	**17**			
18. Mull of Galloway	104	78	99	90	82	56	52	60	78	82	84	93	93	65	62	39	16	**18**		
19. Kirkcudbright	136	111	131	122	114	88	84	92	110	114	116	124	125	97	94	71	48	32	**19**	
20. Douglas (IoM)	146	120	141	132	124	106	94	102	141	130	126	141	135	107	104	84	60	42	45	**20**

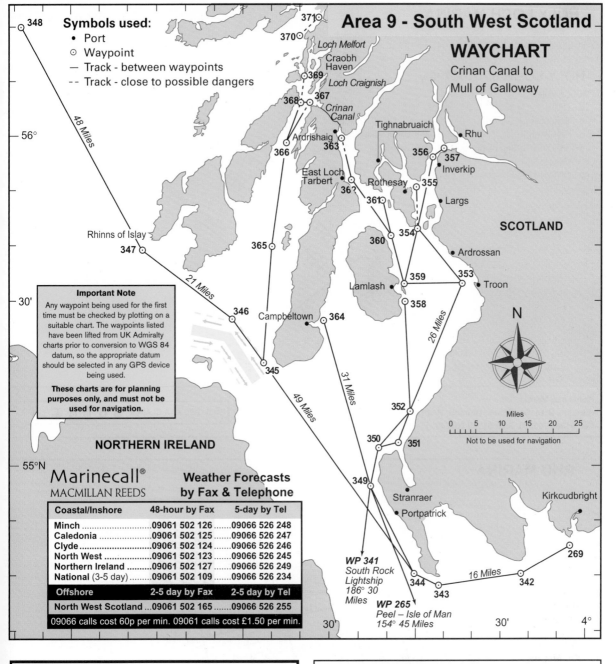

Symbols used:
- • Port
- ⊙ Waypoint
- — Track - between waypoints
- -- Track - close to possible dangers

Area 9 - South West Scotland

WAYCHART
Crinan Canal to
Mull of Galloway

SCOTLAND

NORTHERN IRELAND

Important Note

Any waypoint being used for the first time must be checked by plotting on a suitable chart. The waypoints listed have been lifted from UK Admiralty charts prior to conversion to WGS 84 datum, so the appropriate datum should be selected in any GPS device being used.

These charts are for planning purposes only, and must not be used for navigation.

Map labels: 348, 371, 370, Loch Melfort, Craobh Haven, 369, Loch Craignish, 367, 368, Crinan Canal, Tighnabruaich, Rhu, 356, 357, Inverkip, Ardrishaig, 363, 366, East Loch Tarbert, 362, Rothesay, 355, 361, Largs, 360, 354, Ardrossan, Rhinns of Islay, 347, 365, Lamlash, 359, 353, Troon, 358, 346, Campbeltown, 364, 352, 345, 350, 351, 349, Stranraer, Portpatrick, Kirkcudbright, 269, 344, 343, 342, N

48 Miles, 21 Miles, 31 Miles, 49 Miles, 26 Miles, 16 Miles

WP 341
South Rock Lightship 186° 30 Miles

WP 265
Peel – Isle of Man 154° 45 Miles

Miles
0 5 10 15 20 25
Not to be used for navigation

Marinecall®
MACMILLAN REEDS

Weather Forecasts by Fax & Telephone

Coastal/Inshore	48-hour by Fax	5-day by Tel
Minch	09061 502 126	09066 526 248
Caledonia	09061 502 125	09066 526 247
Clyde	09061 502 124	09066 526 246
North West	09061 502 123	09066 526 245
Northern Ireland	09061 502 127	09066 526 249
National (3-5 day)	09061 502 109	09066 526 234
Offshore	**2-5 day by Fax**	**2-5 day by Tel**
North West Scotland	09061 502 165	09066 526 255

09066 calls cost 60p per min. 09061 calls cost £1.50 per min.

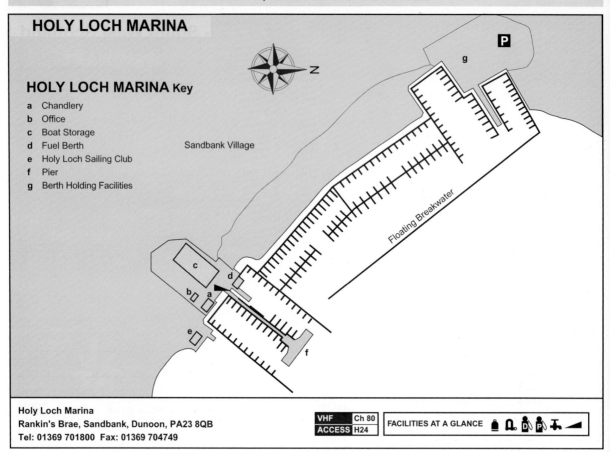

HOLY LOCH MARINA

HOLY LOCH MARINA Key

a Chandlery
b Office
c Boat Storage
d Fuel Berth
e Holy Loch Sailing Club
f Pier
g Berth Holding Facilities

Sandbank Village

Floating Breakwater

Holy Loch Marina
Rankin's Brae, Sandbank, Dunoon, PA23 8QB
Tel: 01369 701800 Fax: 01369 704749

| VHF | Ch 80 |
| ACCESS | H24 |

FACILITIES AT A GLANCE

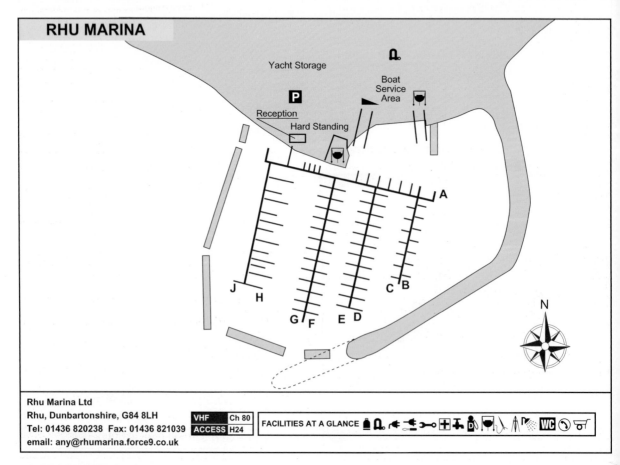

RHU MARINA

Yacht Storage

Boat Service Area

Reception

Hard Standing

J H

G F E D

C B

A

N

Rhu Marina Ltd
Rhu, Dunbartonshire, G84 8LH
Tel: 01436 820238 Fax: 01436 821039
email: any@rhumarina.force9.co.uk

| VHF | Ch 80 |
| ACCESS | H24 |

FACILITIES AT A GLANCE

SANDPOINT MARINA

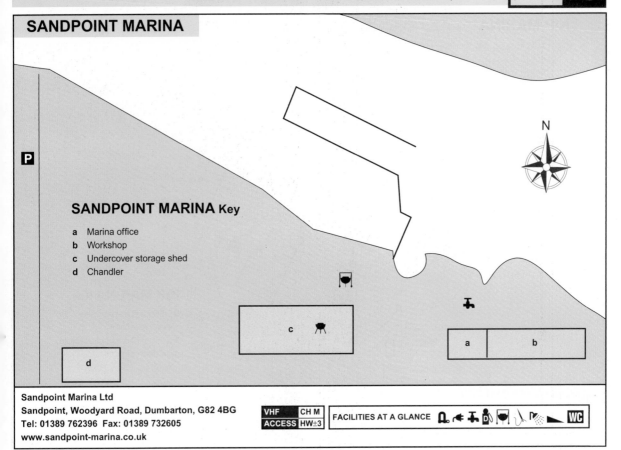

SANDPOINT MARINA Key

a Marina office
b Workshop
c Undercover storage shed
d Chandler

Sandpoint Marina Ltd
Sandpoint, Woodyard Road, Dumbarton, G82 4BG
Tel: 01389 762396 Fax: 01389 732605
www.sandpoint-marina.co.uk

VHF	CH M
ACCESS	HW±3

FACILITIES AT A GLANCE

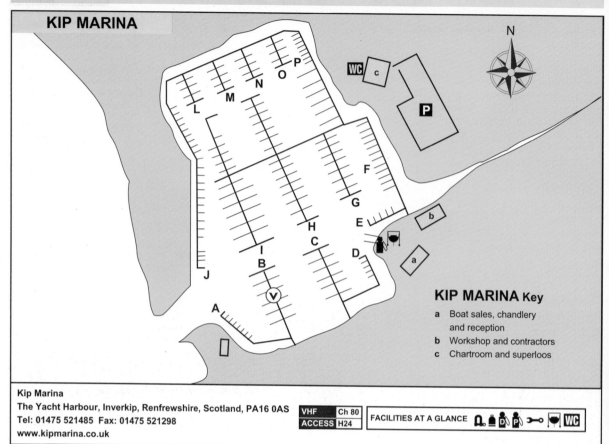

KIP MARINA

KIP MARINA Key

a   Boat sales, chandlery
    and reception
b   Workshop and contractors
c   Chartroom and superloos

Kip Marina
The Yacht Harbour, Inverkip, Renfrewshire, Scotland, PA16 0AS
Tel: 01475 521485 Fax: 01475 521298
www.kipmarina.co.uk

VHF	Ch 80
ACCESS	H24

FACILITIES AT A GLANCE

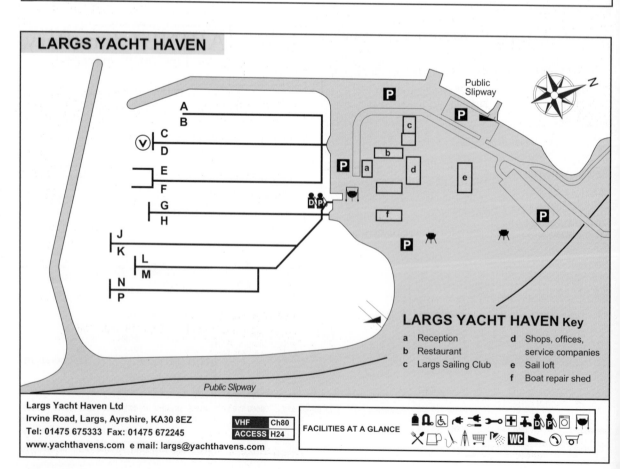

LARGS YACHT HAVEN

LARGS YACHT HAVEN Key

a   Reception
b   Restaurant
c   Largs Sailing Club

d   Shops, offices,
    service companies
e   Sail loft
f   Boat repair shed

Public Slipway

Largs Yacht Haven Ltd
Irvine Road, Largs, Ayrshire, KA30 8EZ
Tel: 01475 675333 Fax: 01475 672245
www.yachthavens.com e mail: largs@yachthavens.com

VHF	Ch80
ACCESS	H24

FACILITIES AT A GLANCE

KIP MARINA
**The Yacht Harbour, Inverkip, Renfrewshire
PA16 0AS.**
Tel: (01475) 521485
Fax: (01475) 521298
www.kipmarina.co.uk
Marina berths for vessels up to 75' LOA, full boatyard facilities including travel hoist, crane, on-site engineers, GRP repairs etc. Bar, restaurant, saunas, launderette and chandlery. Distributors for Moody & Elan, Fairline, Searanger, Rodman & Revenger.

A McCallum & Co Boat Builders
Tarbert — 01880 820209

Alexander Noble and Sons Girvan — 01465 712223

Amsbrisbeg Ltd Port Bannatyne — 01700 502719

ARDFERN YACHT CENTRE LTD
**Ardfern by Lochgilphead, Argyll, Scotland
PA31 8QN**
Tel: (01852) 500247
Fax: (01852) 500624
e-mail: office@ardfernyacht.co.uk
www.ardfernyacht.co.uk
Boatyard and marina facilities in a picturesque natural harbour, comprehensive workshop facilities, extensive chandlery, diesel, gas.

Ardmaleish Boat Building Co
Rothesay — 01700 502007

Ardminish Port Port Ellen — 01583 505254

ARDORAN MARINE
Lerags, Oban, Argyll, Scotland PA34 4SE
Tel: (01631) 566123
Fax: (01631) 566611
e-mail: colin@ardoran.co.uk
www.ardoran.co.uk
West coast Scotland. All marine facilities.

Ardrishaig Boatyard Lochgilphead — 01546 603280

Ardrishaig Police — 01546 603233

Ardrossan Control Tower HM — 01294 463972

Ardrossan Police — 01294 468236

Arthur Duthie Marine Safety
Glasgow — 0141 429 4553

Ayr Yacht and CC Ayr — 01292 476034

Bellanoch Marina Ardrishaig — 01546 603210

Bowling Basin (Dumbarton)
Dumbarton — 01389 877969

BRITISH WATERWAYS
**Crinal Canal Office, Pier Square, Aedrishaig,
Argyll PA30 8DZ**
Tel: (01546) 603210
Fax: (01546) 603941
e-mail: alec.howie@britishways.co.uk
www.scottishcanals.co.uk
The Scottish canals offer the ideal coast to coas'
complemented by excellent marina berthing, id'
and long term moorings.

Brown Son & Ferguson Ltd Glas'

C & C Marine Services Largs	01475 687180
Campbeltown HM	01586 552552
Campbeltown Police	01586 552253
Campbeltown SC Campbeltown	01586 552488
Chattan Shipping Services Ltd Edinburgh	0131 555 3155
Clyde CC (Glasgow) Glasgow	0141 221 2774
Clyde Marina Ltd Ardrossan	01294 607077

CRINAN BOATYARD LTD
Crinan, Lochgilphead, Argyll PA31 8SW
Tel: (01546) 830232
Fax: (01546) 830281
Fully stocked chandlery, slipway, engineering and shipwright work and repairs, swinging moorings, water and diesel, shower and laundry facilities, undercover and outside storage.

Irvine HM	01294 487286
Isle of Bute SC Rothesay	01700 502819
J Henderson Shiskine	01770 860259

JESSAIL
58 Glasgow Street, Ardrossan
KA22 8EH
Tel: (01294) 467311
Fax: (01294) 467311
e-mail: jessail@btinternet.com
Sails, covers, upholstery.

Crinan Canal Office HM	01546 603210
Crinan Canal Police	01546 602222
East Loch Tarbert HM	01859 502444
East Loch Tarbert Police	01880 820200
Estuary Control - Dumbarton HM	01389 726211
Fairlie YC	01294 213940
Helensburgh SC Rhu	01436 672778
Helensburgh	01436 821234
Holy Loch Marina Dunoon	01369 701800
Inverkip Diving Services Inverkip	01475 521281
Inverkip Police	01475 521222

Johnsons Marine Stores Lamlash	01770 600333
JSB Tarbert Ltd Tarbert	01880 820180
Kip Chandlery Inverkip Greenock	01475 521485
Kip Marina	01475 521485
Kirkcudbright HM	01557 331135
Kyle Chandlers Troon	01292 311880
Lamlash Police	01770 302573
Largs Chandlers Largs	01475 686026
Largs Police	01475 674651
Largs SC Largs	01475 670000

ALMANACS & CRUISING COMPANIONS

ALMANACS

Macmillan Reeds Nautical Almanac 2003
The indispensable annual compendium of life dependent navigational data for yachtsmen. Meticulous presentation of all the data required for safe navigation.

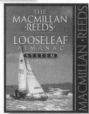

Macmillan Reeds Looseleaf Almanac
• UK & Ireland
• Continental Europe

Update/Pilotage Packs
• UK & Ireland
• Continental Europe
• UK, Ireland
  & Continental Europe

Macmillan Reeds Channel Almanac 2003
The Macmillan Reeds Channel Almanac offers essential data for the South coast of England from the Isles of Scilly to Dover, the Channel Islands and northern France from Calais to L'Aberildut.

Macmillan Reeds Eastern Almanac 2003
including Shetland & Orkney Isles
The Eastern Almanac offers easy access to vital information on the UK East coast from Ramsgate to Cape Wrath, inc Shetlands & Orkneys, plus Dunkerque to Hookseil and Helgoland.

Macmillan Reeds Western Almanac 2003
including Ireland
The Western Almanac offers the cruising and racing yachtsman ready access to essential information by virtue of its clear layout and user friendly format.

PBO Small Craft Almanac 2003
In a practical, handy format the PBO Small Craft Almanac, contains many unique features and represents excellent value.

HANDBOOKS

Macmillan Reeds Yachtsman's Handbook
£34.95   0 333 90451 6
Completely revised and updated, this ultimate reference for yachtsmen is divided into three major sections, covering the navigator the environment and the boat.

CRUISING COMPANION SERIES

The Cruising Companion range covers popular cruising grounds in NW Europe. With superb quality port plans, full-colour aerial photography, and the latest pilotage and approach information. The Cruising Companion series adds 'what to do' information to the 'how to get there' pilotage, with full coverage of shore-side facilities and places of interest.

Channel
£35.00
1 904358 12 8

West Country
£19.95
0 333 90454 0

Solent
£24.95
1 904358 11 X

East Coast Rivers
£19.95
0 333 90455 9

North France & Belgium
£24.95
0 333 98954 6

North Brittany & Channel Is
£24.95
0 333 90452 4

West France
£24.95
0 333 90453 2

NW Spain
£24.95
1 904358 10 1

SW Spain & Portugal
£24.95
0 333 90773 6

Nautical Data Limited • The Book Barn • Westbourne • Hampshire PO10 8RS • UK

tel: +44 (0)1243 389352 • fax: +44 (0)1243 379136 • email: sales@nauticaldata.com • web: www.nauticaldata.com

CLYDE MARINA

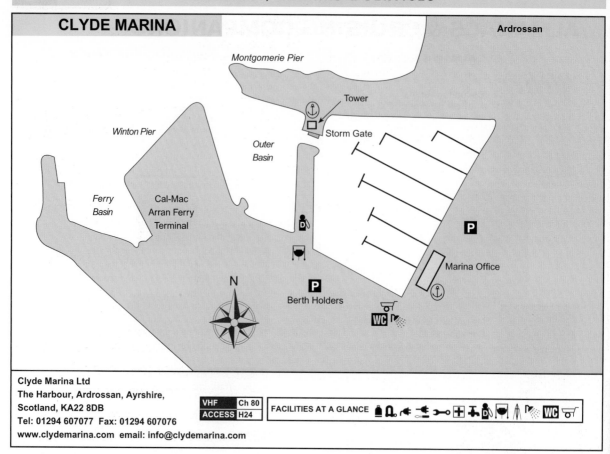

Clyde Marina Ltd
The Harbour, Ardrossan, Ayrshire,
Scotland, KA22 8DB
Tel: 01294 607077 Fax: 01294 607076
www.clydemarina.com email: info@clydemarina.com

VHF	Ch 80
ACCESS	H24

FACILITIES AT A GLANCE

TROON YACHT HAVEN

TROON YACHT HAVEN Key

a Main building
Toilets
Showers
Baths
Laundry
b Marina office

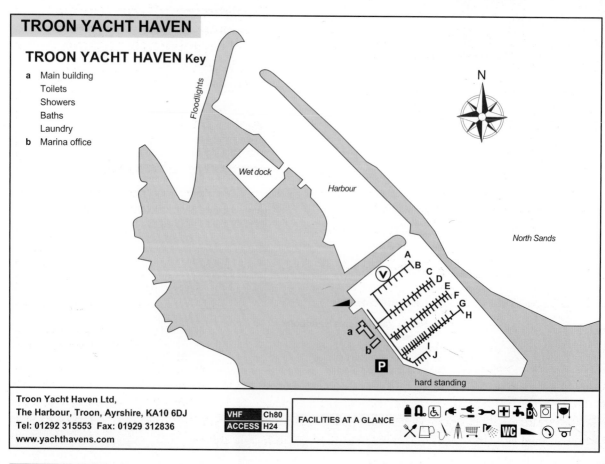

Troon Yacht Haven Ltd,
The Harbour, Troon, Ayrshire, KA10 6DJ
Tel: 01292 315553 Fax: 01929 312836
www.yachthavens.com

VHF	Ch80
ACCESS	H24

FACILITIES AT A GLANCE

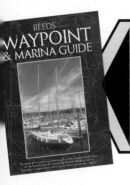

Largs Yacht Haven Largs	01475 675333	**Owen Sails** Gourock	01475 636196
Loch Ryan SC Stranraer	01776 706322	**Portpatrick HM**	01776 810355
Malcolm Sails Fairlie	01475 568500	**Portpatrick Police**	01776 702112
Maramarine Helensburgh	01436 810971	**Prestwick SC** Prestwick	01292 671117
McGruar and Co Ltd Helensburgh	01436 831313	**Queens Gareloch/Rhu HM**	01436 674321
New World Yacht Care Helensburgh	01436 820586	**Rhu Chandlery** Rhu	01436 820584
Nicholson Hughes Sails Rosneath	01436 831356	**Rhu Marina Ltd** Rhu	01436 820238

MARYPORT HARBOUR AND MARINA

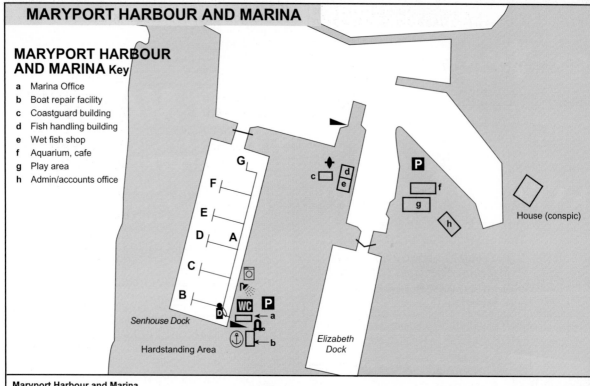

MARYPORT HARBOUR AND MARINA Key

a Marina Office
b Boat repair facility
c Coastguard building
d Fish handling building
e Wet fish shop
f Aquarium, cafe
g Play area
h Admin/accounts office

Maryport Harbour and Marina
Bridge Street, Maryport, Cumbria, CA15 8AE
Tel: 01900 814431/818447 Fax: 01900 810212
www.maryportmarina.com email: enquires@maryport.com

VHF	Ch M
ACCESS	HW±2.5

FACILITIES AT A GLANCE

Rhu Police	01436 672141
Rothesay HM	01700 503842
Rothesay Police	01700 502121
Royal Gourock YC Gourock	01475 632983
Royal Northern and Clyde YC Rhu	01436 820322

Royal Scottish Motor YC	0141 881 1024
Sandpoint Marina Dumbarton	01389 762396
Saturn Sails Largs	01475 689933
Silvers Marine Ltd Helensburgh	01436 831222

SLEAT MARINE SERVICES
Ardvasar, Isle of Skye IV45 8RS
Tel: (01471) 844216
Fax: (01471) 844387
e-mail: services@sleatmarineservices
www.sleatmarineservices.co.uk
Yacht Charter - we offer a choice of yachts in the 10-12 metre
size range. Services to visiting yachts include: 15 ton hoist,
general repairs, diesel, water, mooring and showers. We look
forward to seeing you.

Tarbert Lochfyne YC Tarbert	01880 820376

THE TAYVALLICH INN
Tayvallich, By Lochgilphead, Argyll PA31 8PL
Tel: (01546) 870282
Fax: (01546) 870333
e-mail: tayvallich.inn@virgin.net
www.tayvallich.com
Bar and restaurant situated on the shores of Loch Sween.
Fresh, local seafood a speciality, although plenty for the meat-
eater and vegetarians.

Troon CC Troon	01292 311908
Troon HM	01292 281687
Troon Police	01292 313100
Troon Yacht Haven Troon	01292 315553
Troon YC	01292 315315
UK Customs Nationwide	0845 0109000

Planning a trip?

Met Office

Make it plain sailing
– for your free copy
of the *2002 Marine Weather Services* booklet
call the Met Office Customer Centre
on **0845 300 0300** or go to
www.metoffice.com/leisuremarine/mwsbooklet.html

For a five-day inshore forecast
for Colwyn Bay – Mull of Gallway, and Isle of Man,
dial **09060 100 461*** from your fax machine.

*09060 calls are charged at £1 per minute at all times.

Key to Marina Plans symbols

🔥	Calor Gas	**P**	Parking
	Chandler	✗	Pub/Restaurant
♿	Disabled facilities		Pump out
	Electrical supply		Rigging service
	Electrical repairs		Sail repairs
	Engine repairs	✗	Shipwright
✚	First Aid		Shop/Supermarket
	Fresh Water		Showers
D	Fuel - Diesel		Slipway
P	Fuel - Petrol	**WC**	Toilets
	Hardstanding/boatyard		Telephone
	Laundry facilities		Trolleys
	Lift-out facilities	**V**	Visitors berths

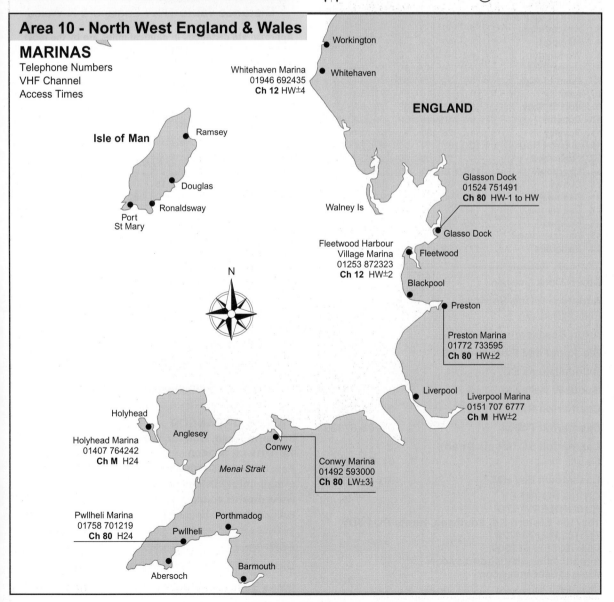

Area 10 - North West England & Wales

MARINAS
Telephone Numbers
VHF Channel
Access Times

Workington

Whitehaven Marina
01946 692435
Ch 12 HW±4

Whitehaven

ENGLAND

Ramsey

Isle of Man

Douglas

Ronaldsway

Port
St Mary

Glasson Dock
01524 751491
Ch 80 HW-1 to HW

Walney Is

Glasso Dock

Fleetwood Harbour
Village Marina
01253 872323
Ch 12 HW±2

Fleetwood

Blackpool

N

Preston

Preston Marina
01772 733595
Ch 80 HW±2

Liverpool

Liverpool Marina
0151 707 6777
Ch M HW±2

Holyhead

Anglesey

Holyhead Marina
01407 764242
Ch M H24

Conwy

Menai Strait

Conwy Marina
01492 593000
Ch 80 LW±3½

Pwllheli Marina
01758 701219
Ch 80 H24

Porthmadog

Pwllheli

Barmouth

Abersoch

Waypoint Guide Area 10 – NW England & N Wales - Mull of Galloway to Bardsey Is

254	**Causeway WCM** - 2M SW	52°39'·90N	04°28'·00W
255	**Abersoch** - 1·2M SE St Tudwal's Is Lt	52°47'·20N	04°26'·80W
256	**Porthmadog** - 1·1M SW Frwy By	52°52'·70N	04°12'·50W
257	**Bardsey Island light** - 4M NNW	52°48'·60N	04°50'·30W
258	**Menai Strait** - 1·4M SW Llanddwyn Is	53°07'·30N	04°26'·80W
259	**Holyhead** - 1M N of W Bkwtr	53°21'·00N	04°37'·00W
260	**Menai Strait** - 1·2M N of Puffin Is	53°20'·50N	04°01'·50W
261	**Liverpool** - 0·7M S of Bar Lt V	53°31'·30N	03°20'·90W
262	**Fleetwood** - 2M SW Lune Dp By	53°54'·10N	03°13'·00W
263	**Douglas** - 1·1M W of Douglas Hd	54°08'·70N	04°26'·00W
264	**Ramsey** - 1·3M ENE of S bkwtr	54°19'·90N	04°20'·20W
265	**Peel** - 1M NW entrance	54°14'·50N	04°42'·50W
266	**Pt St Mary** - 1·2M S of Kallow Pt	54°02'·90N	04°43'·80W
267	**St Bees Head Lt** - 2M W of	54°30'·80N	03°41'·50W
268	**Workington** - 1M WNW of bkwtr.	54°39'·40N	03°36'·30W
269	**Kirkcudbright** -1·5M S Little Ross Lt	54°44'·50N	04°05'·00W

Distance Table - NW England & N Wales

Approximate distances in nautical miles are by the most direct route while avoiding dangers and allowing for Traffic Separation Schemes

	1	2	3	4	5	6	7	8	9	10	11	12	13	14	15	16	17	18	19	20
1. Portpatrick	1																			
2. Mull of Galloway	16	2																		
3. Kirkcudbright	48	32	3																	
4. Maryport	65	49	26	4																
5. Workington	63	47	25	6	5															
6. Ravenglass	70	54	40	30	23	6														
7. Point of Ayre	38	22	28	37	31	34	7													
8. Peel	41	26	46	55	49	52	18	8												
9. Port St Mary	56	41	61	63	57	50	35	18	9											
10. Douglas	60	42	46	50	44	39	19	30	13	10										
11. Ramsey	44	28	34	41	35	34	6	24	27	15	11									
12. Glasson Dock	101	85	74	66	60	37	64	85	69	63	61	12								
13. Fleetwood	95	79	68	59	53	30	58	80	63	57	55	10	13							
14. Liverpool	118	102	97	89	83	60	80	86	76	70	77	52	46	14						
15. Conwy	111	95	95	92	86	58	72	72	57	59	68	62	56	46	15					
16. Beaumaris	109	93	94	95	89	72	71	73	58	58	70	66	60	49	12	16				
17. Caernarfon	117	103	104	105	99	82	81	73	68	68	80	76	70	59	22	10	17			
18. Holyhead	93	81	94	96	90	69	68	62	46	50	65	79	73	68	36	32	26	18		
19. Bardsey Island	127	113	129	129	123	114	107	94	80	88	98	107	101	90	53	41	31	43	19	
20. Fishguard	171	158	175	175	169	160	153	140	126	134	144	153	147	136	100	88	78	89	45	20

Albert Dock Liverpool	0151 709 6558
Aquatech Diving Services Port of St Mary	01624 833037
Arfon Oceaneering Caernarfon	01286 676055
Blackpool and Fleetwood YC	01253 884205
Blundellsands SC	0151 929 2101
Booth W Kelly Ltd Ramsey	01624 812322
Caernarfon HM	01286 672118
Caernarfon Police	01286 673333
Caernarfon SC (Menia Strait) Caernarfon	01286 672861
Castletown Bay HM	01624 823549

CHRIS HORNSEY (CHANDLERY) LTD
152/154 Eastern Rd, Southsea, Hants PO4 8DY
Tel: (02392) 734728
Fax: (02392) 611500
e-mail: sales@chrishornsey.com
www.chrishornsey.com
Established 1970. Close to Southsea Marina.

Conwy HM	01492 596253
Conwy Marina Conwy	01492 593000
Conwy Police	01492 517171
Conwy YC Deganwy	01492 583690
Dave Hudson Trearddur Bay	01407 860628
David Moss (Boatbuilders) Thornton-Cleveleys	01253 893830

DICKIES OF BANGOR
36 Garth Road, Bangor, Gwynedd LL57 2SE
Tel: (01248) 363400
Fax: (01248) 354169
e-mail: info@dickies.co.uk
www.dickies.co.uk
Full yard services, chandlery, brokerage and new boat dealers for Beneteau Sail and power boats and Lagoon power catamarans.

Dickie AM & Sons Ltd Bangor	01248 352775
Dinas Boat Yard Ltd Y Felinheli	01248 671642

Area 10 - North West England

WAYCHART
Mull of Galloway to Bardsey Is
Isle of Man & N. wales

Symbols used:

- • Port
- ⊙ Waypoint
- — Track - between waypoints
- -- Track - close to possible dangers

NORTHERN IRELAND

Important Note
Any waypoint being used for the first time must be checked by plotting on a suitable chart. The waypoints listed have been lifted from UK Admiralty charts prior to conversion to WGS 84 datum, so the appropriate datum should be selected in any GPS device being used.

These charts are for planning purposes only, and must not be used for navigation.

SCOTLAND

Stranraer
Portpatrick
Kirkcudbright
269
Maryport
268 Workington
267 Whitehaven
St Bees Head

S. Rock
Ramsey
265 264
Douglas
Peel 263
Port St Mary
266
Ronaldsway
Walney Is
262
134° 314° 54 Miles

Carlingford

ENGLAND

Glasson Dock
Fleetwood
Blackpool
Preston

Miles
0 10 20 30 40 50
Not to be used for navigation

N

Malahide
228° 048°
65 Miles

Point Lynas
268° 53 Miles
088°
259 260 26 Miles 261
ANGLESEY
Holyhead
Conw
Menai Strait
258
Liverpool

Marinecall®
MACMILLAN REEDS

Weather Forecasts by Fax & Telephone

Coastal/Inshore	48-hour by Fax	5-day by Tel
Northern Ireland	09061 502 127	09066 526 249
Clyde	09061 502 124	09066 526 246
North West	09061 502 123	09066 526 245
Wales	09061 502 122	09066 526 244
Bristol	09061 502 121	09066 526 243
National (3-5 day)	09061 502 109	09066 526 234
Offshore	**2-5 day by Fax**	**2-5 day by Tel**
North West Scotland	09061 502 165	09066 526 255
Irish Sea	09061 502 163	09066 526 253
09066 calls cost 60p per min. 09061 calls cost £1.50 per min.		

Wicklow
072° 252° 65 Miles
Arklow
Pwllheli
Abersoch
257 255
254
59 Miles

REPUBLIC OF IRELAND

DOLPHIN MARITIME SOFTWARE LTD
334 Storey House, White Cross,
South Road, Lancaster LA1 4XQ.
Tel/Fax: (01524) 841946
e-mail: sales@dolphinmaritime.com
www.dolphinmaritime.com
Marine computer programs for IBM PC, Psion and Sharp pocket computers. Specialists in navigation, tidal prediction and other programs for both yachting and commercial uses.

Douglas Bay YC Douglas	01624 673965
Douglas Boatyard Preston	01772 812462
Douglas HM	01624 686628
Douglas Police	01624 631212
Dubois Phillips & McCallum Ltd Liverpool	0151 236 2776
Elton Boatbuilding Ltd Kirkcudbright	01557 330177
Fleetwood Harbour Village Marina Fleetwood	01253 872323
Fleetwood HM	01253 872323
Fleetwood Police	01524 63333
Fylde Coast Sailmaking Co Fleetwood	01253 873476

Garlieston HM	01988 600274
Glasson Dock HM	01524 751724
Glasson Dock Marina Lancaster	01524 751491
Glasson SC Preston	01524 751089
Holyhead HM	01407 763071
Holyhead Marina Holyhead	01407 764242
Holyhead Marine Services Ltd Holyhead	01407 760111
Holyhead Police	01286 673333
Holyhead SC Holyhead	01407 762526
Hoylake SC Wirral	0151 632 2616
Irish Sea Yachts Maryport	01900 816881
Island Boat Services Port of St Mary	01624 832073

CYNGOR SIR
YNYS MÔN
ISLE OF ANGLESEY COUNTY COUNCIL
Maritime Officer
Highways, Transportation & Property Department,
Council Offices, Liang efnf, Anglesey LL77 7TW
Tel: 01248 752331

2003/M&WMD35/eadb

WHITEHAVEN MARINA

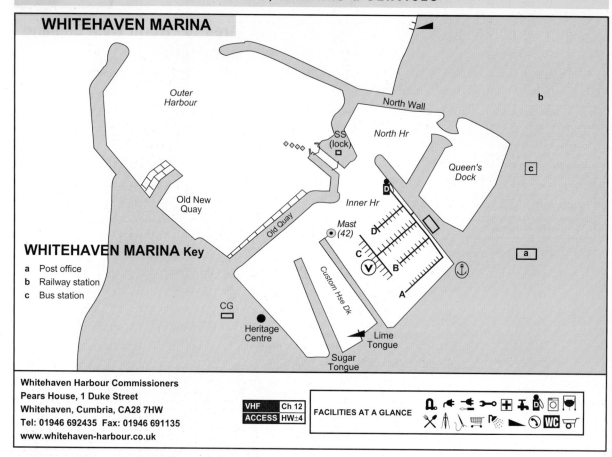

WHITEHAVEN MARINA Key

a   Post office
b   Railway station
c   Bus station

Whitehaven Harbour Commissioners
Pears House, 1 Duke Street
Whitehaven, Cumbria, CA28 7HW
Tel: 01946 692435 Fax: 01946 691135
www.whitehaven-harbour.co.uk

VHF	Ch 12
ACCESS	HW±4

FACILITIES AT A GLANCE

GLASSON DOCK MARINA

GLASSON DOCK MARINA Key

a   Glasson Basin Yacht Co. Ltd
b   Sailing Club
c   Harbour House

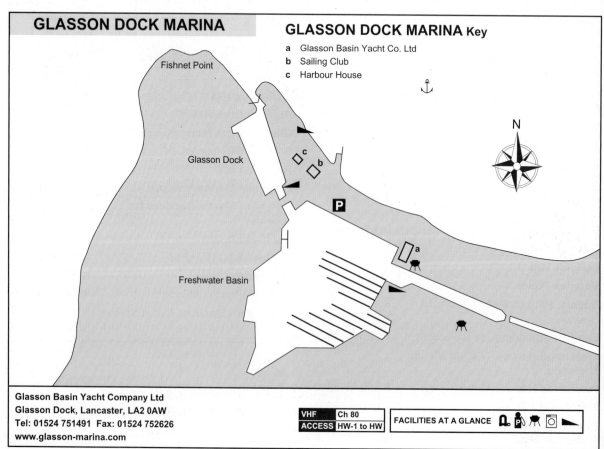

Glasson Basin Yacht Company Ltd
Glasson Dock, Lancaster, LA2 0AW
Tel: 01524 751491 Fax: 01524 752626
www.glasson-marina.com

VHF	Ch 80
ACCESS	HW-1 to HW

FACILITIES AT A GLANCE

FLEETWOOD MARINA

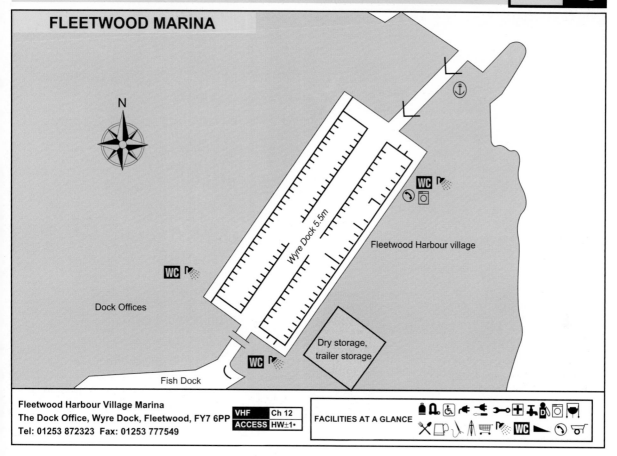

N

Wyre Dock 5.5m

Fleetwood Harbour village

Dock Offices

Dry storage, trailer storage

Fish Dock

Fleetwood Harbour Village Marina
The Dock Office, Wyre Dock, Fleetwood, FY7 6PP
Tel: 01253 872323 Fax: 01253 777549

VHF	Ch 12
ACCESS	HW±1•

FACILITIES AT A GLANCE

Fleetwood Harbour Village Marina
"A Premier Yachting Venue"

An historic fishing port, Fleetwood has established itself as one of the premier yachting venues of the North West.

The sheltered enclosed dock houses a marina with 300 fully serviced berths, a dry storage compound and comprehensive facilities for the leisure sailor. It forms part of an exciting waterfront development by Associated British Ports.

With easy trunk road links to the M55 and M6 it is an ideal base for cruises to Morecambe Bay and the Irish Sea. You'll find our marina a friendly and welcoming haven where ABP's staff pride themselves on giving a personal and professional service.

We look forward to seeing you in Fleetwood as a resident or a visitor.

For further information contact the Marina Superintendent,
Dock Office, Fleetwood, Lancashire FY7 6PP
Telephone 01253 872323 e-mail fleetwood@abports.co.uk
www.abports.co.uk

ABP

2003/M&WM85/b

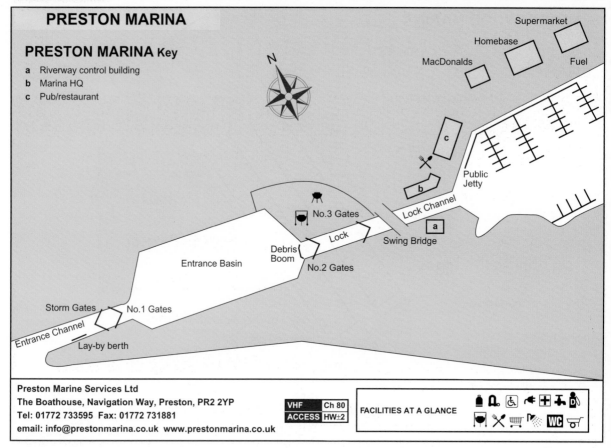

PRESTON MARINA

PRESTON MARINA Key

a Riverway control building
b Marina HQ
c Pub/restaurant

Supermarket
Homebase
MacDonalds
Fuel

Public Jetty
Lock Channel
No.3 Gates
Lock
No.2 Gates
Swing Bridge
Debris Boom
Entrance Basin
Storm Gates
No.1 Gates
Entrance Channel
Lay-by berth

Preston Marine Services Ltd
The Boathouse, Navigation Way, Preston, PR2 2YP
Tel: 01772 733595 Fax: 01772 731881
email: info@prestonmarina.co.uk www.prestonmarina.co.uk

VHF **Ch 80**
ACCESS **HW±2**

FACILITIES AT A GLANCE

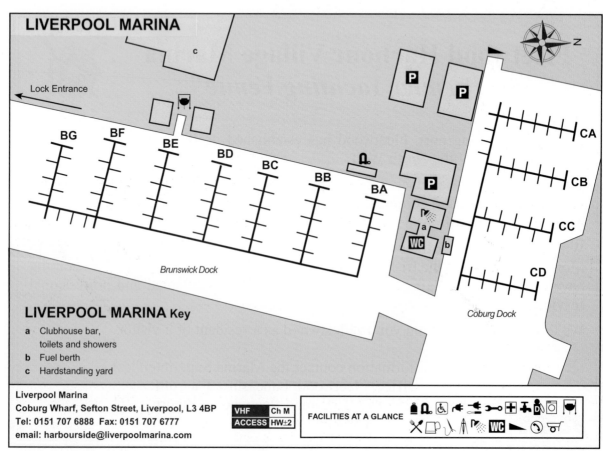

LIVERPOOL MARINA

Lock Entrance

BG BF BE BD BC BB BA

CA
CB
CC
CD

P P P

WC

Brunswick Dock

Coburg Dock

LIVERPOOL MARINA Key

a Clubhouse bar,
toilets and showers
b Fuel berth
c Hardstanding yard

Liverpool Marina
Coburg Wharf, Sefton Street, Liverpool, L3 4BP
Tel: 0151 707 6888 Fax: 0151 707 6777
email: harbourside@liverpoolmarina.com

VHF **Ch M**
ACCESS **HW±2**

FACILITIES AT A GLANCE

Isle of Man YC Port St Mary	01624 832088
J Dawson (Sails) Port Dinorwic	01248 670103
JP Lamb & Sons Ltd Liverpool	0151 709 4861
Kirkcudbright Police	01557 330600
Kirkcudbright SC Kirkcudbright	01557 331727
Kirkcudbright Scallop Gear Ltd Kirkcudbright	01557 330399
Liverpool HM	0151 949 6134/5
Liverpool Marina Liverpool	0151 708 5228
Liverpool Police	0151 709 6010
Mailspeed Marine Warrington	01925 838858
Manx Marine Ltd Douglas	01624 674842
Manx Sailing & CC Ramsey	01624 813494
Maryport Harbour and Marina Maryport	01900 814431
Maryport HM	01900 814431
Maryport Police	01900 602422
Maryport YC	01228 560865

Menai Bridge BC Beaumaris	01248 810583
Menai Strait HM	01248 712312
Menai Strait Police	01286 673333
Mouse Sails Holyhead	01407 763636

NATIONWIDE MARINE HIRE
Units 4 & 5 Clarendon Court, Winwick Quay,
Warrington,Cheshire WA2 8QP
Tel: (01925) 245788
Fax: (01925) 245788
e-mail: sales@zodiacliferafts.co.uk
The company is an approved liferaft service station and is the
leading supplier of Zodiac leisure liferafts in the UK. Zodiac
liferafts to RORC/ORC/SOLAS B specifications are available
for hire. Also EPIRB's, inflatable tenders and lifejackets.

New Tec Diving Services Blackpool	01253 691665
North Wales Boat Centre Conwy	01492 580740
North Wales CC Conwy	01492 593481
North West Venturers YC (Beaumaris) Beaumaris	0161 2921943

PLAS MENAI NATIONAL WATERSPORTS CENTRE
Caernarfon, Gwynedd LL55 1UE
Tel: (01248) 670964
Fax: (01248) 670964
e-mail: plas.menai@scw.co.uk
www.plasmenai.co.uk
Practical and shore-based RYA sailing courses, refresher &
flotilla cruising weekends around the North Wales coast, Ireland,
Isle of Man and southern Scotland Competent Crew to
Yachtmaster and one-day shore-based safety and navigation
skills courses.

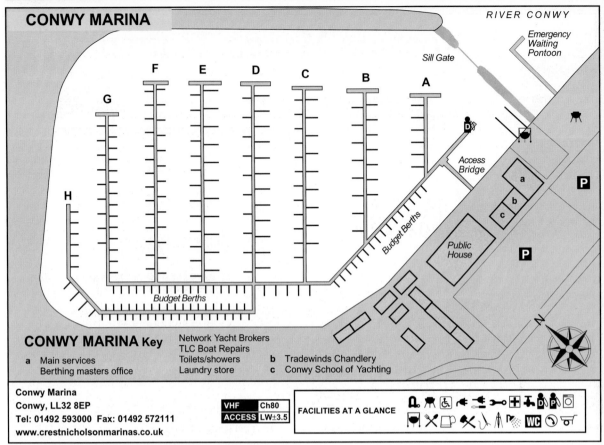

CONWY MARINA

RIVER CONWY

Emergency Waiting Pontoon

Sill Gate

F E D C B A

G

H

Access Bridge

Budget Berths

Budget Berths

a
b
c

Public House

P

P

N

CONWY MARINA Key

a Main services
   Berthing masters office

Network Yacht Brokers
TLC Boat Repairs
Toilets/showers
Laundry store

b Tradewinds Chandlery
c Conwy School of Yachting

Conwy Marina
Conwy, LL32 8EP
Tel: 01492 593000 Fax: 01492 572111
www.crestnicholsonmarinas.co.uk

VHF	Ch80
ACCESS	LW±3.5

FACILITIES AT A GLANCE

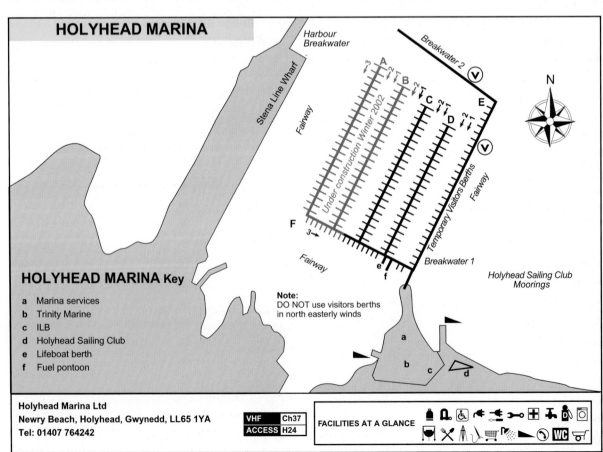

HOLYHEAD MARINA

Harbour Breakwater

Breakwater 2

Stena Line Wharf

Fairway

Under construction Winter 2002

A B C D E

F

Temporary Visitors Berths

Fairway

Fairway

Breakwater 1

e f

Holyhead Sailing Club Moorings

N

Note:
DO NOT use visitors berths
in north easterly winds

a
b c
d

HOLYHEAD MARINA Key

a Marina services
b Trinity Marine
c ILB
d Holyhead Sailing Club
e Lifeboat berth
f Fuel pontoon

Holyhead Marina Ltd
Newry Beach, Holyhead, Gwynedd, LL65 1YA
Tel: 01407 764242

VHF	Ch37
ACCESS	H24

FACILITIES AT A GLANCE

T J RIGGING
9 Vardre Park Deganwy, Conwy LL31 9YQ
Tel: (07780) 972411
e-mail: tj.rigging@virgin.net
Specialist mobile rigging service.

Peel HM	01624 842338
Peel Police	01624 631212
Peel Sailing and CC Peel	01624 842390
Penrhyn Bangor HM	01248 352525
Pollard Marine Port St Mary	01624 835831
Port Dinorwic Marina Y Felinheli	01248 671500
Port St Mary HM	01624 833205
Port St Mary Police	01624 631212
Porth Dinllaen HM	01758 720276

**PREMIUM LIFERAFT SERVICES
ISLE OF MAN**
Tel: (01624) 674842
Freephone: 0800 243673
e-mail: info@liferafts.com
www.liferafts.com
Hire and sales of DoT and RORC approved liferafts and safety equipment.

Preston HM	01772 726711
Preston Marina Preston	01772 733595
Preston Marine Services Ltd Preston	01772 733595
Preston Police	01772 203203
Ramsey HM	01624 812245
Ramsey Police	01624 631212
Ribble CC Lytham St Anne's	01253 739983
River Wyre YC	01253 811948
Royal Anglesey YC (Beaumaris) Anglesey	01248 810295
Royal Mersey YC Birkenhead	0151 645 3204
Royal Welsh YC (Caernarfon) Caernarfon	01286 672599
Royal Welsh YC Aernarfon	01286 672599
Salvesen UK Ltd Liverpool	0151 933 6038
Shipsides Marine Ltd Preston	01772 797079
Silloth HM	016973 31358
Solway YC Kirkdudbright	01556 620312
The Fleetwood Trawlers' Supply Co Ltd Fleetwood	01253 873476
Trinity Marine Holyhead	01407 763855
UK Customs Nationwide	0845 0109000
V Ships (Isle of Man) Douglas	01624 688886
Waterfront Marine Bangor	01248 352513

AREA 10

PWLLHELI MARINA

PWLLHELI MARINA Key

a   Marina offices
  Toilets
  Showers
  Baby change
  Laundrette

b   Domestic refuse point
c   Dinghy park and slipway
d   Short stay boat park
e   pwllheli sailing club
f   Chandlery

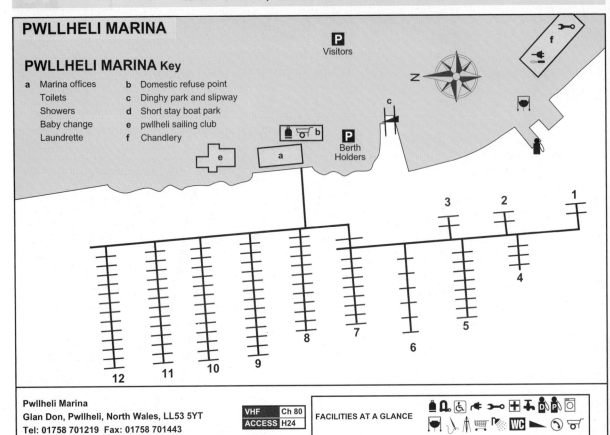

Pwllheli Marina
Glan Don, Pwllheli, North Wales, LL53 5YT
Tel: 01758 701219 Fax: 01758 701443

VHF	Ch 80
ACCESS	H24

FACILITIES AT A GLANCE

West Kirby SC West Kirby	0151 625 5579
Whitehaven Harbour Marina	
Whitehaven	01946 692435
Whitehaven HM	01946 692435
Whitehaven Police	01946 692616
Workington HM	01900 602301
Workington Police	01900 602422

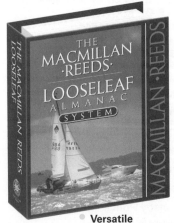

Planning a trip?

Make it plain sailing
– for your free copy
of the *2002 Marine Weather Services* booklet
call the Met Office Customer Centre
on **0845 300 0300** or go to
www.metoffice.com/leisuremarine/mwsbooklet.html

For a five-day inshore forecast
for St. David's Head – Colwyn Bay,
dial **09060 100 460*** from your fax machine.
For Hartland Point – St. David's Head
dial **09060 100 459.***

09060 calls are charged at £1 per minute at all times.

Key to Marina Plans symbols

Calor Gas		P	Parking
Chandler			Pub/Restaurant
Disabled facilities			Pump out
Electrical supply			Rigging service
Electrical repairs			Sail repairs
Engine repairs			Shipwright
First Aid			Shop/Supermarket
Fresh Water			Showers
Fuel - Diesel			Slipway
Fuel - Petrol		WC	Toilets
Hardstanding/boatyard			Telephone
Laundry facilities			Trolleys
Lift-out facilities		V	Visitors berths

Area 11 - South Wales & Bristol Channel

MARINAS

Telephone Numbers
VHF Channel
Access Times

WALES

Barmouth

Aberdovey

Aberystwyth
01970 611422
Ch 80 HW±2
Aberystwyth

Bristol Marina
0117 921 3198
Ch 80 HW-3 to HW

Fishguard

Sharpness Marina
01453 811476
Ch 17 HW-1 to HW

Milford Haven

Burry Port

Penarth Marina
02920 705021
Ch 80 H24

Tenby

Swansea

Milford Marina
01646 696312
Ch M H24

Swansea Marina
01792 470310
Ch 80 HW±4½

Cardiff

Barry

Bristol

Portishead Marina
01275 841941
Ch 80 H±4

Neyland Yacht Haven
01646 601601 **C
h 80** H24

Bristol Channel

Ilfracombe

Watchet

Burnham-on-Sea

Appledore

N

Padstow

Land's End

Isles of Scilly
Round Is

Waypoint Guide Area 11 – South Wales & Bristol Channel - Bardsey Is to Lands End

129	**Runnel Stone Lt By** - 0·3M S of	50°00'·85N	05°40'·30W
130	**Wolf Rk Lt** - 2M S of	49°54'·65N	05°48'·50W
131	**St Mary's, Scilly** - 2M E of St Mary's	49°54'·00N	06°l 5.00'W
233	**Padstow** - 2M NW of Stepper Point	50°35'·70N	04°59'·10W
234	**Hartland Point** - 2·5M NW of	51°02'·80N	04°34'·40W
235	**River Taw** - 1·6M NW Bideford By	51°06'·20N	04°18'·20W
236	**Morte Point** - 2·5M NNW of	51°13'·60N	04°15'·80W
237	**Ilfracombe** - 1·5M N	51°14'·20N	04°06'·80W
238	**Foreland Point** - 1·5 miles N	51°16'·20N	03°47'·20W
239	**Burnham on Sea** - 2·6M N	51°15'·30N	03°07'·80W
240	**Barry & R. Severn** - 2·9M SSW ent	51°21'·00N	03°17'·30W
241	**Ledge SCM By** - 2M S of	51°28'·00N	03°58'·60W
242	**Swansea** - 1M SE Mumbles Hd	51°33'·40N	03°57'·00W
243	**Caldey Island** - 7 miles SE	51°32'·20N	04°35'·20W
244	**Tenby** - 1M SE Caldey Island	51°37'·20N	04°39'·60W
245	**Crow Rock** - 1·3M S of	51°35'·40N	05°03'·50W
246	**Milford Haven** - 1·1M S St Ann's Hd	51°39'·70N	05°10'·60W
247	**Skokholm Island Lt** - 1·6M W of	51°41'·60N	05°19'·70W
248	**South Bishop Is Lt** - 3·0M NW	51°53'·30N	05°27'·80W
249	**Fishguard** - 1·5M N Strumble Hd	52°03'·40N	05°04'·20W
250	**Aberystwyth** - 1·5M W of ent	52°24'·40N	04°08'·00W
251	**Aberdovey** - 1·5M W of hbr bar	52°31'·70N	04°07'·10W
252	**Sarn-y-Bwch WCM** - 1·1M W	52°34'·80N	04°15'·10W
253	**Barmouth** - 1·2M W of hbr bar	52°42'·60N	04°05'·60W
254	**Causeway WCM** - 2M SW	52°39'·90N	04°28'·00W
255	**Abersoch** - 1·2M SE St Tudwal's Is Lt	52°47'·20N	04°26'·80W
256	**Porthmadog** - 1·1M SW Frwy By	52°52'·70N	04°12'·50W
257	**Bardsey Island light** - 4M NNW	52°48'·60N	04°50'·30W

Distance Table - South Wales & Bristol Channel

Approximate distances in nautical miles are by the most direct route while avoiding dangers and allowing for Traffic Separation Schemes

	1	2	3	4	5	6	7	8	9	10	11	12	13	14	15	16	17	18	19	20
1. Bardsey Island	1																			
2. Abersoch	14	2																		
3. Pwllheli	18	5	3																	
4. Barmouth	27	18	18	4																
5. Aberdovey	31	26	25	14	5															
6. Aberystwyth	33	30	30	20	10	6														
7. Fishguard	45	54	58	56	47	40	7													
8. South Bishop	60	70	74	74	67	61	25	8												
9. Milford Haven	83	93	97	97	90	84	48	23	9											
10. Tenby	106	116	120	120	113	107	71	46	28	10										
11. Swansea	129	139	143	143	136	130	94	69	55	36	11									
12. Barry	151	161	165	165	158	152	116	91	77	57	37	12								
13. Cardiff	160	170	174	174	167	161	125	100	86	66	46	9	13							
14. Sharpness	191	201	205	205	198	192	156	131	117	106	75	39	33	14						
15. Avonmouth	174	184	188	188	181	175	139	114	100	89	58	22	20	18	15					
16. Burnham-on-Sea	168	178	182	182	175	169	133	108	94	70	48	18	53	50	33	16				
17. Ilfracombe	127	137	141	141	134	128	92	67	53	35	25	35	44	74	57	45	17			
18. Lundy Island	110	120	124	124	117	111	75	50	38	30	37	54	63	95	78	66	22	18		
19. Padstow	141	151	155	155	148	142	106	81	70	70	76	88	97	127	110	98	55	39	19	
20. Longships	168	178	182	182	175	169	133	108	105	110	120	130	139	169	152	140	95	82	50	20

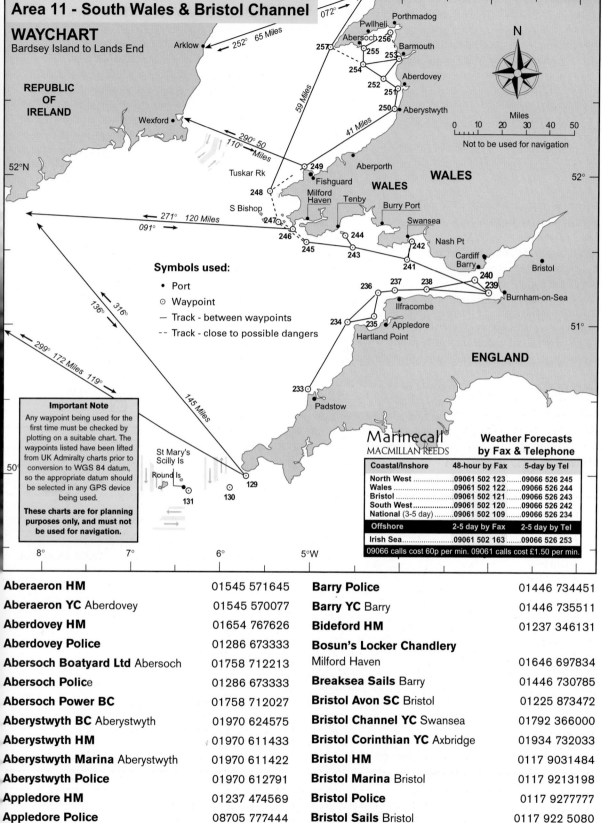

Area 11 - South Wales & Bristol Channel

WAYCHART
Bardsey Island to Lands End

REPUBLIC OF IRELAND

WALES

ENGLAND

Symbols used:
- • Port
- ⊙ Waypoint
- — Track - between waypoints
- -- Track - close to possible dangers

Important Note
Any waypoint being used for the first time must be checked by plotting on a suitable chart. The waypoints listed have been lifted from UK Admiralty charts prior to conversion to WGS 84 datum, so the appropriate datum should be selected in any GPS device being used.

These charts are for planning purposes only, and must not be used for navigation.

Miles
0 10 20 30 40 50
Not to be used for navigation

Marinecall®
MACMILLAN REEDS

Weather Forecasts by Fax & Telephone

Coastal/Inshore	48-hour by Fax	5-day by Tel
North West	09061 502 123	09066 526 245
Wales	09061 502 122	09066 526 244
Bristol	09061 502 121	09066 526 243
South West	09061 502 120	09066 526 242
National (3-5 day)	09061 502 109	09066 526 234

Offshore	2-5 day by Fax	2-5 day by Tel
Irish Sea	09061 502 163	09066 526 253

09066 calls cost 60p per min. 09061 calls cost £1.50 per min.

Aberaeron HM	01545 571645	**Barry Police**	01446 734451
Aberaeron YC Aberdovey	01545 570077	**Barry YC** Barry	01446 735511
Aberdovey HM	01654 767626	**Bideford HM**	01237 346131
Aberdovey Police	01286 673333	**Bosun's Locker Chandlery**	
Abersoch Boatyard Ltd Abersoch	01758 712213	Milford Haven	01646 697834
Abersoch Police	01286 673333	**Breaksea Sails** Barry	01446 730785
Abersoch Power BC	01758 712027	**Bristol Avon SC** Bristol	01225 873472
Aberystwyth BC Aberystwyth	01970 624575	**Bristol Channel YC** Swansea	01792 366000
Aberystwyth HM	01970 611433	**Bristol Corinthian YC** Axbridge	01934 732033
Aberystwyth Marina Aberystwyth	01970 611422	**Bristol HM**	0117 9031484
Aberystwyth Police	01970 612791	**Bristol Marina** Bristol	0117 9213198
Appledore HM	01237 474569	**Bristol Police**	0117 9277777
Appledore Police	08705 777444	**Bristol Sails** Bristol	0117 922 5080
Barmouth HM	01341 280671	**Brunel Chandlery Ltd** Neyland	01646 601667
Barmouth Police	01286 673333	**Bude HM**	01288 353111
Barry HM	01446 732665	**Burnham-on-Sea HM**	01278 782180

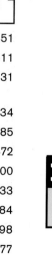

ABERYSTWYTH MARINA

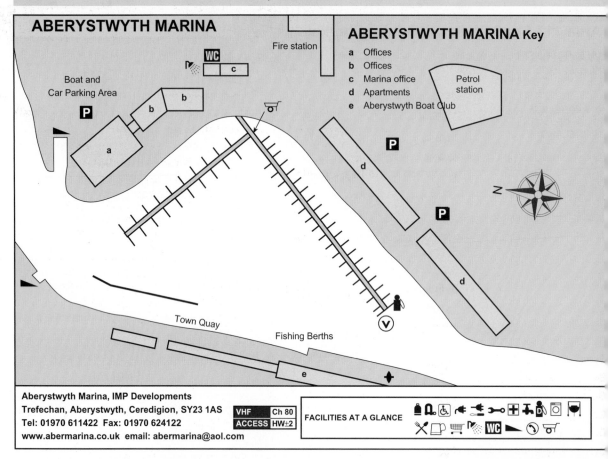

ABERYSTWYTH MARINA Key

a Offices
b Offices
c Marina office
d Apartments
e Aberystwyth Boat Club

Fire station

Petrol station

Boat and Car Parking Area

Fishing Berths

Town Quay

Aberystwyth Marina, IMP Developments
Trefechan, Aberystwyth, Ceredigion, SY23 1AS
Tel: 01970 611422 Fax: 01970 624122
www.abermarina.co.uk email: abermarina@aol.com

VHF Ch 80
ACCESS HW±2

FACILITIES AT A GLANCE

MILFORD MARINA

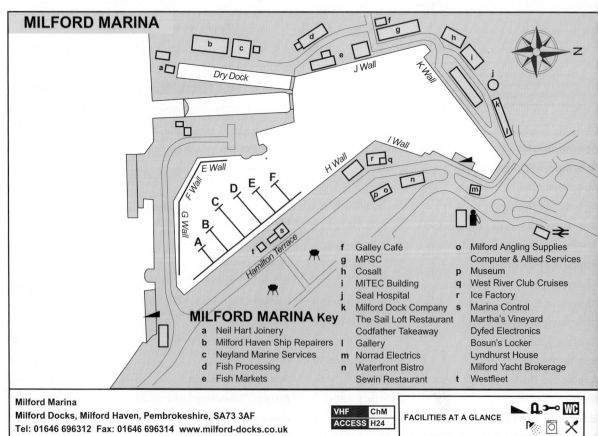

MILFORD MARINA Key

a Neil Hart Joinery
b Milford Haven Ship Repairers
c Neyland Marine Services
d Fish Processing
e Fish Markets
f Galley Café
g MPSC
h Cosalt
i MITEC Building
j Seal Hospital
k Milford Dock Company
The Sail Loft Restaurant
Codfather Takeaway
l Gallery
m Norrad Electrics
n Waterfront Bistro
Sewin Restaurant
o Milford Angling Supplies
Computer & Allied Services
p Museum
q West River Club Cruises
r Ice Factory
s Marina Control
Martha's Vineyard
Dyfed Electronics
Bosun's Locker
Lyndhurst House
Milford Yacht Brokerage
t Westfleet

Dry Dock
J Wall
K Wall
I Wall
E Wall
F Wall
G Wall
H Wall
Hamilton Terrace

Milford Marina
Milford Docks, Milford Haven, Pembrokeshire, SA73 3AF
Tel: 01646 696312 Fax: 01646 696314 www.milford-docks.co.uk

VHF ChM
ACCESS H24

FACILITIES AT A GLANCE

ABERYSTWYTH MARINA - IMP DEVELOPMENTS
Y Lanfa-Aberystwyth Marina, Trefechan, Aberystwyth SY23 1AS
Tel: (01970) 611422
Fax: (01970) 624122
e-mail: abermarina@aol.com
www.abermarina.co.uk
NEW fully serviced marina. Diesel, gas, water, toilets and hot showers.

DALE SAILING CO LTD
Brunel Quay, Neyland, Milford Haven, Pembrokeshire SA73 1PY
Tel: (01646) 603110
Fax: (01646) 601061
e-mail:
enquiries@dale-sailing.co.uk
www.dale-sailing.co.uk
Sales, service and chandlery on site at Neyland Marina UK. Diesel, haulage, storage, engine, GRP, rigging repairs, chandlers, brokerage. Dealer for many inc. Suzuki, Mercury/Mercruiser, Volvo, Selden, Yanmar, Raytheon, Perkins, Lewmar.

Burnham-on-Sea Police	01823 337911
Burnham-on-Sea SC Bridgwater	01278 792911
Burry Port Police	01554 772222
Burry Port YC Burry Port	01554 833635
Cabot CC	0117 9514389
Cambrian Boat Centre Swansea	01792 467263
Cambrian Marine Services Ltd Cardiff	029 20343459
Canard Sails Swansea	01792 367838
Cardiff Bay YC Cardiff	029 20226575
Cardiff HM	029 20400500
Cardiff Police	01446 734451
Cardiff YC Cardiff	029 2046 3697
Chapman & Hewitt Boatbuilders Wadebridge	01208 813487
Crest Nicholson Marinas Ltd - Bristol Bristol	0117-923 6466
Dale YC Haverfordwest	01646 636362
Dickie AM & Sons Ltd Pwllheli	01758 701828
Diving & Marine Engineering Barry	01446 721553
Dovey Marine Aberdovey	01654 767581
Dovey YC Aberdovey	01654 767607
Firmhelm Ltd Pwllheli	01758 612251
Fishguard (Lower Harbour) HM	01348 874726
Fishguard Bay YC Lower Fishguard	01348 872866
Fishguard HM	01348 404425
Fishguard Police	01437 763355
GB Attfield & Company Dursley	01453 547185
Glaslyn Marine Supplies Ltd Porthmadog	01766 513545
Goodwick Marine Fishguard	01348 873955
Hafan Pwllheli Pwllheli	01758 701219

Milford Marina
The Docks, Milford Haven, Prembrokeshire SA73 3AF
Telephone: 01646 696313/2 Fax: 01646 636314
Email: tscoates@milford-docks.co.uk

Milford Marina is set within 22 miles of beautiful sheltered estuary offering all year round sailing. Facilities include – Marina berths, boatyard storage, 16 ton travel hoist, diesel, electricity, gas, laundry etc. Chandlery, Brokerage, restaurants, retail park plus more on site. Staff on duty 24 hours.

2003 M&WMD55/cb

MILFORD MARINA
Milford Haven, Pembrokeshire SA73 3AF
Tel: (01646) 696312/3
Fax: (01646) 696314
e-mail: marina@milford-docks.co.uk
www.milford-docks.co.uk
Marina berths, boat storage, 16t hoist, diesel, electricity, laundery, chandlery, boat & engine repairs, brokerage, engine sales, restaurants, retail park on site, 24 hour staff, 22 miles of sheltered estuary for all year round sailing.

Harris Marine Barry	01446 740924
Hayle HM	01736 754043
Ilfracombe HM	01271 862108
Ilfracombe Police	08705 777444
Ilfracombe YC Ilfracombe	01271 863969
Instow Marine Services Bideford	01271 861081
JKA Sailmakers Pwllheli	01758 613266
Jones & Teague Saundersfoot	01834 813429
Kaymac Diving Services Swansea	01792 793316
Kelpie Boats Pembroke Dock	01646 683661
Lawrenny YC	01646 651212
Madoc YC Porthmadog	01766 512976
Madog Boatyard Porthmadog	01766 514205/513435
Marina BC Pwllheli	01758 612271
Marine Force (Bristol) Bristol	0117 926 8396
Marine Scene Cardiff	029 2070 5780
Merioneth YC Barmouth	01341 280000
Milford Haven HM	01646 696100
Milford Haven Police	01437 763355
Milford Marina Milford Haven	01646 696312
Minehead HM	01643 702566
Minehead Police	01823 337911
Monkstone Cruising and SC Swansea	01792 812229

NEYLAND YACHT HAVEN

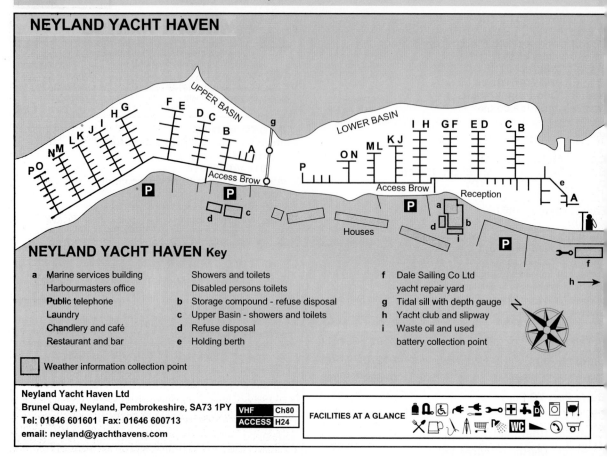

NEYLAND YACHT HAVEN Key

a Marine services building
Harbourmasters office
Public telephone
Laundry
Chandlery and café
Restaurant and bar

Showers and toilets
Disabled persons toilets
b Storage compound - refuse disposal
c Upper Basin - showers and toilets
d Refuse disposal
e Holding berth

f Dale Sailing Co Ltd
yacht repair yard
g Tidal sill with depth gauge
h Yacht club and slipway
i Waste oil and used
battery collection point

☐ Weather information collection point

Neyland Yacht Haven Ltd
Brunel Quay, Neyland, Pembrokeshire, SA73 1PY
Tel: 01646 601601 Fax: 01646 600713
email: neyland@yachthavens.com

VHF	Ch80
ACCESS	H24

FACILITIES AT A GLANCE

SWANSEA MARINA

SWANSEA MARINA Key

a Leisure Centre
b Maritime Museum
c Pumphouse Restaurant
d Yacht Club
e Repair shed
f Mariott Hotel

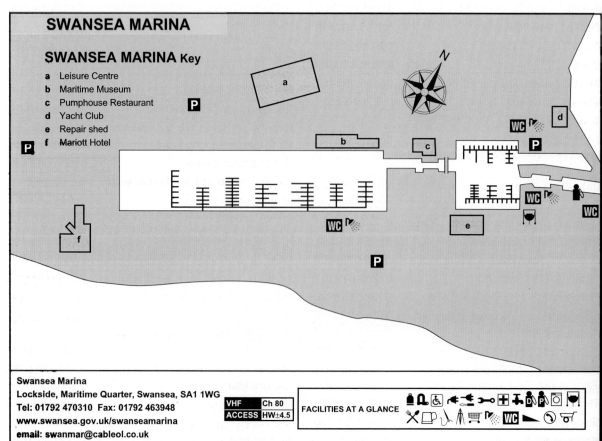

Swansea Marina
Lockside, Maritime Quarter, Swansea, SA1 1WG
Tel: 01792 470310 Fax: 01792 463948
www.swansea.gov.uk/swanseamarina
email: swanmar@cableol.co.uk

VHF	Ch 80
ACCESS	HW±4.5

FACILITIES AT A GLANCE

STEPHEN RATSEY SAILMAKERS
8 Brunel Quay, Neyland, Milford Haven,
Pembrokeshire SA73 1PY.
Tel: (01646) 601561
Fax: (01646) 601968
e-mail: info@ratseys.co.uk
www.stephenratsey.co.uk
Emergency repairs – sails, covers, rigging and upholstery.

NEYLAND YACHT HAVEN LTD
Brunel Quay, Neyland,
Pembrokeshire SA73 1PY
Tel: 01646 601601
Fax: 01646 600713
e-mail: neyland@yachthavens.com
www.yachthavens.com
24 hr access, 360 berth marina, visitors berths available, water, electricity, laundry, payphone, gas, diesel, showers, cafe, bar, chandleries, sailmaker, engineers, yard facilities, weather information, all available in a picturesque location.

PREMIUM LIFERAFT SERVICES
NEYLAND
Tel: (01646) 601946
Freephone: 0800 243673
e-mail: info@liferafts.com
www.liferafts.com
Hire and sales of DoT and RORC approved liferafts and safety equipment.

Mumbles YC Swansea	01792 369321
New Quay YC Aberdovey	01545 560516
Newport and Uskmouth SC Cardiff	01633 271417
Newquay HM	01637 872809
Neyland Yacht Haven Milford Haven	01646 601601
Neyland YC Neyland	01646 600267
North Devon YC Bideford	01271 860367
Padstow HM	01841 532239
Padstow Police	08705 777444
Pembroke Haven YC	01646 684403
Pembrokeshire YC Milford Haven	01646 692799
Penarth Marina Penarth	029 20705021
Penarth YC Penarth	029 20708196
Penrhos Marine Aberdovey	01654 767478
Porlock Weir SC Watchet	01643 862702
Portavon Marina Keynsham	0117 9861626
Porthcawl Harbour BC Swansea	01656 655935
Porthmadog & Trawsfynydd SC Talsarnau	01766 513546
Porthmadog HM	01766 512927
Porthmadog Police	01286 673333
Portishead Police	01934 638272
Portishead Quays Marina Bristol	01275 841941
Pwllheli HM	01758 704081
Pwllheli Police	01286 673333
Pwllheli SC Pwllhelli	01758 613343

R Towy BC Tenby	01267 241755
Ray Harris Marine (1984) Ltd Barry	01446 740924
Reed's Nautical Books Bradford on Avon	01225 868821
RNS Marine Northam	01237 474167
Rock Sailing and Water Ski Club Wadebridge	01208 862431
Rudders Boatyard & Moorings Milford Haven	01646 600288
S Caernarvonshire YC	01758 712338
Seaguard Marine Engineering Ltd Goodwick	01348 872976
Severn Valley Boat Centre Stourport-on-Severn	01299 871165
Severn Valley Cruisers Ltd (Boatyard) Stourport-on-Severn	01299 871165
Sharpness HM	01453 811862/64
Sharpness Marine Berkeley	01453 811476
Sharpness Police	01452 521201
Solva Boat Owners Association Fishguard	01437 721538
South Caernavonshire YC Abersoch	01758 712338
St Ives HM	01736 795018
Steel-kit Borth	01970 871713
Stephen Ratsey Sailmaker Milford Haven	01646 601561

AREA 11

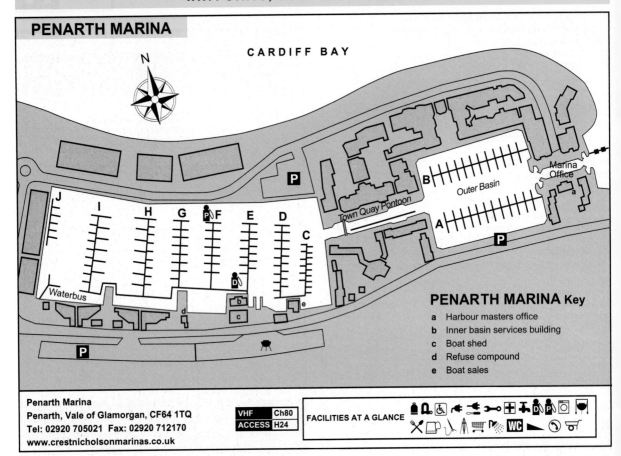

PENARTH MARINA

CARDIFF BAY

PENARTH MARINA Key

a   Harbour masters office
b   Inner basin services building
c   Boat shed
d   Refuse compound
e   Boat sales

Penarth Marina
Penarth, Vale of Glamorgan, CF64 1TQ
Tel: 02920 705021 Fax: 02920 712170
www.crestnicholsonmarinas.co.uk

VHF	Ch80
ACCESS	H24

FACILITIES AT A GLANCE

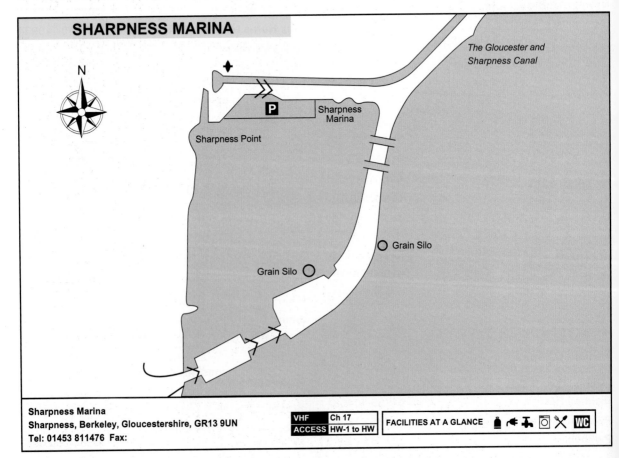

SHARPNESS MARINA

The Gloucester and
Sharpness Canal

Sharpness
Marina

Sharpness Point

Grain Silo

Grain Silo

Sharpness Marina
Sharpness, Berkeley, Gloucestershire, GR13 9UN
Tel: 01453 811476 Fax:

VHF	Ch 17
ACCESS	HW-1 to HW

FACILITIES AT A GLANCE

Swansea HM	01792 653787
Swansea Marina Swansea	01792 470310
Swansea Police	01792 456999
Swansea Yacht & Sub-Aqua Club Swansea	01792 469096
Teifi BC - Cardigan Bay Fishguard	01239 613846
Tenby HM	01834 842717
Tenby Police	01834 842303
Tenby SC Tenby	01834 842762
Tenby YC	01834 842762
TJ Williams Ltd Cardiff	029 20 487676
Underwater Services Dyffryn Arbwy	01341 247702
Watchet Boat Owner Association Watchet	01984 633736
Watchet HM	01984 631264
Watermouth YC Watchet	01271 865048
Weston Bay YC Portishead	01275 620772
WF Price & Co Ltd Bristol	0117 929 2229
Wigmore Wright Marine Services Penarth	029 20709983
William Partington Marine Ltd Pwllheli	01758 612808
Worcester Yacht Chandlers Ltd Barbourne	01905 22522

AREA **11**

BRISTOL MARINA

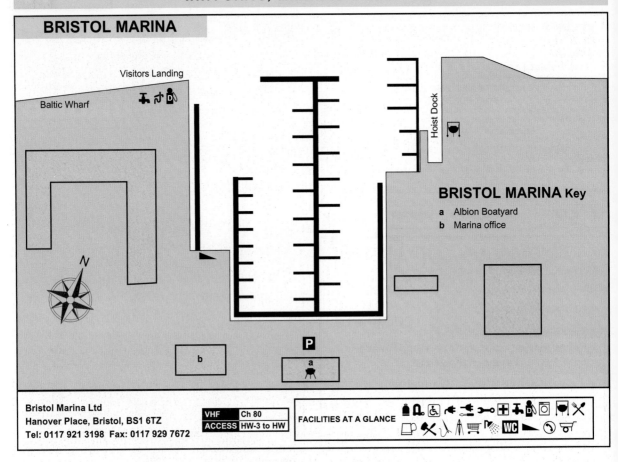

Baltic Wharf

Visitors Landing

Hoist Dock

BRISTOL MARINA Key

a Albion Boatyard
b Marina office

Bristol Marina Ltd
Hanover Place, Bristol, BS1 6TZ
Tel: 0117 921 3198 Fax: 0117 929 7672

VHF	Ch 80
ACCESS	HW-3 to HW

FACILITIES AT A GLANCE

Bristol Marina

Member of the

British Marine Federation

Marina Berthing

Repair Yard • Workshops • Sailmakers • Riggers • Chandlers

30 Ton Boat Hoist

Diesel Fuel • Calor Gas

Full on-site-services owner maintenance

THE **YACHT HARBOUR** ASSOCIATION

HANOVER PLACE, BRISTOL BS1 6UH
Tel: (0117) 921 3198 Fax: (0117) 929 7672

2003/WM 97/-

PORTISHEAD MARINA

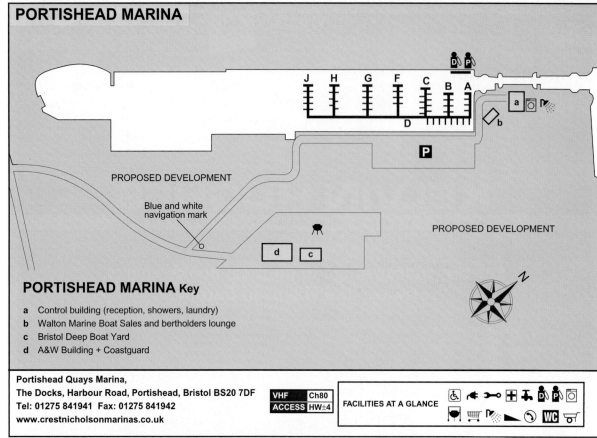

PORTISHEAD MARINA Key

a Control building (reception, showers, laundry)
b Walton Marine Boat Sales and bertholders lounge
c Bristol Deep Boat Yard
d A&W Building + Coastguard

Portishead Quays Marina,
The Docks, Harbour Road, Portishead, Bristol BS20 7DF
Tel: 01275 841941 Fax: 01275 841942
www.crestnicholsonmarinas.co.uk

VHF	Ch80
ACCESS	HW±4

FACILITIES AT A GLANCE

Planning a trip?

Make it plain sailing
– for your free copy
of the *2002 Marine Weather Services* booklet
call the Met Office Customer Centre
on **0845 300 0300** or go to
www.metoffice.com/leisuremarine/mwsbooklet.html

For an overview of Met Office products and
services for leisure mariners, visit our web site at
www.metoffice.com/leisuremarine

09060 calls are charged at £1 per minute at all times.

Met Office

Key to Marina Plans symbols

Calor Gas		P	Parking
Chandler		✗	Pub/Restaurant
Disabled facilities			Pump out
Electrical supply			Rigging service
Electrical repairs			Sail repairs
Engine repairs		✗	Shipwright
First Aid			Shop/Supermarket
Fresh Water			Showers
Fuel - Diesel			Slipway
Fuel - Petrol		WC	Toilets
Hardstanding/boatyard			Telephone
Laundry facilities			Trolleys
Lift-out facilities		V	Visitors berths

Area 12 - South Ireland

MARINAS
Telephone Numbers
VHF Channel
Access Times

REPUBLIC OF IRELAND

Malahide
01 845 4129
Ch M HW±4
Malahide

Howth YC Marina
01 839 2777
Ch M H24

DUBLIN
Dun Laoghaire

Howth

Galway

Wicklow

Arklow Marina
0402 39901
H24

Arklow

Kilrush
065 9052072
Ch 80 H24
Kilrush

R.Shannon

Limerick

Dingle Marina
066 9151629
Ch 14 H24

Fenit 066 713 6231 **Ch 16** H24
Fenit Harbour

Waterford
051 309900
Ch 12 H24
Waterford

Wexford

Dingle

Cahersiveen Marina
066 947 2777
Ch 37

Kilmore Quay

Kilmore Quay
053 29955
Ch M H24

Cahersiveen

Bantry

Cork

Youghal

Kenmare

Schull

Dunmore East

Baltimore

Crosshaven

Castlehaven

Kinsale

Crookhaven

Crosshaven BY Marina 021 483 1161 **Ch M** H24
East Ferry Marina 012 481 1342 **Ch 80** H24
Royal Cork YC Marina 021 483 1023 **Ch M** H24
Salve Marine 021 483 1145 H24

Lawrence Cove
027 75044
Ch 16 H24

Castlepark Marina 021 477 4959 **Ch M** H24
Kinsale YC Marina 021 477 2196 **Ch M** H24

N

Waypoint Guide Area 12 – South Ireland - Malahide south to Liscanor Bay

299	**Loop Head Lt** - 1·6M W of	52°33'·70N	09°58'·60W
300	**Loop Head Lt** - 1·4 miles S of	52°32'·30N	09°55'·80W
301	**Kilrush** - 0·9M S of Kilcredaun Lt	52°33'·90N	09°42'·50W
302	**Tearaght Island Lt** - 2·5M NW	52°06'·20N	10°42'·50W
303	**Great Foze Rock** - 1·8M SW	52°00'·00N	10°43'·20W
304	**Dingle** - 1·2M S of Reenbeg Point	52°05'·60N	10°15'·80W
305	**Bray Head** - 1·4M W of	51°52'·80N	10°28'·00W
306	**The Bull Island Lt** - 1·7M SW	51°34'·30N	10°20'·10W
307	**Crow Head** - 1·9MS of	51°32'·90N	10°09'·40W
308	**Bantry** - 0·8M SW Whiddy Island	51°40'·00N	09°32'·80W
309	**Sheep's Head** Lt - 1·5M W of	51°32'·30N	09°53'·40W
310	**Mizen Head Lt (SW)** - 2M SSW	51°25'·00N	09°50'·30W
311	**Crookhaven** - 1M ESE Streek Hd	51°27'·80N	09°40'·30W
312	**Schull** - 1M S of Long Island Lt	51°29'·20N	09°32'·00W
313	**The Fastnet Rock Lt**	51°23'·33N	09°36'·16W
314	**Cape Clear** - 1·6M SW of	51°24'·20N	09°32'·90W
315	**Baltimore** - 1·5M Sharbour ent	51°26'·90N	09°23'·50W
316	**Toe Head** - 1·5M S of	51°27'·40N	09°13'·00W
317	**Castle Haven** - 1M SE of ent	51°30.30'N	09°09.80'W
318	**Galley Head** - 1·4M S of	51°30'·40N	08°57'·20W
319	**Old Hd of Kinsale Lt** - 1·5M SSE	51°34'·90N	08°30'·80W
320	**Cork Landfall By** - 0·4M E of	51°43'·00N	08°14'·80W
321	**Roche's Point Lt** - 1·2M S of	51°46'·40N	08°15'·40W
322	**Ballycotton Island Lt** - 1·2M S	51°48'·40N	07°58'·80W
323	**Youghal, S** - IM SE Capel Island	51°52'·40N	07°50'·00W
324	**Youghal, SE** - 2M SE Blackball PHB	51°54'·80N	07°45'·60W
325	**Waterford** - 1·4M SSE Dunmore E	52°07'·40N	06°58'·80W
326	**Coningbeg Lt V** - 0·4M N of	52°02'·80N	06°39'·30W
327	**Carnsore Point** - 3·2M ESE of	52°09'·40N	06°16'·40W
328	**Greenore Point** - 1·8M E of	52°14'·70N	06°15'·90W
329	**Wexford** - 1·6M E of entrance	52°20'·50N	06°19'·30W
330	**W Blackwater Pt Mk** - 0·4M W	52°25'·80N	06°14'·00W
331	**Cahore Point** - 1·7 miles SE of	52°32'·50N	06°09'·90W
332	**Arklow** - 1·2M E by S	52°47'·40N	06°06'·40W
333	**Mizen Head (E coast)** - 1M ESE	52°51'·00N	06°01'·90W
334	**Wicklow** - 2·6M E	52°58'·90N	05°57'·80W
335	**Dun Laoghaire** - 2·2M NE	53°19'·60N	06°04'·60W
336	**Ben of Howth** - 1·4M E of	53°22'·40N	06°00'·50W
337	**Malahide** - 1·5M E of Bar	53°27'·00N	06°04'·80W
338	**Rockabill** - 1·2M WSW	53°35'·30N	06°02'·00W

Distance Table - South Ireland

Approximate distances in nautical miles are by the most direct route while avoiding dangers and allowing for Traffic Separation Schemes

		1	2	3	4	5	6	7	8	9	10	11	12	13	14	15	16	17	18	19	20
1.	Carlingford Lough	1																			
2.	Howth	39	2																		
3.	Dun Laoghaire	48	8	3																	
4.	Wicklow	63	25	21	4																
5.	Arklow	75	37	36	15	5															
6.	Tuskar Rock	113	73	70	52	37	6														
7.	Rosslare	108	70	66	47	34	8	7													
8.	Dunmore East	139	101	102	84	69	32	32	8												
9.	Youghal	172	134	133	115	100	63	65	34	9											
10.	Crosshaven	192	154	155	137	122	85	85	59	25	10										
11.	Kinsale	202	164	168	150	135	98	95	69	35	17	11									
12.	Baltimore	239	201	196	177	164	128	132	102	70	54	42	12								
13.	Fastnet Rock	250	212	207	189	174	137	144	112	78	60	49	10	13							
14.	Bantry	281	243	241	223	208	171	174	146	112	94	83	42	34	14						
15.	Darrynane	283	245	240	221	208	172	176	146	114	98	86	44	39	38	15					
16.	Valentia	295	257	252	242	227	184	188	165	131	113	102	56	48	55	16	16				
17.	Dingle	308	270	265	246	233	197	201	171	139	123	111	69	61	63	29	13	17			
18.	Kilrush	361	323	318	299	286	250	254	224	192	176	164	122	114	116	82	66	64	18		
19.	Galway	366	362	357	339	324	287	291	262	228	210	199	159	150	155	119	103	101	76	19	
20.	Slyne Head	317	351	346	328	313	276	283	251	217	199	188	153	139	144	113	97	95	75	49	20

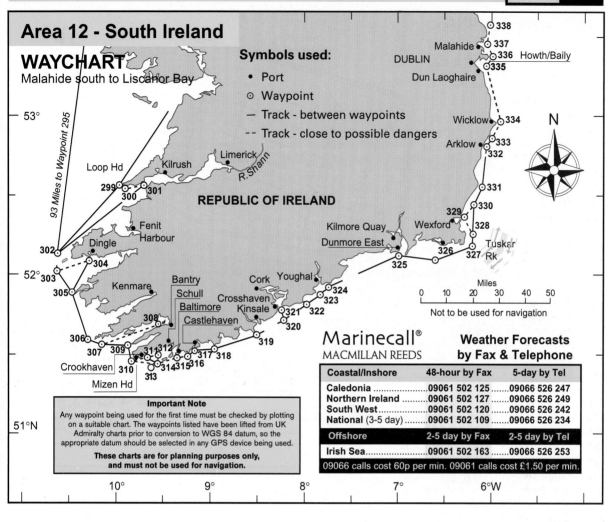

Area 12 - South Ireland

WAYCHART

Malahide south to Liscanor Bay

Symbols used:

- • Port
- ⊙ Waypoint
- — Track - between waypoints
- -- Track - close to possible dangers

REPUBLIC OF IRELAND

Important Note

Any waypoint being used for the first time must be checked by plotting on a suitable chart. The waypoints listed have been lifted from UK Admiralty charts prior to conversion to WGS 84 datum, so the appropriate datum should be selected in any GPS device being used.

These charts are for planning purposes only, and must not be used for navigation.

Marinecall® MACMILLAN REEDS	Weather Forecasts by Fax & Telephone	
Coastal/Inshore	**48-hour by Fax**	**5-day by Tel**
Caledonia	09061 502 125	09066 526 247
Northern Ireland	09061 502 127	09066 526 249
South West..................	09061 502 120	09066 526 242
National (3-5 day)	09061 502 109	09066 526 234
Offshore	**2-5 day by Fax**	**2-5 day by Tel**
Irish Sea......................	09061 502 163	09066 526 253
09066 calls cost 60p per min. 09061 calls cost £1.50 per min.		

Arklow Customs	00353 402 32553
Arklow HM	00353 402 32466
Arklow Marina Arklow	00353 402 39901
Arklow Police	00353 402 32304/5
Arklow SC Arklow	00353 402 33100
Arklow Slipway Arklow	00353 402 33233
Baltimore Boatyard Baltimore	00353 28 20444
Baltimore Diving and Watersports Centre	
West Cork	00353 28 20300
Baltimore HM	00353 28 22145
Baltimore Police	00353 28 20102
Baltimore SC Baltimore	00353 28 20426
Bantry Bay HM	00353 27 53277
Bantry Bay Police	00353 27 50045
Bantry Bay SC Bantry	00353 27 50081
Bantry Customs	00353 27 50061
Bantry Customs	00353 27 50061
Cahersiveen Marina Cahersiveen	00353 669 473214
Carlingford Lough Customs	00353 42 34248

Carroll's Ballyhack Boatyard	
New Ross	00353 51 389164
Castle Haven Police	00353 28 36144
Castlepark Marina Kinsale	00353 21 4774959
Castlepoint Boatyard Crosshaven	00353 21 4832154
CH Marine (Cork) Cork	00353 21 4315700

MALAHIDE MARINA

MALAHIDE MARINA Key

- **a** Boat handling & storage area
- **b** Refuelling bay
- **c** Marina centre
- **d** Boatyard
- **e** Marina access bridge
- **f** Restaurant
- **g** Wash area

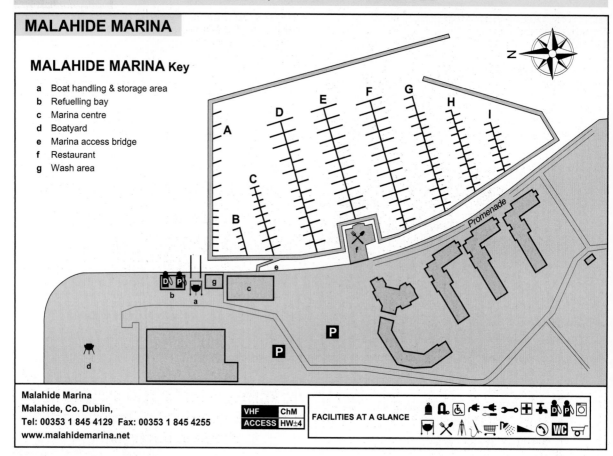

Malahide Marina
Malahide, Co. Dublin,
Tel: 00353 1 845 4129 Fax: 00353 1 845 4255
www.malahidemarina.net

VHF	ChM
ACCESS	HW±4

FACILITIES AT A GLANCE

HOWTH MARINA

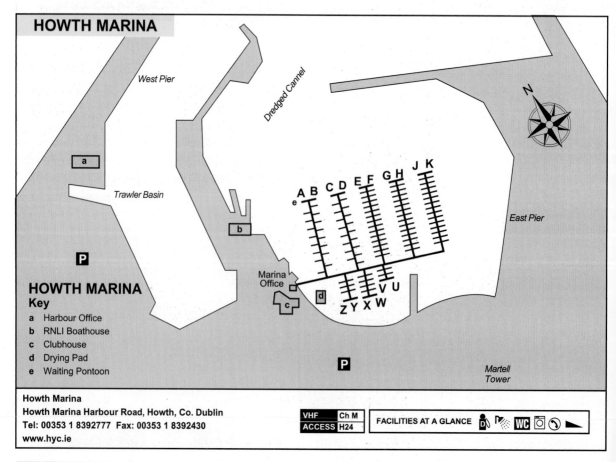

HOWTH MARINA
Key

- **a** Harbour Office
- **b** RNLI Boathouse
- **c** Clubhouse
- **d** Drying Pad
- **e** Waiting Pontoon

Howth Marina
Howth Marina Harbour Road, Howth, Co. Dublin
Tel: 00353 1 8392777 Fax: 00353 1 8392430
www.hyc.ie

VHF	Ch M
ACCESS	H24

FACILITIES AT A GLANCE

HOWTH MARINA - IRELAND
Howth, Co Dublin, Ireland
TEL: 00 353 (1) 839 2777
FAX: 00 353 (1) 839 2430
e-mail: marina@hyc.ie
www.hyc.ie
Modern marina in beautiful sheltered location. Fully services berths with every facility and 24-hour security. Very popular marina for traffic in the Irish Sea. Is available at all stages of tide with extremely easy access. Visitors benefit from temporary membership of Howth Yacht Club.

MALAHIDE MARINA - IRELAND
Malahide, Co Dublin, Ireland.
Tel: +353 1 8454129
Fax: +353 1 8454255
Located next to the picturesque village of Malahide our marina village is the ideal spot to enjoy and relax. There are 350 fully serviced berths, petrol and diesel available. 30-ton hoist with full boatyard facilities with winter storage ashore or afloat. A fine selection of shops, and friendly pubs and restaurants serving good food are close by.

CH Marine Skibbereen	00353 28 23190
CJ Deevy and Co Ltd Waterford	00353 51 855719
Cork Customs	00353 21 311024
Cork HM	00353 21 4273125
Courtmacsherry HM	00353 23 46311/46600
Crookhaven HM	00353 28 35319
Crookhaven SC Crookhaven	087 2379997 mobile
Crosshaven Boatyard Co Ltd Crosshaven	00353 21 831161
Crosshaven Boatyard Marina Crosshaven	00353 21 4831161

D Matthews Ltd Cork	00353 214 277633
Dinghy Supplies Ltd/Sutton Marine Ltd Sutton	00353 1 832 2312
Dingle Customs	00353 66 7121480
Dingle HM	00353 66 9151629
Dingle Marina Dingle	00353 66 915 1629
Dingle Police	00353 66 9151522
Dingle SC Dingle	00353 66 51984
Downer International Sails & Chandlery Dun Laoghaire	00353 1 280 0231
Dublin Customs	00353 1 679 2777
Dublin HM	00353 1 874871
Dublin Police	00353 1 6665000
Dun Laoghaire Customs	00353 1 280 3992
Dun Laoghaire HM	00353 1280 1130/8074

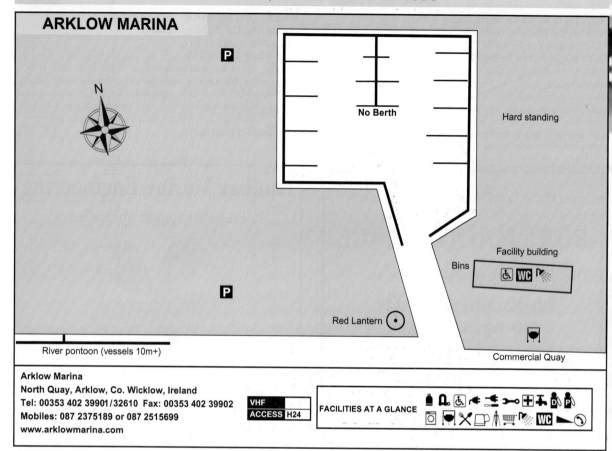

ARKLOW MARINA

No Berth

Hard standing

Facility building

Bins

River pontoon (vessels 10m+)

Red Lantern

Commercial Quay

Arklow Marina
North Quay, Arklow, Co. Wicklow, Ireland
Tel: 00353 402 39901/32610 Fax: 00353 402 39902
Mobiles: 087 2375189 or 087 2515699
www.arklowmarina.com

VHF
ACCESS H24

FACILITIES AT A GLANCE

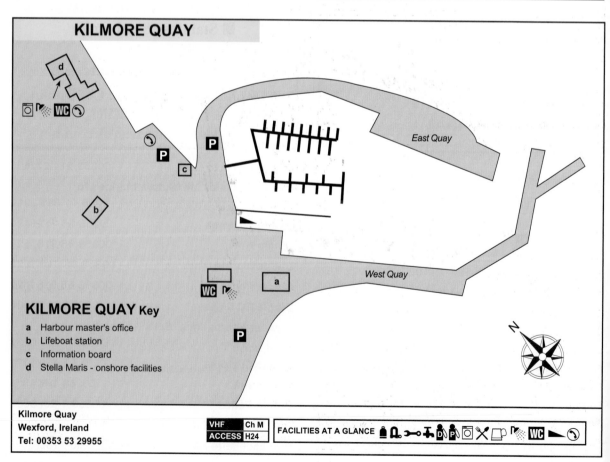

KILMORE QUAY

d

East Quay

P

c

P

b

West Quay

a

WC

KILMORE QUAY Key

a   Harbour master's office
b   Lifeboat station
c   Information board
d   Stella Maris - onshore facilities

P

Kilmore Quay
Wexford, Ireland
Tel: 00353 53 29955

VHF   Ch M
ACCESS H24

FACILITIES AT A GLANCE

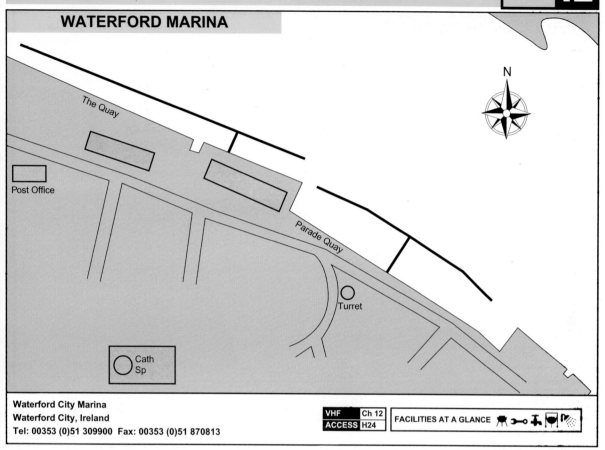

WATERFORD MARINA

The Quay

Post Office

Parade Quay

Turret

Cath
Sp

N

Waterford City Marina
Waterford City, Ireland
Tel: 00353 (0)51 309900 Fax: 00353 (0)51 870813

VHF	Ch 12
ACCESS	H24

FACILITIES AT A GLANCE

HARDWARE & MARINE SUPPLIES
Kilmore Quay, Co. Wexford, Ireland.
Tel: 00 353 (53) 29791
Fax: 00 353 (53) 29803
We are a commercial fishing supplier, with a good selection of leisure boating supplies and general hardware. Diving service to inspect damage also available. Camping Gas, batteries, ropes, shackles, safety equipment, flags and stays made to order.

DUN LAOGHAIRE MARINA
Harbour Road, Dun Laoghaire, Co. Dublin
Tel: ++353 1 2020040
Fax: ++353 1 2020043
e-mail: dlmarina@indigo.ie
www.dlharbour.ie
Located within Dun Laoghaire - 8 miles from Dublin City centre adjacent suburban rail station and all amenities. Facilities include shore power, portable water, showers, laundry, fuel - petrol & diesel, gas, sewage pump out.

Dun Laoghaire MYC	00353 1 288 938
Dunmore East Customs	00353 51 875391
Dunmore East HM	00353 51 383166
Dunmore East Police	00353 51 383112
East Ferry Marina Cobh	00353 21 481 1342
Fenit Harbour Customs	00353 66 36115
Fenit Harbour Marina Fenit	00353 66 7136231
Ferguson Engineering Wexford	00353 6566822133
Ferrypoint Boat Co Youghal	00353 24 94232
Foynes YC Foynes	00353 69 91201

KILMORE QUAY MARINA - IRELAND
Kilmore Quay, Co Wexford, Ireland.
Tel: 353 53 (29) 955
Fax: 353 53 (29) 915
Kilmore Quay in the south east of Ireland has a new Blue Flag marina with 20 pontoon visitor berths. This friendly fishing port has pleasant hotel facilities, pubs and restaurants offering a traditional Irish welcome. Rosslare ferryport is only 15 miles away.

WATERFORD CITY MARINA - IRELAND
Waterford City, Ireland.
Tel: 00 353 (51) 309900
Fax: 00 353 (51) 870813
www.waterfordcorp.ie
Located in the heart of the historic city centre. There are 100 fully serviced berths available. Full CCTV in operation. Showers on-shore nearby in Tower Hotel. Wide range of shops, restaurants, pubs and other amenities available on the doorstep of the marina because of its unique city-centre location. Open all year with both winter and summer season rates available.

Galway Customs	00353 91 567191
George Kearon Ltd Arklow	00353 402 32319
Glenans Irish Sailing School	00353 1 6611481
Hardware and Marine Supplies Kilmore Quay	00353 53 29791
Howth HM	00353 1 832 2252
Howth Marina Howth	00353 1839 2777
Howth YC Howth	00353 1 832 2141

AREA 12

CROSSHAVEN BY MARINA

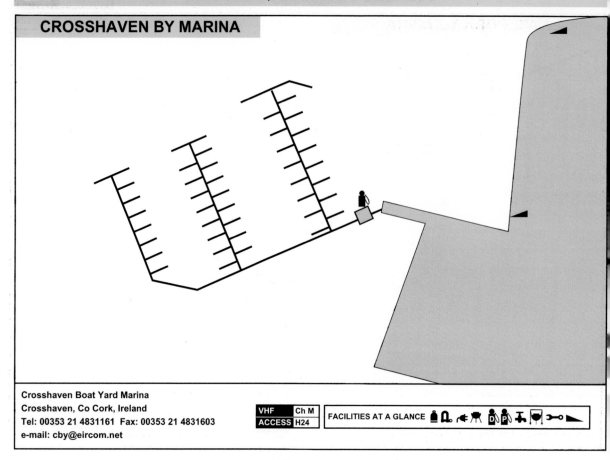

Crosshaven Boat Yard Marina
Crosshaven, Co Cork, Ireland
Tel: 00353 21 4831161 Fax: 00353 21 4831603
e-mail: cby@eircom.net

VHF	Ch M
ACCESS	H24

FACILITIES AT A GLANCE

SALVE MARINE

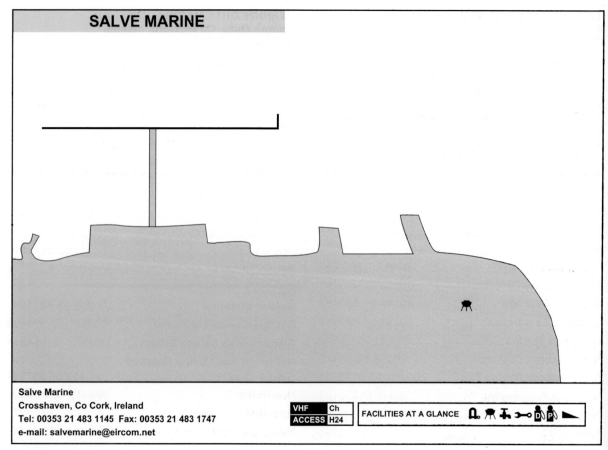

Salve Marine
Crosshaven, Co Cork, Ireland
Tel: 00353 21 483 1145 Fax: 00353 21 483 1747
e-mail: salvemarine@eircom.net

VHF	Ch
ACCESS	H24

FACILITIES AT A GLANCE

ROYAL CORK YC MARINA

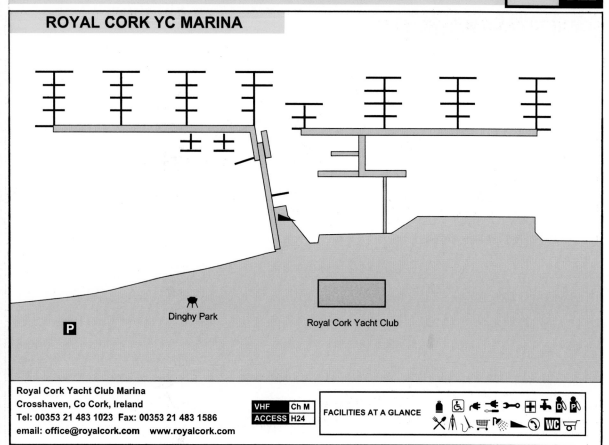

Dinghy Park

Royal Cork Yacht Club

P

Royal Cork Yacht Club Marina
Crosshaven, Co Cork, Ireland
Tel: 00353 21 483 1023 Fax: 00353 21 483 1586
email: office@royalcork.com   www.royalcork.com

VHF	Ch M
ACCESS	H24

FACILITIES AT A GLANCE

CROSSHAVEN BOATYARD MARINA - IRELAND
Crosshaven, Co.
Cork, Ireland
Tel: 00 353 (21) 48 31161
Fax: 00 353 (21) 48 31603
e-mail: cby@eircom.net
All facilities at this 100-berth marina situated 12 miles from Cork City and close to ferryport and airport. Travel lift - 40 tons, full repair and maintenance services, spray painting and approved International Gelshield centre. Storage undercover and outside for 400 boats. Brokerage. Irish agents for Dufour and Oyster yacths, & Kelt White Shark. RNLI and Defence contractors.

SALVE MARINE LTD - IRELAND
Crosshaven, Co. Cork, Ireland.
Tel: 353 214 (83) 1145
Fax: 353 214 (83) 1747
e-mail: salvemarine@eircom.net
The marina is just 20 minutes from Cork City, Cork airport and Ringaskiddy ferry port. Located yards from Royal Cork yacht club and Crosshaven village centre. Facilities for yachts up to 140' x 14' draught including mains electricity 240/380 volts. Slip, telephone, fax, toilets and showers. Stainless steel, aluminium and bronze welding/machining. Repairs and maintenance to hulls and rigging.

Iniscealtra SC Limerick	00353 61 338347	**Kilrush Customs**	00353 61 415366	
Irish CC	00353 214870031	**Kilrush Police**	00353 65 51057	
John Brennan Dun Laoghaire	00353 1 280 5308	**Kinsale Customs**	00353 21 311044	
Kenmare River Police	00353 64 41177	**Kinsale HM**	00353 21 4772503	
Kevin Hunt Tralee	00353 6671 25979	**Kinsale Police**	00353 21 4772302	
Kieran Cotter Baltimore	00353 28 20106	**Kinsale Yacht Club Marina**		
Kilkee Diving Centre Kilkee	00353 6590 56707	Kinsale	00353 21 4772196	
Killybegs Customs	00353 73 31070	**Lawrence Cove Marina** Bear Island	00353 27 75044	
Kilmore Customs	00353 53 33741	**Lough Swilly Customs**	00353 74 21611	
Kilmore Quay HM	00353 53 29955	**Malahide Customs**	00353 1 874 6571	
Kilmore Quay Marina Kilmore Quay	00353 53 29955	**Malahide Marina** Malahide	00353 1 8454129	
Kilmore Quay Police	00353 53 29642	**Malahide Police**	00353 1 6664600	
Kilnsale Boatyard Kinsale	00353 21 4774774	**Malahide YC** Malahide	00353 1 845 3372	
Kilrush Creek Marina Kilrush	00353 65 9052072	**Marindus Engineering** Kilmore Quay	00353 53 29794	

AREA **12**

EAST FERRY MARINA

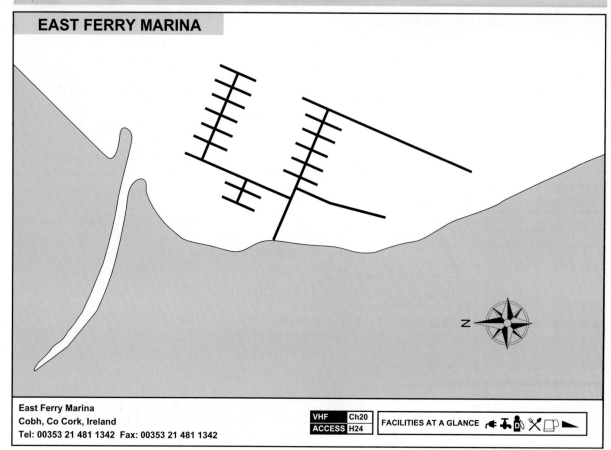

East Ferry Marina
Cobh, Co Cork, Ireland
Tel: 00353 21 481 1342 Fax: 00353 21 481 1342

VHF	Ch20
ACCESS	H24

FACILITIES AT A GLANCE

KINSALE YC MARINA

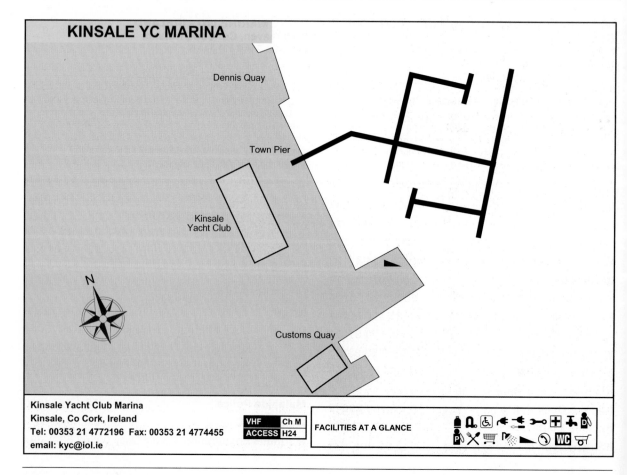

Dennis Quay

Town Pier

Kinsale
Yacht Club

Customs Quay

Kinsale Yacht Club Marina
Kinsale, Co Cork, Ireland
Tel: 00353 21 4772196 Fax: 00353 21 4774455
email: kyc@iol.ie

VHF	Ch M
ACCESS	H24

FACILITIES AT A GLANCE

CASTLEPARK MARINA

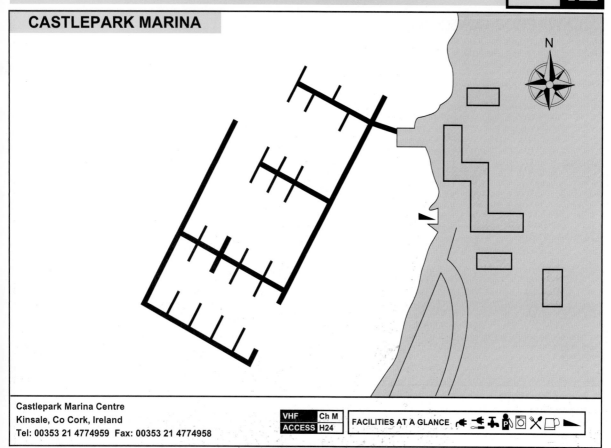

Castlepark Marina Centre
Kinsale, Co Cork, Ireland
Tel: 00353 21 4774959 Fax: 00353 21 4774958

VHF	Ch M
ACCESS	H24

FACILITIES AT A GLANCE

McWilliam Sailmaker Ltd (Crosshaven) Crosshaven	00353 21 4831505
National YC Dun Laoghaire	00353 1 280 5725
Nicholas Murphy Dunmore East	00353 51 383259
O'Sullivans Marine Ltd Tralee	00353 66 7124524
Poolbeg YC	00353 1 660 4681
Prest Customs	00353 94 21131
Rathmullan Customs	00353 74 26324
Rossbrin Boatyard Schull	00353 28 37352
Rosslare Customs	00353 53 33116
Rosslare Harbour HM	00353 53 57921
Royal Cork Yacht Club Marina Crosshaven	00353 21 4831023
Royal Cork YC Crosshaven	00353 21 831023
Royal Irish YC Dun Laoghaire	00353 1 280 9452
Royal St George YC Dun Laoghaire	00353 1 280 1811
Ryan & Roberts Marine Services Askeaton	00353 61 392198
Salve Engineering Marina Crosshaven	00353 21 4831145
Schull Customs	00353 27 51562
Schull Police	00353 28 28111
Schull SC Schull	00353 28 37352
Schull Watersports Centre Schull	00353 28 28554
Shannon Customs	00353 61 471076

AREA **12**

LAWRENCE COVE MARINA

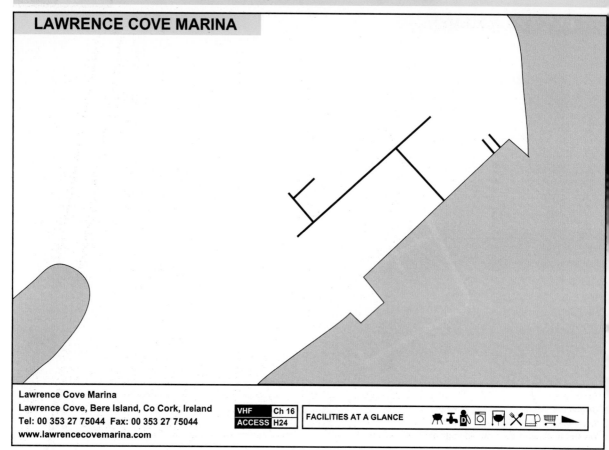

Lawrence Cove Marina
Lawrence Cove, Bere Island, Co Cork, Ireland
Tel: 00 353 27 75044 Fax: 00 353 27 75044
www.lawrencecovemarina.com

VHF	Ch 16
ACCESS	H24

FACILITIES AT A GLANCE

CAHERSIVEEN MARINA

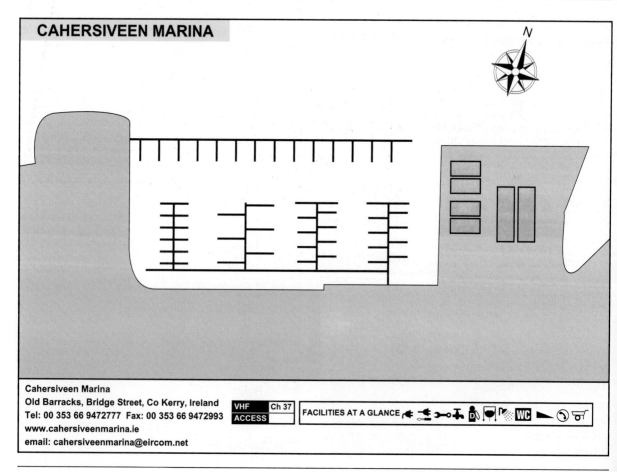

Cahersiveen Marina
Old Barracks, Bridge Street, Co Kerry, Ireland
Tel: 00 353 66 9472777 Fax: 00 353 66 9472993
www.cahersiveenmarina.ie
email: cahersiveenmarina@eircom.net

VHF	Ch 37
ACCESS	

FACILITIES AT A GLANCE

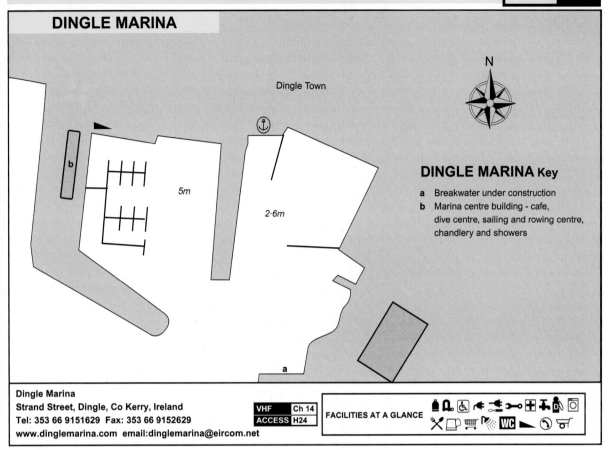

DINGLE MARINA

Dingle Town

DINGLE MARINA Key

a Breakwater under construction
b Marina centre building - cafe, dive centre, sailing and rowing centre, chandlery and showers

Dingle Marina
Strand Street, Dingle, Co Kerry, Ireland
Tel: 353 66 9151629 Fax: 353 66 9152629
www.dinglemarina.com email:dinglemarina@eircom.net

VHF Ch 14
ACCESS H24

FACILITIES AT A GLANCE

DINGLE MARINA - IRELAND
Harbour Master, Strand Street, Dingle, Co Kerry, Ireland.
Tel: 353 66 (91) 51629
Fax: 353 42 (91) 52629
e-mail: dinglemarina@eircom.net
Europe's most westerly marina on the beautiful south west coast of Ireland in the heart of the old sheltered fishing port of Dingle. Visitor berths, fuel and water. Shops, 52 pubs and many restaurants with traditional music and hospitality. Harbour easily navigable day or night.

LAWRENCE COVE MARINA - IRELAND
Bere Island, Bantry Bay, Co Cork, Ireland.
Tel/Fax: 353 27 (75) 044
e-mail: lcm@iol.ie
www.lawrencecovemarina.com
Lawrence Cove Marina is situated in Bantry Bay in the south west corner of Ireland in the heart of the best cruising ground in Europe. It is a fairly new marina, personally run by John and Phil Harrington with full facilities and a very safe haven to leave a boat. It is two hours from Cork airport with good connections. The marina now provides winter storage having acquired a hoist and all your boating problems can be solved.

Shannon Estuary Customs	00353 69 415366	**Watson Sails** Dublin 13	00353 1 832 6466
Skinners Boat Yard Baltimore	00353 28 20114	**Western Marine** Dalkey	00353 1280 0321
Sligo Customs	00353 71 61064	**Western YC** Kilrush	00353 87 2262885
South Cork SC	00353 28 36383	**Wexford Customs**	00353 53 331116
Sutton Marine (Dublin) Sutton	00353 1 832 2312	**Wexford Customs**	00353 53 33292
Tralee SC Tralee	00353 66 36119	**Wexford HBC** Wexford	00353 53 22039
Tuskar Rock Marine Rosslare	00353 53 33376	**Wexford Police**	00353 404 67107
Union Chandlery Cork	00353 21 4554334	**Wicklow Customs**	00353 404 67222
Viking Marine Ltd Dun Laoghaire	00353 1 280 6654	**Wicklow HM**	00353 404 67455
Waterford City Marina Waterford	00353 51 309926	**Wicklow Police**	00353 404 67107
Waterford Customs	00353 51 875391	**Wicklow SC** Wicklow	00353 404 67526
Waterford Harbour SC Dunmore East	00353 51 383230	**Youghal HM**	00353 24 92626
		Youghal Police	00353 24 92200
Waterford HM	00353 51 874907	**Youghal SC** Youghal	00353 24 92447

AREA 12

FENIT HARBOUR

FENIT HARBOUR Key

- **a** Fenit Seaworld
- **b** Fish store
- **c** Warehouse
- **d** Marina services, harbour office lifeboat station

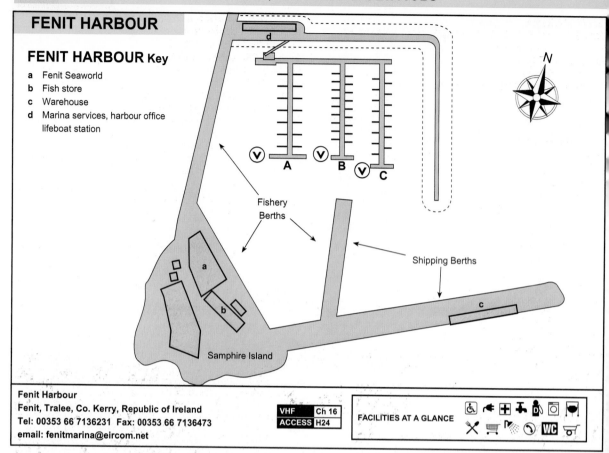

Fishery Berths

Shipping Berths

Samphire Island

Fenit Harbour
Fenit, Tralee, Co. Kerry, Republic of Ireland
Tel: 00353 66 7136231 Fax: 00353 66 7136473
email: fenitmarina@eircom.net

| VHF | Ch 16 |
| ACCESS | H24 |

FACILITIES AT A GLANCE

KILRUSH MARINA

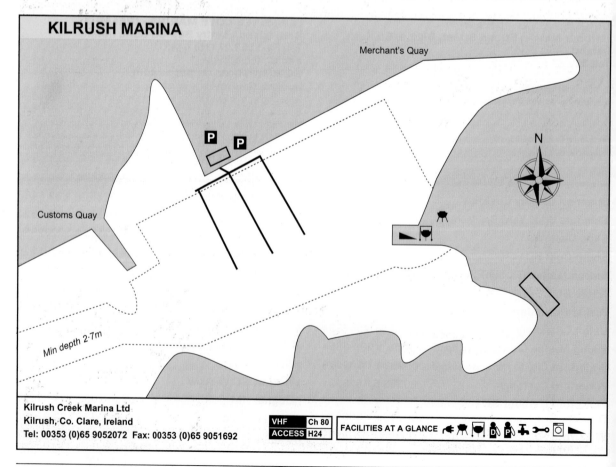

Merchant's Quay

Customs Quay

Min depth 2·7m

Kilrush Creek Marina Ltd
Kilrush, Co. Clare, Ireland
Tel: 00353 (0)65 9052072 Fax: 00353 (0)65 9051692

| VHF | Ch 80 |
| ACCESS | H24 |

FACILITIES AT A GLANCE

FENIT MARINA,
TRALEE & FENIT HARBOUR COMMISSIONERS
Fenit, County Kerry, Ireland
Tel: 353 66 (71) 36231
Fax: 353 66 (71) 36473
e-mail: fenitmarina@eircom.net
Marina operators.

> **When replying to adverts please mention the Waypoint & Marina Guide**

KILRUSH MARINA & BOATYARD - IRELAND
Kilrush, Co Clare, Ireland
Tel: 00 353 (65) 9052072
Fax: 00 353 (65) 9051692
Mobile: 00 353 862313870
VHF Ch80
e-mail: kcm@shannon.dev.ie
www.shannon-dev.ie/kcm
Marina on Ireland's beautiful west coast, is a new marina with 120 fully serviced berths. The marina has all shore facilities including a modern boatyard with 45-ton hoist. It adjoins the busy market town of Kilrush which has every facility required by the visiting yachtsman.

MACMILLAN

REEDS
Looseleaf Almanac System

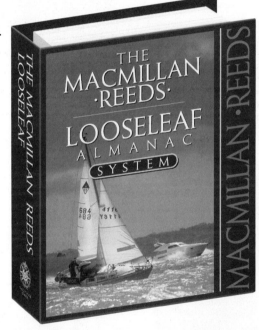

The Macmillan Reeds Looseleaf Almanac is an innovative and versatile system that lets you completely customise the navigational information you carry on board. Remove unneeded sections and add your own notes and navigational data from other sources. Bound securely in a sturdy binder, your almanac will always include just as much, or as little, information as you need for your cruising area – or even for a single voyage.

The ongoing cost is low, too. It is easy to extend or update the information in your Looseleaf Almanac – replace the relevant sections with new information from the Update/Pilotage packs as and when needed.

The Macmillan Reeds Looseleaf Almanac is available in two editions: one covers the UK and Ireland (including the Channel Islands), the other covers the coast of Continental Europe, from Skagen at the tip of Denmark, all the way to Gibraltar. The update/pilotage packs follow the same areas, adding a Combined edition, which includes the contents of both the Continental and the UK and Ireland packs.

Description	Price	Code
UK & Ireland edition (includes binder)	£34.95	ND50
Continental Europe edition (includes binder)	£34.95	ND51
UK & Ireland Update/Pilotage Pack	£12.95	ND52
Continental Europe Update/Pilotage Pack	£12.95	ND53
Combined Update/Pilotage Pack	£16.50	ND54

- **Versatile**
- **Value for money**
- **Convenient**
- **Flexible**
- **Updateable**

AREA **12**

Nautical Data Limited • tel: +44 (0)1243 389352 • web: www.nauticaldata.com

Planning a trip?

Make it plain sailing
– for your free copy
of the *2002 Marine Weather Services* booklet
call the Met Office Customer Centre
on **0845 300 0300** or go to
www.metoffice.com/leisuremarine/mwsbooklet.html

For an overview of Met Office products and
services for leisure mariners, visit our web site at
www.metoffice.com/leisuremarine

09060 calls are charged at £1 per minute at all times.

Met Office

Key to Marina Plans symbols

▮	Calor Gas	**P**	Parking
♫	Chandler	✕	Pub/Restaurant
♿	Disabled facilities	♒	Pump out
⚡	Electrical supply	♈	Rigging service
⚡	Electrical repairs	⚓	Sail repairs
➤	Engine repairs	✂	Shipwright
✚	First Aid	🛒	Shop/Supermarket
⚓	Fresh Water	☔	Showers
D	Fuel - Diesel	◣	Slipway
P	Fuel - Petrol	**WC**	Toilets
⚒	Hardstanding/boatyard	◔	Telephone
◻	Laundry facilities	🛒	Trolleys
⚖	Lift-out facilities	Ⓥ	Visitors berths

Area 13 - North Ireland

MARINAS
Telephone Numbers
VHF Channel
Access Times

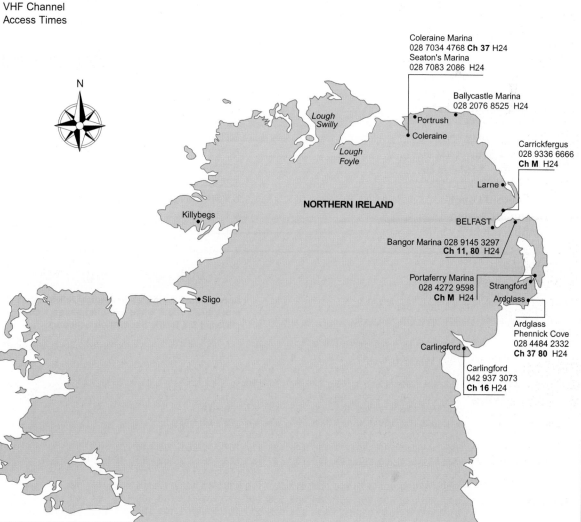

Coleraine Marina
028 7034 4768 **Ch 37** H24
Seaton's Marina
028 7083 2086 H24

Ballycastle Marina
028 2076 8525 H24

Carrickfergus
028 9336 6666
Ch M H24

Lough
Swilly

Lough
Foyle

• Portrush

• Coleraine

Larne •

NORTHERN IRELAND

• Killybegs

BELFAST •

Bangor Marina 028 9145 3297
Ch 11, 80 H24

Portaferry Marina
028 4272 9598
Ch M H24

Strangford

Ardglass •

• Sligo

Ardglass
Phennick Cove
028 4484 2332
Ch 37 80 H24

Carlingford •

Carlingford
042 937 3073
Ch 16 H24

Waypoint Guide Area 13 – North Ireland - Lambay Island north to Liscanor Bay

270	**Mew Is Lt** - 1·3M ENE	54°42'·30N	05°29'·90W
271	**Belfast 0·7M ENE No.1 By**	54°42'·00N	05°45'·20W
272	**Black Hd Lt** - 1·3 M ENE	54°46'·50N	05°39'·20W
273	**Isle of Muck** - 1·1M NE	54°51'·70N	05°41'·85W
274	**Larne Lough** - 1M N of Barr's pt	54°52'·50N	05°46'·80W
275	**E Maiden Lt** - 1·7M SW	54°54'·50N	05°45'·50W
276	**Torr Head** - 0·6M ENE of	55°12'·20N	06°02'·80W
277	**Fair Head** - 0·9M N of	55°14'·60N	06°09'·00W
278	**L. Foyle 4·8M NNE Inishowen Lt**	55°17'·90N	06°52'·20W
279	**Malin Head** - 2M NNE	55°25'·00N	07°21'·20W
280	**Lough Swilly** - 1M N of ent	55°18'·20N	07°34'·30W
281	**Tory Island** - 1·2M SE of	55°14'·00N	08°11'·00W
282	**Rinrawros Pt Lt, Aran** - 1·3M NW	55°01'·75N	08°35'·40W
283	**Rathlin O'Birne Is Lt** -1·9M WSW	54°39'·20N	08°52'·90W
284	**Killibegs** - 2·4M WNW S.John's Pt Lt	54°34'·70N	08°31'·80W
285	**Sligo** - 2·7M N of Aughris Hd	54°19'·50N	08°45'·30W
286	**The Stags rocks 1·3M N of**	54°23'·40N	09°47'·40W
287	**Broadhaven** - 1M N of the bay	54°20'·40N	09°56'·00W
288	**Eagle Island** - 1·4M NW of	54°17'·80N	10°07'·40W
289	**Black Rock** - 2·7M NE by N of	54°06'·20N	10°16'·60W
290	**Achill Head** - 1·4M SW	53°57'·30N	10°17'·90W
291	**Clew Bay** - 1M SW Achillbeg Is Lt	53°50'·80N	09°57'·90W
292	**Westport** - 1·5M WSW Inishgort Lt	53°49'·00N	09°42'·60W
293	**Clew Bay** - 1·5M NW Roonah Hd	53°46'·90N	09°57'·80W
294	**Inishturk Island** - 1·2M NW	53°43'·60N	10°08'·80W
295	**Inishshark Island** - 1·8M W of	53°36'·50N	10°21'·00W
296	**Slyne Hd Lt** - 1·6M SW	53°22'·90N	10°16'·00W
297	**Rock Is Lt** - 5·3M NW by W of	53°11'·80N	09°58'·60W
333	**Mizen Head (E coast)** - 1M ESE	52°51'·00N	06°01'·90W
334	**Wicklow** - 2·6M E	52°58'·90N	05°57'·80W
335	**Dun Laoghaire** - 2·2M NE	53°19'·60N	06°04'·60W
336	**Ben of Howth** - 1·4M E of	53°22'·40N	06°00'·50W
337	**Malahide** - 1·5M E of Bar	53°27'·00N	06°04'·80W
338	**Rockabill** - 1·2M WSW	53°35'·30N	06°02'·00W
339	**Carlingford Lough**	53°58'·40N	06°00'·00W
340	**Strangford Lough**	54°18'·40N	05°27'·70W
341	**South Rock Lt V** - 1·1M E	54°24'·30N	05°20'·00W

Distance Table - North Ireland

Approximate distances in nautical miles are by the most direct route while avoiding dangers and allowing for Traffic Separation Schemes

		1	2	3	4	5	6	7	8	9	10	11	12	13	14	15	16	17	18	19	20
1.	Dun Laoghaire	1																			
2.	Carlingford Lough	50	2																		
3.	Strangford Lough	71	36	3																	
4.	Bangor	96	61	34	4																
5.	Carrickfergus	101	66	39	6	5															
6.	Larne	108	73	45	16	16	6														
7.	Carnlough	118	78	50	25	26	11	7													
8.	Altacarry Head	135	102	74	45	45	31	21	8												
9.	Portrush	150	115	87	58	60	48	35	19	9											
10.	Lough Foyle	157	121	92	72	73	55	47	30	11	10										
11.	L Swilly (Fahan)	200	166	138	109	104	96	81	65	48	42	11									
12.	Tory Island	209	174	146	117	113	105	90	74	57	51	35	12								
13.	Burtonport	218	182	153	130	130	116	108	90	74	68	49	18	13							
14.	Killybegs	267	232	204	175	171	163	148	132	115	109	93	58	43	14						
15.	Sligo	281	246	218	189	179	177	156	146	123	117	107	72	51	30	15					
16.	Eagle Island	297	262	234	205	198	193	175	162	147	136	123	88	72	62	59	16				
17.	Westport	337	323	295	266	249	240	226	207	193	187	168	137	120	108	100	57	17			
18.	Slyne Head	352	317	289	260	257	248	234	217	201	195	178	143	128	117	114	55	44	18		
19.	Galway	348	366	338	309	307	297	284	266	253	245	227	192	178	166	163	104	94	49	19	
20.	Kilrush	318	361	364	335	332	323	309	291	276	270	251	220	203	191	183	142	119	75	76	20

Area 13 - North Ireland

WAYCHART
Lambay Island, north to Liscanor Bay

Symbols used:

- • Port
- ⊙ Waypoint
- — Track - between waypoints
- -- Track - close to possible dangers

Marinecall®
MACMILLAN REEDS

Weather Forecasts
by Fax & Telephone

Coastal/Inshore	48-hour by Fax	5-day by Tel
Caledonia	09061 502 125	09066 526 247
Northern Ireland	09061 502 127	09066 526 249
Clyde	09061 502 124	09066 526 246
National (3-5 day)	09061 502 109	09066 526 234

Offshore	2-5 day by Fax	2-5 day by Tel
Irish Sea	09061 502 163	09066 526 253
North West Scotland	09061 502 165	09066 526 255

09066 calls cost 60p per min. 09061 calls cost £1.50 per min.

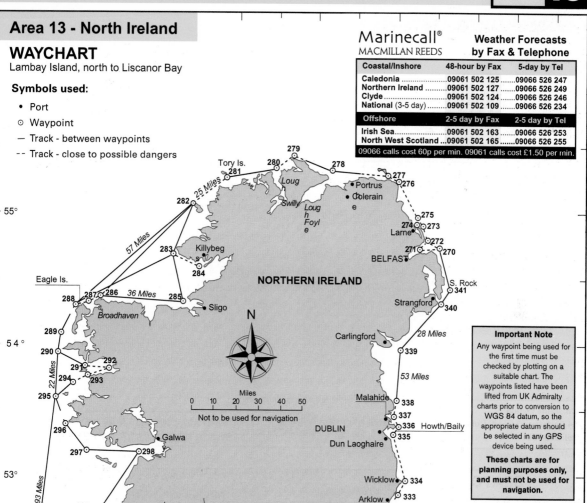

Important Note
Any waypoint being used for the first time must be checked by plotting on a suitable chart. The waypoints listed have been lifted from UK Admiralty charts prior to conversion to WGS 84 datum, so the appropriate datum should be selected in any GPS device being used.

These charts are for planning purposes only, and must not be used for navigation.

A Morrison Killyleagh	028 44828215	**Corrib Rowing & YC** Galway City	00353 91 564560
Abco Divers Belfast	028 90610492	**Courtmacsherry Police**	00353 23 46122
Albert Clarke Newtownards	01247 872325	**Down Marine Co** Ltd Belfast	028 90480247
Ardglass HM	028 4484 1291	**DV Diving**	028 91 464671
Ardglass Marina	028 4484 2332	**E A Gaw** Belfast	028 90451905
Ardglass Police	028 4461501	**East Antrim BC** Antrim	028 28 277204
Ballycastle Marina Ballycastle	028 2076 8525	**East Belfast YC** Belfast	028 9065 6283
Ballyholme YC Bangor	028 91271467	**Galway Bay HM**	00353 91 561874
Bangor Marina Bangor	028 91 453297	**Galway Bay Police**	00353 91 538000
Belfast Lough HM	028 90 553012	**Galway Bay SC**	00353 91 794527
Belfast Lough Police	028 91 454444	**Galway Maritime** Galway	00353 91 566568
Belfast River Manager	028 90 328507	**Glandore Police**	00353 23 48162
BJ Marine Ltd Bangor	028 91271434	**Glénans Irish SC (Westport)**	00353 98 26046
Burtonport HM	00353 075 42155	**Groomsport Bay HM**	028 91 278040
Carlingford Lough Police	042 9373102	**Hilary Keller** Buncrana	00353 77 62146
Carlingford Lough YC Rostrevor	028 4173 8604	**Holywood YC** Holywood	028 90423355
Carlingford Marina Carlingford	00353 42 937073	**Howth Police**	00353 1 6664900
Carnlough Harbour HM	07703 606763	**J McCready and Co Ltd** Belfast	028 90232842
Carrickfergus Marina Carrickgergus	028 93 366666	**J Parkinson (Sinbad Marine Services)** Killybegs	00353 73 31417
Carrickfergus SC Whitehead	028 93 351402	**Jamison and Green Ltd** Belfast	028 90322444
Caters Carrick Ltd Carrickfergus	028 93351919	**Killybegs HM**	00353 73 31032
Co Antrim YC Carrickfergus	028 9337 2322	**Killybegs Police**	00353 73 31002
Coleraine Marina Coleraine	028 7034 4768	**Killyleagh YC** Killyleagh	028 4482 8250
Coleraine YC Coleraine	028 703 44503		

COLERAINE MARINA

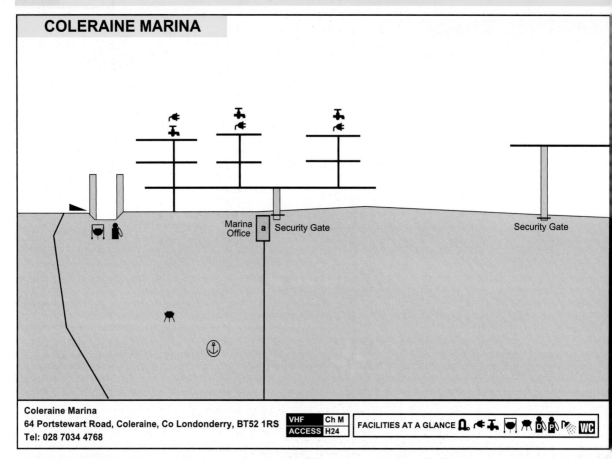

Coleraine Marina
64 Portstewart Road, Coleraine, Co Londonderry, BT52 1RS
Tel: 028 7034 4768

VHF	Ch M
ACCESS	H24

FACILITIES AT A GLANCE

SEATON'S MARINA

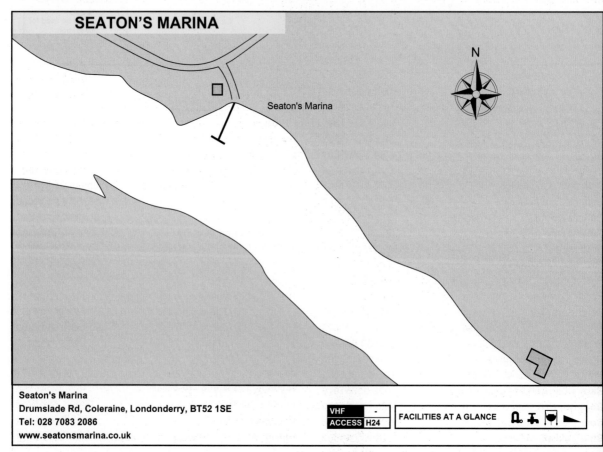

Seaton's Marina
Drumslade Rd, Coleraine, Londonderry, BT52 1SE
Tel: 028 7083 2086
www.seatonsmarina.co.uk

VHF	-
ACCESS	H24

FACILITIES AT A GLANCE

BALLYCASTLE MARINA

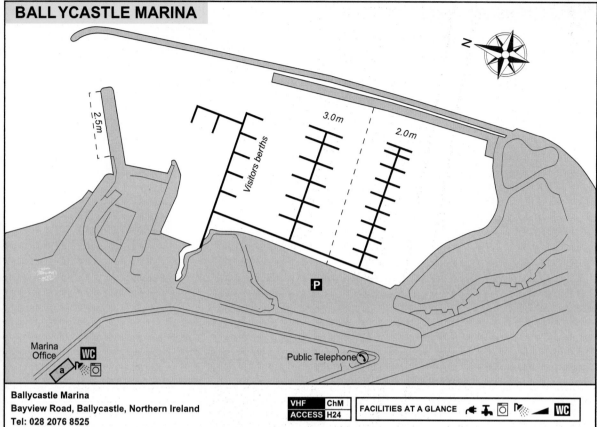

Ballycastle Marina
Bayview Road, Ballycastle, Northern Ireland
Tel: 028 2076 8525

VHF	ChM
ACCESS	H24

FACILITIES AT A GLANCE

Kircubbin SC Kirkcubbin	028 4273 8422
Larne HM	02828 872100
Larne Police	02828 272266
Larne Rowing & SC Larne	028 2827 4573
Lomax Boatbuilders Cliffony	00353 71 66124
Lough Foyle HM	028 7186 0555
Lough Foyle Police	028 77766797
Lough Swilly Police	00353 72 51102
Lough Swilly YC Fahn	00353 74 22377
Mayo SC (Rosmoney) Rosmoney	00353 98 27772
McCready Sailboats Ltd Holywood	028 9042 1821
McWilliam Sailmaker (Killinchy) Killinchy	028 97542345
Mooney Boats Killybegs	00353 73 31152/31388
Nautical World (Bangor) Bangor	028 91460330
Newtownards SC Newtownards	028 9181 3426
Noel Higgins	00353 872027650
Pat Rynn Engineering Galway	00353 91 562568
Phennick Cove Marina Ardglass	028 44842332
Portaferry Marina Portaferry	00353 28 4272 9598
Portrush HM	028 70822307
Portrush Police	028 70344122
Portrush YC Portrush	028 70 823932
Quoile YC Downpatrick	028 44 612266
River Bann & Coleraine HM	028 7034 2012
River Bann and Coleraine Police	028 70344122
Rossreagh Boatyard Rathmullan	00353 74 51082
Royal North of Ireland YC	028 90 428041
Royal Ulster YC Bangor	028 91 270568

Seaton Marina Coleraine	028 703 832086
Skerries SC Carlingdford Lough	00353 1 849 1233
Sketrick Marine Centre Killinchy	028 9754 1400
Sligo HM	00353 71 61197
Sligo Police	00353 71 57000
Sligo YC Sligo	00353 71 77168
Strangford Lough HM	028 44 881637
Strangford Lough Marina Portaferry	00353 1247 729598
Strangford Lough Police	028 44615011
Strangford Lough YC Newtownards	028 97 541883
Strangford SC Downpatrick	028 4488 1404
Sunset Marine & Watersports Sligo	00353 71 62792
Sunset Sails Sligo	00353 71 62792

TODD CHART AGENCY LTD
Navigation House, 85 High Street, Bangor, County Down, Northern Ireland BT20 5BD
Tel: 028 9146 6640
Fax: 028 9147 1070
e-mail:admiralty@toddchart.co.uk
www.nautical-charts.com
International Admiralty Chart Agent, chart correction service and nautical booksellers. Programming Centre for C-MAP NT and Navionics electronic charts. Stockist of Imray charts and books, navigation and chartroom instruments, binoculars, clocks etc. UK agent for Icelandic Hydrographic Service. Mail order - Visa, Mastercard, American Express and Switch/Delta accepted.

UK Customs Nationwide	0845 0109000
Warrenpoint BC Warrenpoint	028 4175 2137
Westport Police	00353 98 25555
Wilson Alan c/o Portrush YC Portrush	028 2076 2225

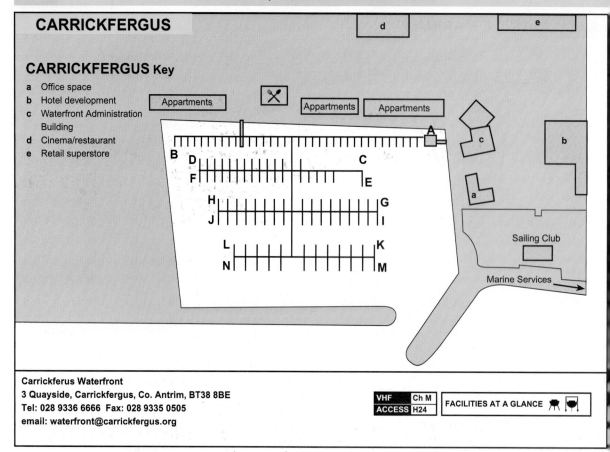

CARRICKFERGUS

CARRICKFERGUS Key

a Office space
b Hotel development
c Waterfront Administration Building
d Cinema/restaurant
e Retail superstore

Carrickferus Waterfront
3 Quayside, Carrickfergus, Co. Antrim, BT38 8BE
Tel: 028 9336 6666 Fax: 028 9335 0505
email: waterfront@carrickfergus.org

VHF	Ch M
ACCESS	H24

FACILITIES AT A GLANCE

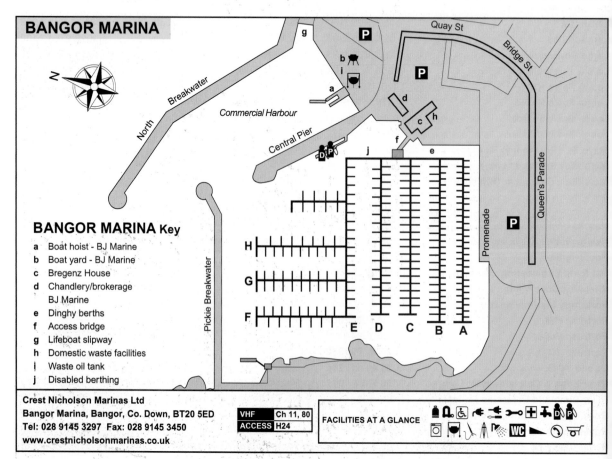

BANGOR MARINA

BANGOR MARINA Key

a Boat hoist - BJ Marine
b Boat yard - BJ Marine
c Bregenz House
d Chandlery/brokerage BJ Marine
e Dinghy berths
f Access bridge
g Lifeboat slipway
h Domestic waste facilities
i Waste oil tank
j Disabled berthing

Crest Nicholson Marinas Ltd
Bangor Marina, Bangor, Co. Down, BT20 5ED
Tel: 028 9145 3297 Fax: 028 9145 3450
www.crestnicholsonmarinas.co.uk

VHF	Ch 11, 80
ACCESS	H24

FACILITIES AT A GLANCE

PORTAFERRY MARINA

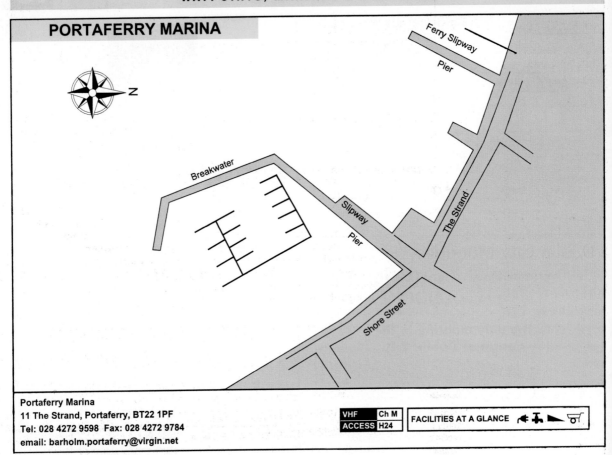

Portaferry Marina
11 The Strand, Portaferry, BT22 1PF
Tel: 028 4272 9598 Fax: 028 4272 9784
email: barholm.portaferry@virgin.net

VHF	Ch M
ACCESS	H24

FACILITIES AT A GLANCE

ARDGLASS

PHENNICK COVE MARINA Key

a Administration building
b Boat storage

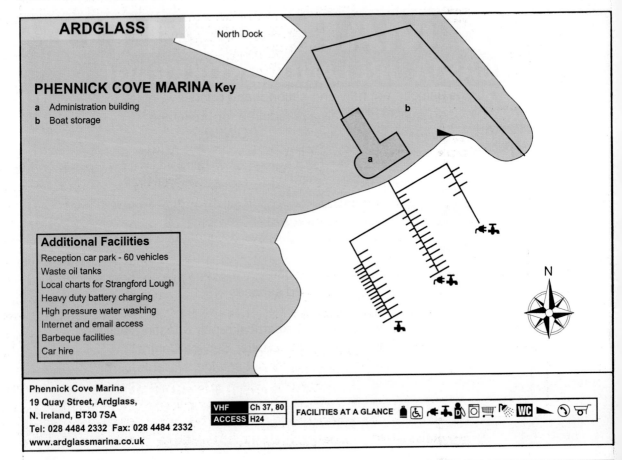

Additional Facilities
Reception car park - 60 vehicles
Waste oil tanks
Local charts for Strangford Lough
Heavy duty battery charging
High pressure water washing
Internet and email access
Barbeque facilities
Car hire

Phennick Cove Marina
19 Quay Street, Ardglass,
N. Ireland, BT30 7SA
Tel: 028 4484 2332 Fax: 028 4484 2332
www.ardglassmarina.co.uk

VHF	Ch 37, 80
ACCESS	H24

FACILITIES AT A GLANCE

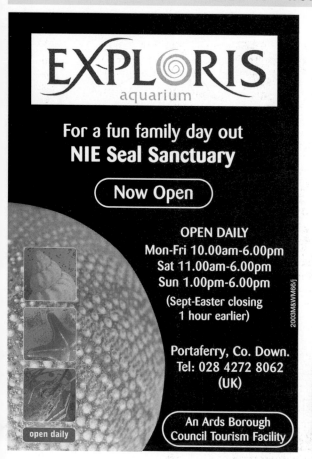

CARLINGFORD MARINA

CARLINGFORD MARINA Key

a Bar and restaurant
b Toilets, showers and laundry
c Refuse
d Adventure centre
e Chandlery
f Marina office
g Waiting pontoon

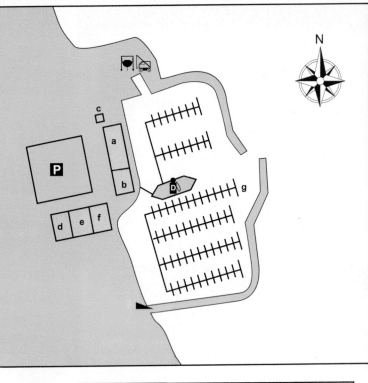

Carlingford Marina
Co. Louth, Ireland
Tel: 00353 (0)42 937 3073
Fax: 00353 (0)42 937 3075
www.carlingfordmarina.com

VHF	Ch 16
ACCESS	H24

FACILITIES AT A GLANCE

CARLINGFORD MARINA - IRELAND
Carlingford, Co Louth, Ireland.
Tel/Fax: +353 42 9373073
www.carlingfordmarina.com
VHF Ch16 and 37

Superb location in beautiful setting close to historic village of Carlingford, our friendly marina provides a top class service for all boat users. Waterside bar and restaurant, chandlery, slipway, 50-ton cranage, power, diesel, water, laundry and showers. Visitors are always welcome.

Planning a trip?

Met Office

Make it plain sailing
– for your free copy
of the *2002 Marine Weather Services* booklet
call the Met Office Customer Centre
on **0845 300 0300** or go to
www.metoffice.com/leisuremarine/mwsbooklet.html

For a five-day inshore forecast
for the Channel Islands,
dial **09060 100 466*** from your fax machine.

*09060 calls are charged at £1 per minute at all times.

Key to Marina Plans symbols

Calor Gas		**P** Parking	
Chandler		Pub/Restaurant	
Disabled facilities		Pump out	
Electrical supply		Rigging service	
Electrical repairs		Sail repairs	
Engine repairs		Shipwright	
First Aid		Shop/Supermarket	
Fresh Water		Showers	
Fuel - Diesel		Slipway	
Fuel - Petrol		**WC** Toilets	
Hardstanding/boatyard		Telephone	
Laundry facilities		Trolleys	
Lift-out facilities		**V** Visitors berths	

Area 14 - Channel Islands

MARINAS
Telephone Numbers
VHF Channel
Access Times

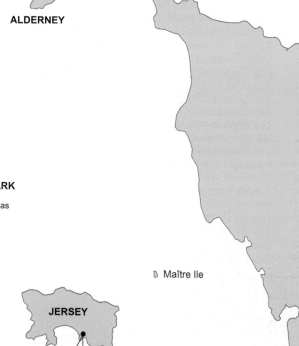

ALDERNEY

Beaucette Marina
01481 245000
Ch 80 H±3

GUERNSEY

HERM

SARK

St Peter Port Marinas
01481 720229
Ch 20 H±2½

Victoria Marina
01481 725 987
Ch 12 H±2½

Maître Ile

N

JERSEY

St Helier Marina
01534 885588

La Collette Marina
01534 885588
Ch 14 H24

MAPTECH®
www.maptech.co.uk

• **Navigational Software**
• Chart Navigator • Cruising Navigator • Offshore Navigator

• **Navigational Digital Charts**

Telephone: 01243 389352

Waypoint Guide Area 14 – Channel Islands - Guernsey, Jersey, Alderney

35	**Alderney - Bray Harbour** - 1M NNE	49°45'·00N	02°10'·75W
36	**The Swinge** - turning way point	49°43'·50N	02°14'·40W
37	**Casquets** -1 mile W of	49°43'·38N	02°24'·06W
38	**Guernsey NE** - 1·2m E of Beaucette	49°30'·13N	02°28'·30W
39	**St Peter Port** - 0·5M E of ent	49°27'·40N	02°30'·70W
40	**Big Russel** - mid way south	49°25'·30N	02°26'·00W
41	**Guernsey** - 1M SE of St Martin's Pt	49°24'·66N	02°30'·53W
42	**Guernsey** - 1·5M S of Pleinmont Pt	49°24'·00N	02°40'·00W
43	**Guernsey** - 1·8M W of Les Hanois	49°26'·16N	02°45'·00W
44	**Sark** - 0·3M S of Brecou	49°25'·47N	02°23'·30W
45	**Sark** - 1M E of Creux Harbour	49°25'·80N	02°19'·00W
46	**Jersey** - 1·75M NW of Grosnez Pt	49°16'·60N	02°16'·75W
47	**Jersey** - 1M WSW of La Corbiere	49°10'·46N	02°16'·32W
48	**Jersey** - 0·15M S of Normant Pt	49°09'·80N	02°10'·00W
49	**St Helier** - 0·3M S of Breakwater	49°09'·97N	02°07'·33W
50	**St Helier** - 0·3M S of Demie de Ras	49°08'·77N	02°06'·06W
51	**SE Jersey** - 1st turning pt going E	49°08'·05N	02°03'·35W
52	**SE Jersey** - 2nd turning pt to Gorey	49°07'·60N	01°57'·90W
53	**SE Jersey** - 3rd turning pt to Gorey	49°08'·70N	01°57'·20W
54	**Gorey Entrance** - 298°, 1·6 miles	49°11'·10N	01°59'·12W
55	**St Catherine, Jersey** - 0·5M SE	49°13'·10N	02°00'·00W
56	**Les Écrehou** - 1·4M S of Maitre Ile Bn	49°15'·70N	01°55'·50W
57	**Minquiers NCM** - 0·1M W	48°59'·70N	02°20'·65W
58	**SW Minquiers WCM** - 0·1M SW	48°54'·34N	02°19'·42W
59	**Roches Douvres Lt** - 3M NW of	49°08'·60N	02°52'·10W
60	**Roches Douvres Lt** - 2·5M NE	49°08'·10N	02°46'·20W
61	**Lezardrieux** - 1·5m N La Horaire Bn	48°55'·07N	02°55'·15W
81	**Iles Chausey** - 1M S of entrance	48°51'·10N	01°49'·00W
82	**Granville** - 0·7M SW of Granville Lt	48°49'·62N	01°37'·55W
83	**Iles Chausey** - 0·5M E of Anvers ECM	48°54'·00N	01°40'·00W
84	**SE Minquiers ECM** - 1M SE	48°53'·20N	01°58'·90W
85	**Les Ardentes ECM By** - 0·2M E	48°57'·90N	01°51'·15W
86	**NE Minquiers ECM** - 0·1M NE	49°00'·97N	01°55'·11W
87	**Les Écrehou SE** - 0·4M SE of Écrevière By	49°15'·10N	01°51'·65W
88	**Carteret** - 1·75M SW	49°20'·90N	01°49'·20W
89	**Carteret** - 0·3M SW Trois Grunes WCM By	49°21'·65N	01°55'·30W
90	**Cap de Flamanville** - 2M W of	49°31'·65N	01°56'·30W
91	**Diellette** - 1M NW of on transit	49°33'·80N	01°53'·00W
92	**Cap de La Hague** - 4M SSW of	49°40'·54N	02°01'·55W
93	**Cap de La Hague** - 2M W of	49°43'·37N	02°00'·28W
94	**Cap de La Hague** - 1·5M N of La Plate Lt	49°45'·50N	01°55'·70W
95	**Omonville** - 1M E of, in white sec	49°42'·55N	01°48'·25W

Distance Table - Channel Islands

Approximate distances in nautical miles are by the most direct route while avoiding dangers and allowing for Traffic Separation Schemes

		1	2	3	4	5	6	7	8	9	10	11	12	13	14	15	16	17	18	19	20
1.	Cherbourg	**1**																			
2.	Cap de la Hague	14	**2**																		
3.	Carteret	41	23	**3**																	
4.	Granville	75	61	38	**4**																
5.	St Malo	87	73	49	23	**5**															
6.	Casquets	31	17	32	63	70	**6**														
7.	Braye (Alderney)	23	9	26	66	73	8	**7**													
8.	Beaucette	39	25	34	59	58	15	19	**8**												
9.	St Peter Port	42	28	31	55	54	18	23	4	**9**											
10.	Les Hanois	49	35	37	58	56	23	29	14	10	**10**										
11.	Creux (Sark)	37	23	23	50	52	18	22	11	10	16	**11**									
12.	St Helier	59	45	28	30	38	43	46	33	29	32	24	**12**								
13.	Gorey (Jersey)	47	33	16	29	38	36	35	32	29	35	20	13	**13**							
14.	Dahouet	88	74	62	44	28	70	72	62	58	57	53	41	47	**14**						
15.	St Quay-Portrieux	88	74	64	54	35	71	73	55	56	48	51	46	52	12	**15**					
16.	Paimpol	91	77	65	56	42	67	70	54	50	45	50	45	53	24	24	**16**				
17.	Lézardrieux	88	74	68	54	49	65	68	52	48	42	38	47	55	33	21	14	**17**			
18.	Tréguier	94	80	72	72	60	66	72	56	52	42	58	53	63	58	46	29	22	**18**		
19.	Roscoff	117	103	95	96	84	87	94	77	73	63	79	80	93	71	59	58	54	41	**19**	
20.	L'Aberwrac'h	145	131	126	128	116	115	122	107	103	93	109	110	123	103	91	88	84	72	32	**20**

Area 14 - Channel Islands

WAYCHART
Guernsey, Jersey & Alderney

Marinecall®
MACMILLAN REEDS

Weather Forecasts by Fax & Telephone

Coastal/Inshore	48-hour by Fax	5-day by Tel
Channel Islands	-	.........09066 526 250
Mid Channel	09061 502 119	.........09066 526 241
South West.................	09061 502 120	.........09066 526 242
National (3-5 day) 09061 502 109		.........09066 526 234
Offshore	**2-5 day by Fax**	**2-5 day by Tel**
English Channel 09061 502 161		......09066 526 251
Biscay	09061 502 164	......09066 526 254

09066 calls cost 60p per min. 09061 calls cost £1.50 per min.

Important Note

Any waypoint being used for the first time must be checked by plotting on a suitable chart. The waypoints listed have been lifted from UK Admiralty charts prior to conversion to WGS 84 datum, so the appropriate datum should be selected in any GPS device being used.

These charts are for planning purposes only, and must not be used for navigation.

Symbols used:

- • Port
- ⊙ Waypoint
- — Track - between waypoints
- -- Track - close to possible dangers

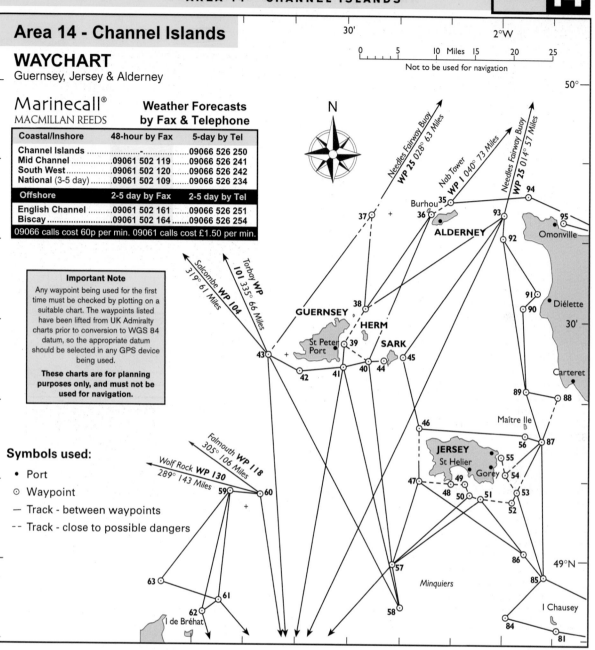

Not to be used for navigation

Alderney & Burhou HM	01481 822620
Alderney and Burhou Police	01481 725111
Alderney SC Alderney	01481 822959
Aqua-Star Ltd St Sampsons	01481 244550
Battricks Boatyard St Aubin	01534 743412
Beaucette HM	01481 245000
Beaucette Marina Vale	01481 245000
Boat Works Ltd St Peter Port	01481 726071
Boatworks + Ltd St Peter Port	01481 726071
Chicks Marine Ltd Guernsey	01481 724536
Collins Marine St Helier	01534 732415
Elizabeth Marina St Helier	01534 885530

Gorey HM	01534 853616
Graham Scott & Co St Peter Port	01481 728989
Guernsey Police	01481 725111
Guernsey YC St Peter Port	01481 722838
Iron Stores Marine St Helier	01534 877755
Islands Yachts St Helier	01534 25048
Jackson Yacht Services Jersey	01534 743819
Jersey Harbours Dept St Helier	01534 885588
La Collette Yacht Basin St Helier	01534 885588
Mainbrayce Marine Alderney	01481 822772
Marquand Brothers St Peter Port	01481 720962
North Quay Marine St Sampson's	01481 246561

BEAUCETTE MARINA

BEAUCETTE MARINA Key

- **a** Harbour office
- **b** Restaurant
- **c** Showers/toilets
- **d** Laundry & telephone
- **e** Manager's cabin
- **f** Boatyard

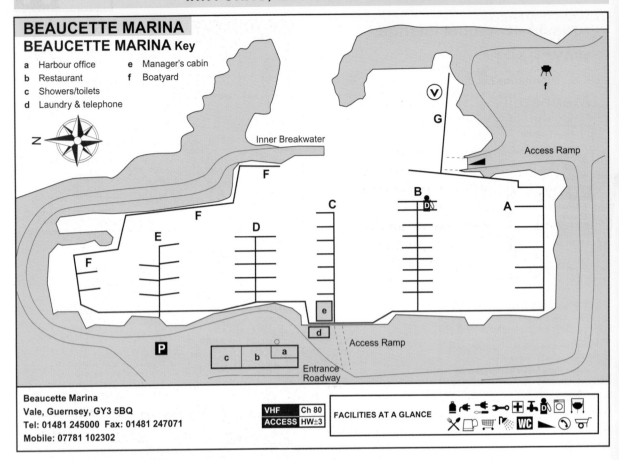

Beaucette Marina
Vale, Guernsey, GY3 5BQ
Tel: 01481 245000 Fax: 01481 247071
Mobile: 07781 102302

VHF	Ch 80
ACCESS	HW±3

FACILITIES AT A GLANCE

GUERNSEY VICTORIA MARINA

GUERNSEY VICTORIA MARINA Key

- **a** Toilets, showers, launderette and shops
- **b** Royal Channel Islands Yacht Club
- **c** Refuse skip
- **d** Marina control, port office
- **e** Dinghy/tender landing pontoon
- **f** Pub/restaurant

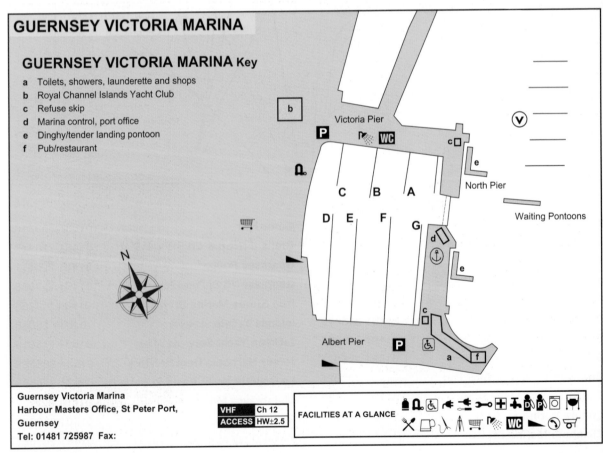

Guernsey Victoria Marina
Harbour Masters Office, St Peter Port,
Guernsey
Tel: 01481 725987 Fax:

VHF	Ch 12
ACCESS	HW±2.5

FACILITIES AT A GLANCE

BEAUCETTE MARINA
Vale, Guernsey, Channel Islands GY3 5BQ
Tel: (01481) 245000
Fax: (01481) 247071
e-mail: beaucette@premiermarinas.com
www.premiermarinas.com
Situated on the north east coast, Beaucette is one of Europe's most charming deep water marinas. With 115 berths, the marina offers all the services and facilities you would expect. Beaucette is a PREMIER MARINA.

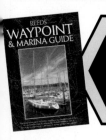

PREMIUM LIFERAFT SERVICES
CHANNEL ISLANDS
Tel: (01481) 720485
Freephone: 0800 243673
e-mail: info@liferafts.com
www.liferafts.com
Hire and sales of DoT and RORC approved liferafts and safety equipment.

Royal Channel Islands YC (Jersey)	
St Aubin	01534 745783
Sark HM	01481 832323
Seaquest Marine Ltd St Peter Port	01481 721773
South Pier Shipyard St Helier	01534 519700
St Helier HM	01534 885588
St Helier Marina St Helier	01534 885588
St Helier Police	01534 612612
St Helier YC St Helier	01534 721307/32229
St Peter Port HM	01481 720229
St Peter Port Marinas St Peter Port	01481 720229

UK Customs Nationwide	0845 0109000
Victoria Marina St Peter Port	01481 725987

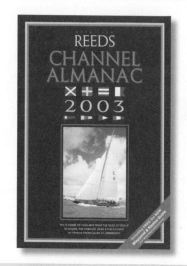

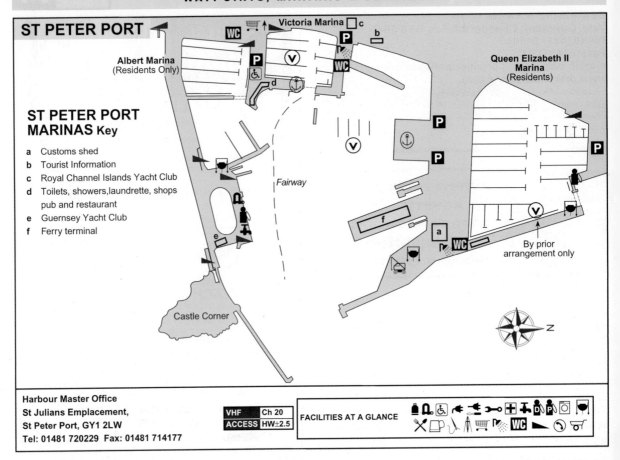

ST PETER PORT

ST PETER PORT MARINAS Key

- **a** Customs shed
- **b** Tourist Information
- **c** Royal Channel Islands Yacht Club
- **d** Toilets, showers, laundrette, shops pub and restaurant
- **e** Guernsey Yacht Club
- **f** Ferry terminal

Harbour Master Office
St Julians Emplacement,
St Peter Port, GY1 2LW
Tel: 01481 720229 Fax: 01481 714177

VHF	Ch 20
ACCESS	HW±2.5

FACILITIES AT A GLANCE

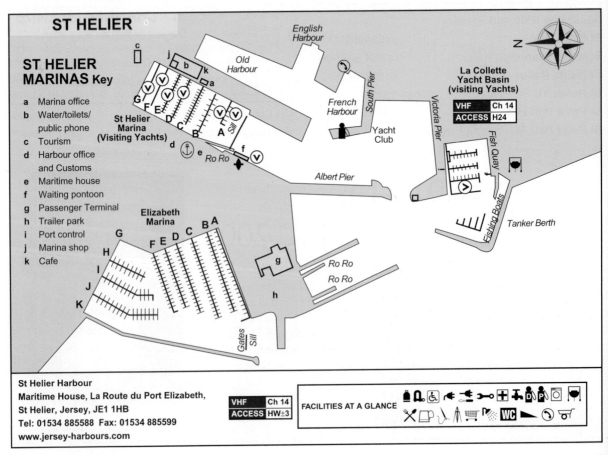

ST HELIER

ST HELIER MARINAS Key

- **a** Marina office
- **b** Water/toilets/ public phone
- **c** Tourism
- **d** Harbour office and Customs
- **e** Maritime house
- **f** Waiting pontoon
- **g** Passenger Terminal
- **h** Trailer park
- **i** Port control
- **j** Marina shop
- **k** Cafe

La Collette Yacht Basin (visiting Yachts)	
VHF	Ch 14
ACCESS	H24

St Helier Harbour
Maritime House, La Route du Port Elizabeth,
St Helier, Jersey, JE1 1HB
Tel: 01534 885588 Fax: 01534 885599
www.jersey-harbours.com

VHF	Ch 14
ACCESS	HW±3

FACILITIES AT A GLANCE

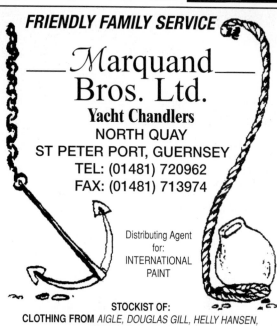
An introduction to Jersey, its harbours and waters

 ## States of Jersey

Tel: 01534 885588   Fax: 01534 885599
Email: jsyhbr@itl.net

This is Jersey - an island with an independent history which has kept many of it's ancient traditions alive - an island which has also taken what the world can offer so that it can support a buoyant economy with high employment while seeking to preserve all that is best. An island with it's own laws and currency - an island of traditional agriculture and modern finance - an island, above all, at which a welcome is assured whether you stop off for a couple of nights on your passage back from St Malo and the Brittany coast or whether you take several days off to explore Jersey - and why not? It is well worth it.

"You may only want to laze on your boat or you may wish to explore and enjoy what Jersey has to offer, whatever your preference we are here to welcome you and ensure you have a pleasant and enjoyable holiday in Jersey's five gold anchor marinas."

Brian Nibbs

Captain Brian Nibbs
Chief Executive
Jersey Harbours

2003M&WM84/je

MARINE SUPPLIES AND SERVICES

SECTION 2
MARINE SUPPLIES AND SERVICES GUIDE

ADHESIVES

CC MARINE (RUBBAWELD) LTD
P.O. Box 155, Chichester, W.
Sussex PO20 8TS
Tel: (01243) 672606
Fax: (01243) 673703
Manufacturer of marine adhesive tapes.

SIKA LTD
Watchmead, Welwyn Garden City,
Hertfordshire AL7 1BQ
Tel: (01707) 394444
Fax: (01707) 329129
e-mail:
waktins.terry@uk.sika.com
www.sika.com
Sikaflex watertight bonding. Deck caulking
and glazing.

ASSOCIATIONS

**ROYAL INSTITUTE OF
NAVIGATION**
1 Kensington Gore, London
SW7 2AT
Tel: (020) 7591 3130
Fax: (020) 7591 3131
e-mail: info@rin.org.uk
www.rin.org.uk
Forum for all interested in navigation - Air:
Sea: Land: Space.

BERTHS & MOORINGS

BRITISH WATERWAYS
Crinal Canal Office, Pier Square,
Aedrishaig, Argyll PA30 8DZ
Tel: (01546) 603210
Fax: (01546) 603941
e-mail:
alec.howie@britishways.co.uk
www.scottishcanals.co.uk
The Scottish canals offer the ideal coast
to coast cruising links complemented by
excellent marina berthing, ideal for both
visitor and long term moorings.

BURGH CASTLE MARINA
Butt Lane, Burgh Castle, Norfolk
NR31 9PZ
Tel: (01493) 780331
Fax: (01493) 780163
e-mail:
burghcastlemarina@aol.com
Safe pontoon moorings with full tidal
access on river Waveney and Bellamy
Goldaways Holiday Park. One hour sail
from sea. Central for Broadland cruising.
Amenities include pub-restaurant, pool,
showers, laundery & exhibition centre.

CHELSEA HARBOUR LTD
The Chambers, Chelsea Harbour,
London SW10 0XF.
TEL: 020 7225 9108
FAX: 020 7352 7868
A tranquil and intimate marina of 55
berths close to the heart of the West End

of London. 5-Star hotel, restaurants and
bars. Overnight pontoon and amenities.
24-hour security patrols and CCTV.

DUBLIN CITY MOORINGS
Custom House Quay, Dublin 1,
Ireland
Tel: +353 1 8183300
Fax: +353 8183399
e-mail: info@dublindocklands.ie
www.dublindocklands.ie
The only moorings in the centre of Dublin
City. Beside the Custom House and
IFSC. Opened in 1999 with berthing for
up to 25 boats. Electricity/water,
showers/toilets. 24-hour security. Swipe
card access.

**EMSWORTH YACHT
HARBOUR LTD**
Thorney Road, Emsworth,
Hampshire PO10 8BP.
Tel: (01243) 377727
Fax: (01243) 373432
www.emsworth-marina.co.uk
Friendly marina in Chichester harbour.
Water, electricity, diesel, Calor gas,
40-tonne mobile crane, slipways,
hard-standing and storage areas.
Showers and toilets, car parking,
chandlery, engineers and boat repairs.

HAFAN PWLLHELI
Glan Don, Pwllheli, Gwynedd
LL53 5YT
Tel: (01758) 701219
Fax: (01758) 701443 VHF Ch80
Hafan Pwllheli has over 400 pontoon
berths and offers access at virtually all
states of the tide. Ashore, its modern
purpose-built facilities include luxury
toilets, showers, launderette, a secure
boat park for winter storage, 40-ton travel
hoist, mobile crane and plenty of space
for car parking. Open 24-hours a day, 7
days a week.

JERSEY HARBOURS
Maritime House,
La Route du Port Elizabeth,
St Helier,
Jersey JE1 1HB.
Tel: (01534) 885588
Fax: (01534) 885599
e-mail: jsyhbr@itl.net
www.jersey-harbours.com
A warm welcome to visiting yachts!
Come and enjoy our 5 Gold anchor
facilities. Visiting yachts can stay at La
Collette Yacht Basin, which is open 24
hours, or closer to town at St Helier
Marina, which is open 3 hours ± HW.

NEPTUNE MARINA LTD
Neptune Quay, Ipswich,
Suffolk IP4 1AX
Tel: (01473) 215204
Fax: (01473) 215206
e-mail:
enquiries@neptune-marina.com
www.neptune-marina.com
Accessible through continuously
operating lockgates (VHF Channel 68)

**British
Waterways
Scotland**

WELCOME

TO SCOTLAND'S CANALS

Marina and Yachting Facilities

- Superb value Marina Berthing

- Winter Lay-up at keen prices

- Skipper's Guides and Passage Information

- A network of Waterways linking Scotland's cruising waters

- A comprehensive range of licence options to suit your needs

Shoreside

- Experience the unique Falkirk Wheel

- Cycle or walk the canal banks

- Magnificent scenery rich in wildlife

- There is so much to see and do – the ideal family experience

Website

- Everything you need to know Online!

www.scottishcanals.co.uk

Neptune Marina (VHF Channels 80 or 37) is located on the north side of Ipswich wet dock immediately adjacent to the town centre and integrated into the rapidly regenerating northern quays.

ORKNEY MARINAS LIMITED
Scotts Road, Hatston, Kirkwall, Orkney KW15 1GR
www.orkneymarinas.co.uk
Cruise the Okney Islands using our secure, serviced pontoon. Berthing for visitors in three new marinas at Kirkwall, Stromness and Westray for Summer 2003.

PADSTOW HARBOUR COMMISSIONERS
Harbour House, Padstow, Cornwall PL28 8AQ
Tel: (01841) 532239
Fax: (01841) 533346
e-mail:
padstowharbour@compuserve.com
www.padstow-harbour.co.uk
Inner harbour controlled by tidal gate - opens HW±2 hours. Minimum depth 3 metres at all times. Yachtsmen must be friendly as vessels raft together. Services include showers, toilets, diesel, water and ice. Security by CCTV.

PETERHEAD BAY AUTHORITY
Bath House, Bath Street, Peterhead AB42 1DX
Tel: (01779) 474020
Fax: (01779) 475712
www.peterhead-bay.co.uk
Contact Ken Bennions. Peterhead Bay Marina offers fully serviced pontoon berthing for local and visiting boat owners. Local companies provide a comprehensive range of supporting services. Ideal stopover for vessels heading to/from Scandinavia or the Caledonian Canal.

SARK MOORINGS -
Channel Islands
Tel: (01481) 832260
Fax: (01481) 832364
Mobile: 07781 106065
Channel 10
e-mail: simon@sarkci.com
www.sarkmoorings.com
Visitors' moorings now available at Havre Gossellin (West Coast), and La Grève de la Ville (East Coast by Point Robert lighthouse). Call up Ch 10 or mobile

07781 106065. Look for the yellow buoys and experience the charm and beauty of Sark.

SUTTON HARBOUR MARINA
North Quay House, Sutton Harbour, Plymouth PL4 0RA
Tel: (01752) 204186
Fax: (01752) 205403
Our historic harbour is a firm favourite with today's yachtsmen. Our friendly staff pride themselves on giving our visitors a warm welcome and offer excellent facilities including chandlery, boat repairs, fuel, servicing and car parking.

BOAT STORAGE

CALEY MARINA
Canal Road, Inverness IV3 8NF
Tel: (01463) 233437
Fax: (01463) 238323
e-mail: info@caleymarina.co.uk
www.caleymarina.co.uk
Marina with all usual facilities. Engine workshops & new & used engine sales & parts etc. Chandlery - largest in Scotland. Boat sales - new & used. Also canoe department.

EMSWORTH YACHT HARBOUR LTD
Thorney Road, Emsworth, Hampshire PO10 8BP.
Tel: (01243) 377727
Fax: (01243) 373432
www.emsworth-marina.co.uk
Friendly marina in Chichester harbour. Water, electricity, diesel, Calor gas, 40-tonne mobile crane, slipways, hard-standing and storage areas. Showers and toilets, car parking, chandlery, engineers and boat repairs.

MILFORD MARINA
Milford Haven, Pembrokeshire SA73 3AF
Tel: (01646) 696312/3
Fax: (01646) 696314
e-mail:
marina@milford-docks.co.uk
www.milford-docks.co.uk
Marina berths, boat storage, 16t hoist, diesel, electricity, laundery, chandlery,

boat & engine repairs, brokerage, engine sales, restaurants, retail park on site, 24 hour staff, 22 miles of sheltered estuary for all year round sailing.

BOAT BUILDERS & REPAIRS

ARDFERN YACHT CENTRE LTD
Ardfern by Lochgilphead, Argyll, Scotland PA31 8QN
Tel: (01852) 500247
Fax: (01852) 500624
e-mail: office@ardfernyacht.co.uk
www.ardfernyacht.co.uk
Boatyard and marina facilities in a picturesque natural harbour, comprehensive workshop facilities, extensive chandlery, diesel, gas.

BOATWORKS + LTD
Castle Emplacement, St Peter Port, Guernsey, Channel Islands GY1 1AU.
Tel: (01481) 726071
Fax: (01481) 714224
Boatwork + provides a comprehensive range of services including boatbuilding and repairs, chandlery, clothing and fuel supplies.

LANGLEY MARINE SERVICES LTD
Sovereign Harbour Marina, Pevensey Bay Road, Eastbourne, East Sussex BN23 6JH
Tel: (01323) 470244
Fax: (01323) 470255
Offering a complete service to the boat owner, engineering, GRP repairs, shipwrighting, electronics, rigging, cleaning, etc. We specialise in the refit and repair of large pleasurecraft and commercial vessels and are contractors to the RNLI.

NORTHSHORE
The Boat Yard, Brancaster Staithe, King's Lynn, Norfolk PE31 8BP
Tel: (01485) 210236
e-mail:
info@northshoresport.co.uk
www.sailcraft.co.uk
Northshore - situated at the head of

Brancaster Staithe harbour - is Norfolk's premier chandlery. Stockists of Barton - Harken etc. Suppliers of Musto - Gill & Henri Lloyd. Plus Sailcraft Sea School - dinghy & powerboat & shore based yachtmaster training.

RILEY MARINE
Cinque Ports Arms. Western Docks, Dover CT17 9DQ
Tel: (01304) 214544
Fax: (01304) 214544
e-mail: riley.marine@virgin.net
Modern and traditional boat skills and repairs. Wood steel GRP painting, varnishing, osmosis repairs, marine engineering, engine installations, repairs & servicing, most known marine engines, main dealer for Epifan, Awlgrip, Rockoil, Tahatsu outboard motors.

ROSSITER YACHTS LTD
Rossiters Quay, Bridge St, Christchurch, Dorset BH23 1DZ
Tel: (01202) 483250
Fax: (01202) 490164
e-mail:
rossiteryachts@hotmail.com
www.rossiteryachts.co.uk
Builders of Curlew and Pontail + repairs & restorations in wood and GRP, osmosure treatment centre. Marine engineering: diesel, petrol, inboard, outboard, marine diesel sales, rigging service, cranage & storage, chandlery, brokerage, moorings.

SEAFIT MARINE SERVICES
Falmouth Marina, North Parade, Falmouth, Cornwall TR11 2TD
Tel: (01326) 313713
Fax: (01326) 211521
Mobile: (07971) 196175
All repair and service work undertaken.

SILVERS MARINA LTD
Silverhills, Rosneath, Helensburgh G84 0RW
Tel: (01436) 831222
Fax: (01436) 831879
Yacht storage, repairs, riggins, osmosis treatment, spray painting, engineering.

STONE PIER YACHT SERVICES
Stone Pier Yard, Shore Road, Warsash, Hampshire SO31 9FR
Tel: (01489) 885400
Fax: (01489) 482049
e-mail: jgale82246@aol.com
High quality workmanship at reasonable prices, friendly and professional repair, refit and restoration facilities for GRP and timber vessels in our spacious workshop. Call Jon Gale for personal solutions to your problems, large or small.

WINTERS MARINE LIMITED
(Lincombe Boatyard)
Lincombe, Salcombe, Devon TQ8 8NQ.
Tel: (01548) 843580
e-mail:
lincombeboatyard@eclipse.co.uk
Deep water pontoon moorings. Winter

storage for 150 boats. All maintenance and repair facilities. Slipway capacity 30 tonnes. Short and long-term lifecraft hire.

BOATYARD SERVICES & SUPPLIES

A & P Ship Care
Ramsgate   01843 593140
A Blagdon Plymouth   01752 561830
A McCallum & Co Boat Builders
Tarbert   01880 820209
A Morrison Killyleagh 028 44828215
AA Coombes Bembridge 01983 872296
Abersoch Boatyard Ltd
Abersoch   01758 712213
Alexander Noble and Sons
Girvan   01465 712223
Amble Boat Co Ltd
Amble   01665 710267
Amsbrisbeg Ltd
Port Bannatyne   01700 502719

ARDORAN MARINE
Lerags, Oban, Argyll, Scotland PA34 4SE
Tel: (01631) 566123
Fax: (01631) 566611
e-mail: colin@ardoran.co.uk
www.ardoran.co.uk
West coast Scotland. All marine facilities.

Ardmair Boat Centre
Ullapool   01854 612054
Ardmaleish Boat Building Co
Rothesay   01700 502007
Ardrishaig Boatyard
Lochgilphead   01546 603280
Arfon Oceaneering
Caernarfon   01286 676055
Arklow Slipway
Arklow   00353 402 33233
B & G Marine
Maylandsea   01621 743546
Baltic Wharf Boatyard
Totnes   01803 867922
Baltimore Boatyard
Baltimore   00353 28 20444
Battricks Boatyard
St Aubin   01534 743412
Bedwell and Co
Walton-on-the-Naze   01255 675873
Berthon Boat Co
Lymington   01590 673312
Birdham Shipyard
Chichester   01243 512310
BJ Marine Ltd Bangor 028 91271434
Boatworks + Ltd
St Peter Port   01481 726071
Booth W Kelly Ltd
Ramsey   01624 812322
Brightlingsea Boatyard
Brightlingsea   01206 302003/8

Brighton Marina Boatyard
Brighton   01273 819919
Bristol Marina (Yard)
Bristol   0117 921 3198
Buckie Shipyard Ltd
Buckie   01542 831245
Bucklers Hard Boat Builders Ltd
Brockenhurst   01590 616214
Bure Marine Ltd
Great Yarmouth   01493 656996
C & J Marine Services
Newcastle Upon Tyne   0191 295 0072
C Lallow Isle of Wight 01983 292112
C Toms and Son Ltd
Fowey   01726 870232

CALEY MARINA
Canal Road, Inverness IV3 8NF
Tel: (01463) 233437
Fax: (01463) 238323
e-mail: info@caleymarina.co.uk
www.caleymarina.co.uk
Marina with all usual facilities. Engine workshops & new & used engine sales & parts etc. Chandlery - largest in Scotland. Boat sales - new & used. Also canoe department.

Cambrian Boat Centre
Swansea   01792 467263
Cambrian Marine Services Ltd
Cardiff   029 20343459
Cantell and Son Ltd
Newhaven   01273 514118
Carroll's Ballyhack Boatyard
New Ross   00353 51 389164
Castlepoint Boatyard
Crosshaven   00353 21 4832154
Chapman & Hewitt Boatbuilders
Wadebridge   01208 813487
Coastal Marine Boatbuilders
(Berwick upon Tweed)
Eyemouth   01890 750328
Coastcraft Ltd
Cockenzie   01875 812150

COATES MARINE LTD
Northern Spars & rigging Services, The Marina Boatyard, Whitby, North Yorkshire YO21 1EU
Tel: (01947) 604486
Fax: (01947) 600580
Boat storage and repairs, full rigging services, repairs, clothing, chandlery.

Coombes Boatyard
Chichester   01243 866663
Corpach Boatbuilding Company
Fort William   01397 772861

CRAOBH MARINA
A member of the Holt Leisure Group
By Lochgilphead, Argyll PA31 8UA.
Tel: (01852) 500222
Fax: (01852) 500252

MARINE SUPPLIES AND SERVICES

BERTHS & MOORINGS – BOATYARDS

VHF Ch37 and 80 (M).
250-berth marina on Loch Shuna. Water, electricity, diesel and gas. Full boatyard services. Chandlery. Brokerage. Insurance. Shops, bar, restaurant, car hire, 24-hour access.

Creekside Boatyard (Old Mill Creek)
Dartmouth   01803 832649

CRINAN BOATYARD LTD
Crinan, Lochgilphead, Argyll
PA31 8SW
Tel: (01546) 830232
Fax: (01546) 830281
Fully stocked chandlery, slipway, engineering and shipwright work and repairs, swinging moorings, water and diesel, shower and laundry facilities, undercover and outside storage.

Crosshaven Boatyard Co Ltd
Crosshaven   00353 21 831161

DALE SAILING CO LTD
Brunel Quay, Neyland,
Milford Haven, Pembrokeshire
SA73 1PY
Tel: (01646) 603110
Fax: (01646) 601061
e-mail:
enquiries@dale-sailing.co.uk
www.dale-sailing.co.uk
Sales, service and chandlery on site at Neyland Marina UK. Diesel, haulage, storage, engine, GRP, rigging repairs, chandlers, brokerage. Dealer for many inc. Suzuki, Mercury/Mercruiser, Volvo, Selden, Yanmar, Raytheon, Perkins, Lewmar.

DARTHAVEN MARINA LTD
Brixham Road, Kingswear,
Devon TQ6 0SG
Tel: (01803) 752242
Fax: (01803) 752722
www.darthaven.co.uk
Darthaven provides "one stop shop" for all repairs/maintenance. Experienced staff. Extensive Chandlery stocks, all leading brands, Volvo Penta, Yanmar, Raymarine,

B&G, etc. 7 days, 35 tonne mobile hoist. Visitors pontoon - Channel 80. Engineering Emergency - 07973 280584.

Dartside Quay
Brixham   01803 845445

Dauntless Co
Canvey Island   01268 793782

David Hillyard
Littlehampton   01903 713327

David Moss (Boatbuilders)
Thornton-Cleveleys   01253 893830

Davis's Boatyard Poole 01202 674349

DICKIES OF BANGOR
36 Garth Road, Bangor,
Gwynedd LL57 2SE
Tel: (01248) 363400
Fax: (01248) 354169
e-mail: info@dickies.co.uk
www.dickies.co.uk
Full yard services, chandlery, brokerage and new boat dealers for Beneteau Sail and power boats and Lagoon power catamarans.

Dinas Boat Yard Ltd
Y Felinheli   01248 671642

Dorset Yachts Poole   01202 674531

Douglas Boatyard
Preston   01772 812462

Dover Yacht Co Dover   01304 201073

DUN LAOGHAIRE MARINA
Harbour Road, Dun Laoghaire,
Co. Dublin
Tel: ++353 1 2020040
Fax: ++353 1 2020043
e-mail: dlmarina@indigo.ie
www.dlharbour.ie
Located within Dun Laoghaire - 8 miles from Dublin City centre adjacent suburban rail station and all amenities. Facilities include shore power, portable water, showers, laundry, fuel - petrol & diesel, gas, sewage pump out.

Elephant Boatyard
Southampton   023 80403268

Elton Boatbuilding Ltd
Kirkcudbright   01557 330177

ER Birch Boatbuilders 01268 696094

Fairways Marine Engineers
Maldon   01621 852866

Farrow & Chambers Yacht Builders
Humberston   01472 632424

Felixstowe Ferry Boatyard
Felixstowe   01394 282173

Ferguson Engineering
Wexford   00353 6566822133

Ferry Marine South
Queensferry   0131 331 1233

Ferrybridge Marine Services Ltd
Weymouth   01305 781518

Findhorn Boatyard
Findhorn   01309 690099

Firmhelm Ltd Pwllheli 01758 612251

Fishbourne Quay Boatyard
Ryde   01983 882200

FORREST MARINE LTD
Kerswell Grange, Old Dawlish
Road, Kennford, Exeter,
Devon EX6 7LR
Tel: (01392) 833504
Fax: (01392) 833608
e-mail:
forrest.transport@virgin.net
UK & European specialist yacht and cruiser overland transport.

Fowey Boatyard Fowey 01726 832194

FOX's MARINA IPSWICH LTD
The Strand, Ipswich,
Suffolk
IP2 8SA
Tel: (01473) 689111
Fax: (01473) 601737
Comprehensive boatyard. New 100ft workshop. Specialists in osmosis and spray painting. Marina access 24hrs. Diesel dock, travel hoists to 70 tons, 10 ton crane. Full electronics, rigging, engineering, stainless steel services. Extensive chandlery.

Frank Halls & Son
Walton on the Naze   01255 675596

George Hewitt Binham 01328 830078

Goodchild Marine Services
Great Yarmouth   01493 782301

Gweek Quay Boatyard
Helston   01326 221657

Haines Boatyard
Chichester   01243 512228

Harbour Marine Services Ltd
Southwold   01502 724721

Harbour Marine
Plymouth   01752 204690/1

Harold Hayles Yarmouth 01983 760373

Harris Marine Barry   01446 740924

Hartlepool Marine Engineering
Hartlepool   01429 867883

Heron Marine
Whitstable   01227 361255

HOLYHEAD MARINA & TRINITY MARINE LTD
Newry Beach, Holyhead LL65 1YA.
Tel: (01407) 764242
Fax: (01407) 769152
e-mail:
info@holyhead-marina.co.uk
Marine engineering and comprehensive boatyard facilities for all types of craft up to 100 tonnes. 500-berth pontoon marina under construction Summer 2001, including all shoreside amenities, exclusive apartments and chandlery. Access at all tides. Berths now available.

Ian Richardson Boatbuilders
Stromness   01856 850321

Instow Marine Services
Bideford   01271 861081

IPSWICH HAVEN MARINA
New Cut East, Ipswich, Suffolk IP3 0EA
Tel: (01473) 236644
Fax: (01473) 236644
e-mail:
ipswichhaven@abports.co.uk
5 gold anchor marina, access through lock manned 24 hours, 70 tonne boat hoist, storage ashore, licenced club house, chronology, new and used boat sales, 5 mins walk from Ipswich town centre, 10 mins to station.

IRON WHARF BOATYARD
Abbeyfields, Faversham, Kent ME13 7BT
Tel: (01795) 537122
Fax: (01795) 532020
Moorings, storage, cranage, chandlery, brokerage and fuel.

J. B. TIMBER LTD
56 Woodgates Lane, North Ferriby, Yorks HU14 3JY
Tel: (01482) 631765
Fax: (01482) 634846
Boatbuilding timbers: Larch, Oak, Iroko, Opepe.

Island Boat Services
Port of St Mary   01624 832073

J Buchan & Son Ltd
Peterhead   01779 475395

J Fleming Engineering 01851 703488

J Henderson Shiskine   01770 860259

J McCaughty (Boatbuilders)
Wick   01955 602858

J Moore & Son
St Austell   01726 842964

Jersey Harbours Dept
St Helier   01534 885588

Jim Spencer Sailing Services
Brightlingsea   01206 302911

John Brennan
Dun Laoghaire   00353 1 280 5308

Jones & Teague
Saundersfoot   01834 813429

K Latham Poole   01202 748029

Kilnsale Boatyard
Kinsale   00353 21 4774774

KILRUSH MARINA & BOATYARD - IRELAND
Kilrush, Co Clare, Ireland
Tel: 00 353 (65) 9052072
Fax: 00 353 (65) 9051692
Mobile: 00 353 862313870
VHF Ch80
e-mail: kcm@shannon.dev.ie
www.shannon-dev.ie/kcm
Marina on Ireland's beautiful west coast, is a new marina with 120 fully serviced berths. The marina has all shore facilities including a modern boatyard with 45-ton hoist. It adjoins the busy market town of Kilrush which has every facility required by the visiting yachtsman.

Lake Yard   01202 674531

Lincombe Boat Yard
Salcombe   01548 843580

Lomax Boatbuilders
Cliffony   00353 71 66124

LYMINGTON YACHT HAVEN
King's Saltern Road, Lymington, Hampshire SO41 3QD.
Tel: (01590) 677071
Fax: (01590) 678186
e-mail:
lymington@yachthavens.com
Perfectly situated at the mouth of the Lymington River giving instant access to the Western Solent. Full marina services, boatyard, brokerage, diesel, petrol, gas, restaurant and bar.

MacDougalls Marine Services
                         01681 700294

Macduff Shipyard Ltd
Macduff   01261 832234

Madog Boatyard
Porthmadog   01766 514205/513435

Mainbrayce Marine
Alderney   01481 822772

Malakoff and Moore
Lerwick   01595 695544

Mallaig Boat Building and Engineering Mallaig   01687 462304

Maramarine
Helensburgh   01436 810971

Marindus Engineering
Kilmore Quay   00353 53 29794

MARINE GLEAM
14 Fromond Close, Lymington, Hants SO41 9LQ
Tel: 0800 074 4672
e-mail:
enquiries@marinegleam.biz
www.marinegleam.biz
A full cleaning programme to meet your specific requirements from a one off, or a regular clean to a full exterior polish, teak, canopy and covers, anti-fouling, full interior, engine & bilges cleaned.

Mariners Farm Boatyard
Gillingham   01634 233179

McGruar and Co Ltd
Helensburgh   01436 831313

MIKE LUCAS YACHTING
Lymcourt Lodge, Middle Lincombe Road, Torquay, Devon TQ1 2HE
Tel: (01803) 212840
Fax: (01803) 212818
e-mail:
mike@mikelucasyachting.co.uk
www.mikelucasyachting.co.uk
Saga Sabler Starlight Specialized broker agent.

Mitchell's Boatyard
Poole   01202 747857

Mooney Boats
Killybegs   00353 73 31152/31388

Norman Pearn and Co
Looe   01503 262244

North Pier (Oban) Oban 01631 562892

North Wales Boat Centre
Conwy   01492 580740

Northshore Yacht Yard
Chichester   01243 512611

Oban Yachts and Marine Services
By Oban   01631 565333

Parker Yachts and Dinghys Ltd
Nr Boston   01205 722697

Pat Rynn Engineering
Galway   00353 91 562568

Penrhos Marine
Aberdovey   01654 767478

Penzance Dry Dock and Engineering Co Ltd. Penzance   01736 363838

MARINE SUPPLIES AND SERVICES

BOATYARD SERVICES & SUPPLIES

Peter Leonard Marine
Newhaven   01273 515987

Philip & Son Dartmouth 01803 833351

Ponsharden Boatyard
Penryn   01326 372215

**POWERSAIL AND ISLAND
CHANDLERS LTD**
East Cowes Marina,
Clarence Road, East Cowes,
Isle-of-Wight PO32 6YB
Tel: (01983) 299800
Fax: (01983) 299800
Chandlery provisions, all boating needs.

R K Marine Ltd
Swanwick   01489 583572

Rat Island Sailboat Company (Yard)
St Mary's   01720 423399

Retreat Boatyard Ltd
Exeter   01392 874270/875934

RF Upson and Co
Aldeburgh   01728 453047

Rice and Cole Ltd
Burnham-on-Crouch   01621 782063

Richardsons Boatbuilders
Binfield Newport   01983 821095

Riverside Yard
Shoreham Beach   01273 592456

RJ Prior (Burnham) Ltd
Burnham-on-Crouch   01621 782160

Robertsons Boatyard
Woodbridge   01394 382305

Rossbrin Boatyard
Schull   00353 28 37352

Rossiter Yacht Builders Ltd
Christchurch   01202 483250

Rossreagh Boatyard
Rathmullan   00353 74 51082

Rudders Boatyard & Moorings
Milford Haven   01646 600288

Ryan & Roberts Marine Services
Askeaton   00353 61 392198

S Cook Boatbuilders and Repairers
Whitby   01947 820521

Sandbanks Yacht Company
Poole   01202 707500

Sandy Morrison Engineering
Uig   01470 542300

Scarborough Marine Engineering Ltd
Scarborough   01723 375199

Severn Valley Cruisers Ltd (Boatyard)
Stourport-on-Severn   01299 871165

Shepherds Wharf Boatyard Ltd
Cowes   01983 297821

SHOTLEY MARINA LTD
Shotley Gate, Ipswich,
Suffolk IP9 1QJ.
Tel: (01473) 788982
Fax: (01473) 788868
e-mail:
sales@shotley-marina.co.uk
www.shotley-marina.co.uk
A modern state of the art marina with 350
berths offering all the services expected.
Open 24-hours with full security. Access
all states of tide, ideal cruising base. Well
stocked chandlery and general store,

repair facilities, laundry and ironing centre,
showers/baths and toilets. Restaurants,
bar, children's room, TV/video and
function rooms with dance floor and bar.
Disabled facilities.

Shotley Marine Services Ltd
Ipswich   01473 788913

SILVERS MARINA LTD
Silverhills, Rosneath,
Helensburgh G84 0RW
Tel: (01436) 831222
Fax: (01436) 831879
Yacht storage, repairs, riggins, osmosis
treatment, spray painting, engineering.

Skinners Boat Yard
Baltimore   00353 28 20114

SLEAT MARINE SERVICES
Ardvasar, Isle of Skye IV45 8RS
Tel: (01471) 844216
Fax: (01471) 844387
e-mail:
services@sleatmarineservices
www.sleatmarineservices.co.uk
Yacht Charter - we offer a choice of yachts
in the 10-12 metre size range. Services to
visiting yachts include: 15 ton hoist,
general repairs, diesel, water, mooring and
showers. We look forward to seeing you.

Smith & Gibbs
Eastbourne   01323 734656

**South Dock (Seaham Harbour Dock
Co)** Seaham   0191 581 3877

Sparkes Boatyard
Hayling Island   023 92463572

Standard House Boatyard
Wells-next-the-Sea   01328 710593

Steel-kit Borth   01970 871713

Strand Shipyard Rye   01797 222070

Surry Boatyard
Shoreham-by-Sea   01273 461491

Tarquin Boat Co
Emsworth   01243 375211

TITCHMARSH MARINA
Coles Lane, Walton-on-the-Naze,
Essex CO14 8SL
Tel: (01255) 672185
Fax: (01255) 851901
www.titchmarshmarina.com
Friendly service in the peaceful
backwaters. Visiting yachtsmen welcome.
Sheltered marina berths. Full marina
facilities: Travel-lift, cranage, 16-amp
electricity, diesel. Winter storage.
Brokerage. Restaurant and bar (see
Harbour Lights Restaurant.)

TOLLESBURY MARINA
The Yacht Harbour, Tollesbury,
Maldon, Essex CM9 8SE
Tel: (01621) 869202
Fax: (01621) 868489
e-mail:
brokerage@woodrolfe.demon.co.uk
www.woodrolfe.com
VHF Ch37 and 80
Dedicated to customer service, this
family-run marina can offer 240 marina
berths with water and electricity on all

pontoons. Cruising club with bar, restaurant, swimming pool and tennis courts. Repair workshop, osmosis treatment centre. Full brokerage service listing over 200 boats.

T J RIGGING
9 Vardre Park Deganwy,
Conwy LL31 9YQ
Tel: (07780) 972411
e-mail: tj.rigging@virgin.net
Specialist mobile rigging service.

Trinity Marine Holyhead 01407 763855

Trouts Boatyard (River Exe)
Topsham   01392 873044

VJ Pratt and Sons
King's Lynn   01553 764058

Weir Quay Boatyard
Bere Alston   01822 840474

West Solent Boatbuilders
Lymington   01590 642080

Wicor Marine Fareham 01329 237112

Winters Marine Ltd (Lincombe
Boatyard) Salcombe   01548 843580

Woodrolfe Boatyard
Maldon   01621 869202

BOOKS, CHARTS & PUBLISHERS

Adlard Coles Nautical
London   0207 7580200

Fernhurst Books
Brighton   01903 882277

Imray, Laurie, Norie & Wilson
Huntingdon   01480 462114

Kelvin Hughes
Southampton   023 8063 4911

MARINE CHART SERVICES
Belgrade Centre, Denington
Road, Denington Industrial
Estate, Wellingborough,
Northants NN8 2QH
Tel: (01933) 441629
Fax: (01933) 442662
e-mail: info@chartsales.co.uk
www.chartsales.co.uk
Save 40% or more on current edition navigation charts. Over 25,000 charts in stock including Admiralty, Imray, Dutch, Norwegian, USA, and more. Worldwide coverage and worldwide delivery. Also pilot books, flags and navigational equipment.

REED'S NAUTICAL
The Barn, Ford Farm, Bradford
Leigh, Bradford-on-Avon, Wilts.
BA15 2RP

Tel: (01225) 868821
Fax: (01225) 868831
e-mail:
sales@abreed.demon.co.uk
www.reedsnautical.com
Specialists in worldwide mail order of nautical books, charts and prints for boating people everywhere - book & chart catalogues available.

STANFORDS CHARTS
PO Box 2747, West Mersea,
Essex CO5 8FT
Tel: (01206) 381580
Fax: (01206) 381580
e-mail:
info@allweathercharts.co.uk
www.allweathercharts.co.uk
Publishers of the only UK charts printed on plastic - 100% waterproof, tough and tear-resistant. With a format to meet every navigational need: large sheets, charts-packs, local series charts. The Yachtsman's allweather charts.

TODD CHART AGENCY LTD
Navigation House,
85 High Street, Bangor,
County Down,
Northern Ireland BT20 5BD

Tel: 028 9146 6640
Fax: 028 9147 1070
e-mail:admiralty@toddchart.co.uk
www.nautical-charts.com
International Admiralty Chart Agent, chart correction service and nautical booksellers. Programming Centre for C-MAP NT and Navionics electronic charts. Stockist of Imray charts and books, navigation and chartroom instruments, binoculars, clocks etc. UK agent for Icelandic Hydrographic Service. Mail order - Visa, Mastercard, American Express and Switch/Delta accepted.

UK HYDROGRAPHICS OFFICE
Admiralty Way, Taunton,
Somerset TA1 2DN
Tel: (01823) 337900
e-mail:
generalenquiries@ukho.gov.uk
www.ukho.gov.uk
Suppliers of navigational charts and
publications, including the Admiralty
Leisure series.

BOW THRUSTERS

WESTERN MARINE POWER LTD
Western Hangar, Mount Batten,
Plymouth, Devon PL9 9SJ.
Tel: (01752) 408804
Fax: (01752) 408807
e-mail: info@wmp.co.uk
www.wmp.co.uk
Suppliers and installers of:- Watermakers,
Air Conditioning, Generators, Electrical
Systems, Electronic Engine Controls,
Bow and Stern Thrusters, Teak Decks,
Davits, Passarelles and Cranes, Galley
and Sanitation Equipment. ISO 9002
Quality Assurance.

BREAKDOWN

SEAFIT MARINE SERVICES
Falmouth Marina, North Parade,
Falmouth, Cornwall TR11 2TD
Tel: (01326) 313713

Fax: (01326) 211521
Mobile: (07971) 196175
All repair and service work undertaken.

CHANDLERS

Acamar Marine Services/Sirius Yacht
Training Christchurch   01202 488030

Aladdin's Cave Chandlery Ltd (Port
Hamble) Southampton   023 80454858

Aladdins Cave Chandlery Ltd
(Deacons) Bursledon   023 8040 2182

Aladdin's Cave Chandlery Ltd (Hamble
Point) Southampton   023 80455058

Aladdins Cave Chandlery Ltd
(Mercury) Southampton   023 80454849

Aladdins Cave Chandlery Ltd
(Swanwick) Swanwick   01489 575828

Aladdin's Cave Camper Nicholsons
Gosport   023 80402182

Albert Clarke
Newtownards   01247 872325

Aqua-Star Ltd
St Sampsons   01481 244550

AQUA TOGS/SHIPMATES
GROUP
115 High Street, Cowes,
Isle of Wight PO31 7AX
Tel: (01983) 295071
Fax: (01983) 290169
e-mail: sales@chandlery.co.uk
www.chandlery.co.uk
Leading suppliers of brand name
technical marine clothing, leisurewear,
safety kit and footwear, specialist
chandleries in Cowes and Dartmouth,
book and chart agents, mail order
available. Branches in Cowes, Lymington,
Dartmouth, Salcombe, Seaview and Ryde.

Arbroath Fishermens Association
Arbroath   01241 873132

ARDFERN YACHT CENTRE LTD
Ardfern by Lochgilphead, Argyll,
Scotland PA31 8QN
Tel: (01852) 500247
Fax: (01852) 500624
e-mail: office@ardfernyacht.co.uk
www.ardfernyacht.co.uk
Boatyard and marina facilities in a
picturesque natural harbour,
comprehensive workshop facilities,
extensive chandlery, diesel, gas.

Arun Aquasports Littlehampton
01903 713553

Arun Canvas and Rigging Ltd
Littlehampton   01903 732561

Arun Nautique Littlehampton
01903 730558

Aruncraft Chandlers
Littlehampton   01903 723667

A.S.A.P. SUPPLIES -
EQUIPMENT & SPARES
WORLDWIDE
Beccles, Suffolk England
NR34 7TD
Tel: (0845) 1300 870
Fax: (0800) 316 2727
e-mail: mma@asap-supplies.com
www.asap-supplies.com
Catalogue sales of quality marine
equipment.

Bluecastle Chandlers
Portland   01305 822298

BOATWORKS + LTD
Castle Emplacement,
St Peter Port,
Guernsey, Channel Islands
GY1 1AU.
Tel: (01481) 726071
Fax: (01481) 714224
Boatwork + provides a comprehensive
range of services including boatbuilding
and repairs, chandlery, clothing and fuel
supplies.

Boatacs
Westcliffe on Sea   01702 475057

Bosun's Locker Chandlery
Milford Haven   01646 697834

Bosun's Locker
Ramsgate   01843 597158

Bradwell Chandlery
Bradwell-on-Sea   01621 776147

Brancaster Sailing and Sailboard Centre Kings Lynn   01485 210236

Brigantine Teignmouth 01626 872400

Brixham Chandlers
Brixham   01803 882055

Brixham Yacht Supplies Ltd
Brixham   01803 882290

Brunel Chandlery Ltd
Neyland   01646 601667

Burghead Boat Centre
Findhorn   01309 690099

C & M Marine
Bridlington   01262 672212

C.J. DEEVY & CO LTD
48 Pomoell St, Waterford,
Ireland.
Tel: 00 353 (51) 855717
Fax: 00 353 (51) 855710
e-mail: sales@deevys.com
www.deevys.com
Motor & marine supplies for the South East region of Ireland. Est 1935. Offering a comprehensive range of products to both marine enthusiasts and motor enthusiasts. Branches in Waterford and Clonmell.

C Q Chandlers Ltd
Poole   01202 682095

Cabin Yacht Stores
Rochester   01634 718020

Captain O M Watts
London   020 7493 4633

Caters Carrick Ltd
Carrickfergus   028 93351919

CH Marine (Cork)
Cork   00353 21 4315700

CH Marine Skibbereen 00353 28 23190

Charity & Taylor Ltd
Lowestoft   01502 581529

Chicks Marine Ltd
Guernsey   01481 724536

CHRIS HORNSEY (CHANDLERY) LTD
152/154 Eastern Rd, Southsea, Hants PO4 8DY
Tel: (02392) 734728
Fax: (02392) 611500
e-mail: sales@chrishornsey.com
www.chrishornsey.com
Established 1970. Close to Southsea Marina.

Christchurch Boat Shop
Christchurch   01202 482751

Clapson & Son (Shipbuilders) Ltd
Barton-on-Humber   01652 635620

Cliff Reynolds Hartlepool   01429 272049

Coastal Marine Boatbuilders Ltd
(Dunbar) Eyemouth   01890 750328

Coates Marine Ltd/Northern Spar Services Whitby   01947 604486

Collins Marine St Helier 01534 732415

Compass Point Chandlery
Southampton   023 80452388

Cosalt International Ltd
Aberdeen   01224 588327

Crinan Boats Ltd
Lochgilphead   01546 830232

CTC MARINE & LEISURE
Saltwater House, Longlands Road, Middlesbrough TS4 2JR
Tel: (01642) 230123
Fax: (01642) 232007
www.clevelandtrailers.co.uk
Chandlers & general marine equipment & spares.

D Matthews Ltd
Cork   00353 214 277633

DALE SAILING CO LTD
Brunel Quay, Neyland, Milford Haven, Pembrokeshire SA73 1PY
Tel: (01646) 603110
Fax: (01646) 601061
e-mail:
enquiries@dale-sailing.co.uk
www.dale-sailing.co.uk
Sales, service and chandlery on site at Neyland Marina UK. Diesel, haulage, storage, engine, GRP, rigging repairs, chandlers, brokerage. Dealer for many inc. Suzuki, Mercury/Mercruiser, Volvo, Selden, Yanmar, Raytheon, Perkins, Lewmar.

Danson Marine Sidcup 0208 304 5678

Dart Chandlers
Dartmouth   01803 833772

David Carne (Sales) Ltd
Falmouth   01326 318314

David Carne (Sales) Ltd
Penryn   01326 374177

Davis's Yacht Chandler
Littlehampton   01903 722778

Denholm Fishselling
Scrabster   01847 896968

Dickie AM & Sons Ltd
Bangor   01248 352775

Dickie AM & Sons Ltd
Pwllheli   01758 701828

Dinghy Supplies Ltd/Sutton Marine Ltd Sutton   00353 1 832 2312

Diverse Yacht Services
Hamble   023 80453399

Dovey Marine Aberdovey 01654 767581

Down Marine Co Ltd
Belfast   028 90480247

Dubois Phillips & McCallum Ltd
Liverpool   0151 236 2776

DUNCAN YACHT CHANDLERS
7 Scotland St, Glasgow G5 8NL
Tel: (0141) 429 6044
Fax: (0141) 429 3078
e-mail: duncanyacht@aol.com
www.duncanyacht.com
Scotland's largest independant chandlery and clothing store stocking everything from a needle to an anchor including a large range of electronics.

East Anglian Sea School
Ipswich   01473 659992

Eccles Marine Co
Middlesbrough   01642 230123

Emsworth Chandlery
Emsworth   01243 375500

Exe Leisure Exeter   01392 879055

Fairways Chandlery
Burnham-on-Crouch   01621 782659

Fathom Marine
Bridport   01308 420988

Ferrypoint Boat Co
Youghal   00353 24 94232

Fishermans Mutual Asssociation (Eyemouth) Ltd
Eyemouth   01890 750373

French Marine Motors Ltd
Brightlingsea   01206 302133

Galway Maritime
Galway   00353 91 566568

GB Attfield & Company
Dursley   01453 547185

George Kearon Ltd
Arklow   00353 402 32319

Gibbons Ship Chandlers Ltd
Sunderland   0191 567 2101

Gibbs Chandlery
Shepperton   01932 242977

Glaslyn Marine Supplies Ltd
Porthmadog   01766 513545

Goodwick Marine
Fishguard   01348 873955

Gorleston Marine Ltd
Great Yarmouth   01493 661883

GP Barnes Ltd
Shoreham   01273 591705/596680

Greenham Marine
Emsworth   01243 378314

Harbour Marine Services Ltd (HMS)
Southwold   01502 724721

HARDWARE & MARINE SUPPLIES
Kilmore Quay, Co. Wexford, Ireland.
Tel: 00 353 (53) 29791
Fax: 00 353 (53) 29803
We are a commercial fishing supplier, with a good selection of leisure boating supplies and general hardware. Diving service to inspect damage also available. Camping Gas, batteries, ropes, shackles, safety equipment, flags and stays made to order.

Hardway Marine Store
Gosport   023 92580420

Hartlepool Marine Supplies
Hartlepool   01429 862932

HARWOODS
St James' Square, Yarmouth, Isle of Wight PO41 0NS
Tel: (01983) 760258
Fax: (01983) 760245
e-mail: help@harwoods-yacht-chandlers.co.uk
www.harwoods-yacht-chandlers.co.uk
Yacht chandlers, marine and country clothing & shoes. Books and charts. Kite surfing & extreme sports equipment. Fishing tackle, dinghys, kitchenware, ironmongers.

Inverness Boat Centre
North Kessock   01463 731383

Iron Stores Marine
St Helier   01534 877755

Isles of Scilly Steamship Co
St Mary's   01720 422710

Jackson Yacht Services
Jersey   01534 743819

Jamison and Green Ltd
Belfast   028 90322444

Jeckells and Son Ltd
Lowestoft   01502 565007

Jimmy Green Marine
Fore St Beer   01297 20744

JNW Services Peterhead 01779 477346

John Bridger Marine
Exeter   01392 216420

John Hawkins Marine Shipstores
Rochester   01634 840812

Johnsons Marine Stores
Lamlash   01770 600333

Johnston Brothers
Mallaig   01687 462215

JP Lamb & Sons Ltd
Liverpool   0151 709 4861

JS Duncan Ltd Wick   01955 602689

JSB Tarbert Ltd
Tarbert   01880 820180

Kelpie Boats
Pembroke Dock   01646 683661

Kelvin Hughes Ltd
Southampton   023 80634911

Kieran Cotter
Baltimore   00353 28 20106

Kildale Marine Hull   01482 227464

Kingfisher Marine
Weymouth   01305 766595

Kip Chandlery Inverkip
Greenock   01475 521485

Kirkcudbright Scallop Gear Ltd
Kirkcudbright   01557 330399

Kyle Chandlers Troon   01292 311880

Largs Chandlers Largs 01475 686026

LH Morgan & Sons Marine
Brightlingsea   01206 302003

Looe Chandlery
West Looe   01503 264355

Mailspeed Marine
Warrington   01925 838858

Manx Marine Ltd
Douglas   01624 674842

Marine & Leisure Europe Ltd
Plymouth   01752 268826

Marine Connections
Bitterne   023 803 36200

MarineForce (Bristol)
Bristol   0117 926 8396

MarineForce (Poole)
Poole   01202 723311

MarineForce
Burnham-on-Crouch   01621 782890

MarineForce Chichester 01243 771111

MarineForce London   020 7247 0521

MarineForce London   020 7247 2047

MarineForce London   020 7480 6630

MarineForce Lymington 01590 673698

MarineForce
Southend-on-Sea   01702 444444

MARINEFORCE LTD
Unit 6, Waterloo Industrial Estate, Flanders Rd, Hedge End, Hampshire SO30 2QT
Tel: (0870) 010 4877
Fax: (0870) 010 4885
e-mail: enquiries@marineforce.com
www.marineforce.com
The UK's leading marine retailer, featuring 10 retail outlets, a huge mail order catalogue and a full trading website. Thousands of stock lines available across clothing, electronics, general chandlery, boats and engines, books and charts.

Marine Instruments
Falmouth   01326 312414

Marine Scene Cardiff   029 2070 5780

MARINESTORE CHANDLERS
Shipways, North St., Maldon,
Essex CM9 5HN
Tel: (01621) 854380
Fax: (01621) 843849
e-mail:
chandler@marinestore.co.uk
www.marinestore.co.uk
East coast chandlers. Specialists in
traditional chandlery. Mail order service
available worldwide. Privately owned boat
company.

Marine Store
Walton on the Naze   01255 679028

Marine Superstore Port Solent
Chandlery Portsmouth   023 92219843

Marquand Brothers
St Peter Port   01481 720962

Martello Yacht Services
Canvey Island   01268 681970

MARYPORT HARBOUR AND
MARINA
Bridge Street, Maryport,
Cumbria CA15 8AE
Tel: (01900) 818447/4431
Fax: (01900) 818672
e-mail:
enquiries@maryportmarina.com
www.maryportmarina.com
Located on the beautiful Lake District
coast. Awarded the European 'Blue Flag'
Award in 2000 and 2001. Pontoon
berths, chandlery, boat repair facility,
12-ton hoist, hardstanding, shower
facilities and laundery room.

Mayflower Chandlery
Plymouth   01752 500121

McCready Sailboats Ltd
Holywood   028 9042 1821

Mengham Marine
Hayling Island   023 92464333

Mylor Chandlery & Rigging
Falmouth   01326 375482

Nancy Black Oban   01631 562550

Nautical World (Bangor)
Bangor   028 91460330

New World Yacht Care
Helensburgh   01436 820586

Nicholas Murphy
Dunmore East   00353 51 383259

NICK COX YACHT CHARTER LTD
Kings Saltern Road, Lymington,
Hampshire SO41 3QD
Tel: (01590) 673489
Fax: (01590) 673489
Lymington's hardware & technical
specialist.

Norfolk Marine Chandlery Shop
Norwich   01603 783150

Norfolk Marine
Great Yarmouth   01692 670272

North Quay Marine
St Sampson's   01481 246561

OCEAN LEISURE LTD
11-14 Northumberland Avenue,
London WC2N 5AQ
Tel: (020) 7930 5050
Fax: (020) 7930 3032
e-mail: info@oceanleisure.co.uk
www.oceanleisure.co.uk
Situated right in the heart of the capital,
Ocean Leisure is London's premier
watersports store. We stock everything
from foul weather gear to marine
electronics, and we have expert staff on
site to assist you.

Ocean World Ltd
Cowes   01983 291744

One Stop Chandlery
Chelmsford   01245 380680

O'Sullivans Marine Ltd
Tralee   00353 66 7124524

Outriggers/Upper Deck Marine
Fowey   01726 833233

PA Lynch Ltd Morpeth   01670 512291

Pascall Atkey & Sons Ltd
Isle of Wight   01983 292381

Paterson A Macduff   01261 832784

Peter Dixon Chandlery
Exmouth   01395 273248

Peterhead Watersports Centre
Peterhead   01779 480888

Peters PLC Chichester   01243 511033

Piplers of Poole Poole   01202 673056

PIRATES CAVE LTD
Unit 14, Northpoint Business
Estate, Enterprise Close,
Medway City Estate, Frindsbury,
Rochester ME2 4LX
Tel: (01634) 295233
Fax: (01634) 722326
e-mail:
piratescaveuk@yahoo.co.uk
We hold a very large stock of general
chandlery as well as being main dealers
for XM, Silva, Raymarine, Whale, Jabsco,
Barton, Spincock and ECS products.
Staffed by people with boating
experience.

POWERSAIL AND ISLAND CHANDLERS LTD
East Cowes Marina,
Clarence Road, East Cowes,
Isle-of-Wight PO32 6YB
Tel: (01983) 299800
Fax: (01983) 299800
Chandlery provisions, all boating needs.

Preston Marine Services Ltd
Preston   01772 733595

PURPLE SAILS & MARINE
137-138 Stafford Street,
Walsall WS2 8EA
Tel: (01922) 614787
Fax: (01922) 630766
e-mail: purple-marine@virgin.net
www.teampurple.co.uk
Retailers of all chandlery goods for all
types of sailing. For a copy of our latest
mail order catalogue, please call now.

QUAY WEST CHANDLERS
Mitchells Boatyard, Turks Lane,
Parkstone, Poole, Dorset
BH14 8EW
Tel: (01202) 742488
Fax: (01202) 742489
General yacht chandlers, covering all
aspects of water useage, with practical
hands on experience and loads of
patience!!

R. ARTHURS CHANDLERY
59-61 Forton Road, Gosport,
Hampshire PO12 4TD

Tel: (023) 9252 6522
Fax: (023) 9252 6522
e-mail:
arthurschandlery@aol.com
For all your marine chandlery.
International, Blakes, XM, Coopers,
Sikkens, Epifanes, Jabsco, Rule, Whale,
Attwood, Aquasignal, Hella, Stanfords,
Imray, Admiralty, Liros Ropes. Ocean
Safety Rigging Service.

RACECOURSE YACHT BASIN (WINDSOR) LTD
Maidenhead Road, Windsor,
Berkshire SL4 5HT
Tel: (01753) 851501
Fax: (01753) 868172
e-mail: marina@ryb.co.uk
www.ryb.co.uk
Marina - full facilities - shop - sales -
brokerage.

Ray Harris Marine (1984) Ltd
Barry   01446 740924

Reed's Nautical Books
Bradford on Avon   01225 868821

Reg Landon Marine
Truro   01872 272668

RHP Marine Cowes   01983 290421

Rhu Chandlery Rhu   01436 820584

RNS Marine Northam   01237 474167

Rob Perry Marine
Axminster   01297 631314

Ron Davis Marine
Portland   01305 821175

Ron Hale Marine
Portsmouth   023 92732985

Russell Simpson Marine Ltd
Brighton   01273 681543

Russell Simpson Marine Ltd
Eastbourne   01323 470213

Russell Simpson Marine Ltd
Newhaven   01273 612612

Salcombe Boatstore
Salcombe   01548 843708

Salterns Chandlery
Poole   01202 701556

Sandrock Marine Rye   01797 222679

Schull Watersports Centre
Schull   00353 28 28554

Sea & Shore Ship Chandler
Dundee   01382 202666

Sea Cruisers of Rye Rye 01797 222070

Sea Span Edinburgh   0131 552 2224

Sea Teach Ltd Emsworth 01243 375774

Seafare Tobermory   01688 302277

Seamark-Nunn & Co
Felixstowe   01394 275327

SEAQUEST MARINA LTD
16 Fountain Street, St. Peter
Port, Guernsey GY1 1BX
Tel: (01481) 721773
Fax: (01481) 716738
e-mail: seaquk@yahoo.co.uk
We are a general chandlery specialising in marine electronics, admiralty charts and books, water sports equipment and inflatable dinghys. We are main agents for Avon Inflatables and Garmin Electronics. Lowest prices on the Island.

Seaway Marine
Macduff   01261 832877

Severn Valley Boat Centre
Stourport-on-Severn   01299 871165

Sharp & Enright Dover   01304 206295

Shipmates Chandlery
Dartmouth   01803 839292

Shipmates Chandlery
Salcombe   01548 844555

Shipshape Marine
King's Lynn   01553 764058

Shipsides Marine Ltd
Preston   01772 797079

Shorewater Sports
Chichester   01243 672315

Sketrick Marine Centre
Killinchy   028 9754 1400

Smith AM (Marine) Ltd
London   020 8529 6988

Solent Marine Chandlery Ltd
Gosport   023 92584622

South Coast Marine
Christchurch   01202 482695

South Pier Shipyard
St Helier   01534 519700

Southampton Yacht Services Ltd
Southampton   023 803 35266

Spinnaker Yacht Chandlery
Bembridge   01983 874324

Standard House Chandlery
Wells-next-the-Sea   01328 710593

Stornoway Fishermen's Co-op
Stornoway   01851 702563

Storrar Marine Store
Newcastle upon Tyne   0191 266 1037

Sunset Marine & Watersports
Sligo   00353 71 62792

Sussex Marine Centre
Shoreham   01273 454737

Sussex Marine
St Leonards on Sea   01424 425882

Sutton Marine (Dublin)
Sutton   00353 1 832 2312

T C S Chandlery Grays   01375 374702

The Bosuns Locker
South Queensferry 0131 331 3875/4496

THE DINGHY STORE
**The Sea Wall, Whitstable, Kent
CT5 1BX**
Tel: (01227) 274168
Fax: (01227) 772750
e-mail:
sales@thedinghystore.co.uk

www.thedinghystore.co.uk
One of the largest marine chandlers in Kent. 1st floor: Harken, Holt, RWO, Marlow, International Paints, charts, books. 2nd floor: Musto, Henri Lloyd, Gill, Crewsaver, Chatham, Icom radios. Open seven days a week in summer months.

**The Fleetwood Trawlers' Supply Co
Ltd** Fleetwood   01253 873476

The Foc'sle Exeter   01392 874105

Thomas Gunn Navigation Services
Aberdeen   01224 595045

TJ Williams Ltd Cardiff   029 20 487676

Torbay Boating Centre
Paignton   01803 558760

Torquay Chandlers
Torquay   01803 211854

Trafalgar Yacht Services
Fareham   01329 823577

Trident UK North Shields   0191 259
6797

Union Chandlery Cork   00353 21
4554334

Upper Deck Marine and Outriggers
Fowey   01726 832287

V Ships (Isle of Man)
Douglas   01624 688886

Viking Marine Ltd
Dun Laoghaire   00353 1 280 6654

W L Bussell & Co
Weymouth   01305 785633

Waterfront Marine
Bangor   01248 352513

Western Marine
Dalkey   00353 1280 0321

WF Price & Co Ltd
Bristol   0117 929 2229

Whitstable Marine
Whitstable   01227 262525/274168

William Partington Marine Ltd
Pwllheli   01758 612808

Worcester Yacht Chandlers Ltd
Barbourne   01905 22522

Wyatts Chandlery Ltd
Colchester   01206 384745

XM Yachting Ltd
Polegate   01323 870092

Yacht & Sports Gear Ltd
Chichester   01243 784572

YACHT PARTS PLYMOUTH
**Victoria Building, Queen Anne's
Battery Marina, Plymouth,
Devon PL4 0LP.**
Tel: (01752) 252489
Fax: (01752) 225899
e-mail: sales@yachtparts.co.uk
www.yachtparts.co.uk
From anchors to zinc anodes – probably the best stocked chandler in the country. Open seven days with free easy parking. Our large clothing department caters for everyone from the dinghy sailor to the ocean going yachtsman.

Yachtmail Ltd Lymington 01590 672784

Yare Boatique Norwich 01603 715289

CHART AGENTS

A M Smith (Marine) Ltd
London................020 8529 6988

B Cooke & Son Ltd
Hull..................01482 223454

Brown Son & Ferguson Ltd
Glasgow...............0141 429 1234

Chattan Shipping Services Ltd
Edinburgh.............0131 555 3155

Eland Exeter.........01392 255788

Imray Laurie Norie and Wilson Ltd
Huntingdon...........01480 462114

John Lilley & Gillie Ltd
North Shields.........0191 257 2217

John Lilley and Gillie Ltd
North Shields.........0191 258 3519

Kelvin Hughes
Southampton..........023 8063 4911

MARINE CHART SERVICES
Belgrade Centre,
Denington Road,
Denington Industrial Estate,
Wellingborough,
Northants NN8 2QH
Tel: (01933) 441629
Fax: (01933) 442662
e-mail: info@chartsales.co.uk
www.chartsales.co.uk
Save 40% or more on current edition navigation charts. Over 25,000 charts in stock including Admiralty, Imray, Dutch, Norwegian, USA, and more. Worldwide coverage and worldwide delivery. Also pilot books, flags and navigational equipment.

Sea Chest Nautical Bookshop
Plymouth.............01752 222012

Seath Instruments (1992) Ltd
Lowestoft............01502 573811

SOUTH BANK MARINE CHARTS LTD
Hutton Rd, Fish Docks,
Grimsby, N.E. Lincs
DN31 3PT
Tel: (01472) 361137
Fax: (01472) 346673
e-mail:
southbankcharts@talk21.com
Extensive stock of charts and publications.

STANFORDS CHARTS
PO Box 2747, West Mersea,
Essex CO5 8FT
Tel: (01206) 381580
Fax: (01206) 381580
e-mail:
info@allweathercharts.co.uk
www.allweathercharts.co.uk
Publishers of the only UK charts printed on plastic - 100% waterproof, tough and tear-resistant. With a format to meet every navigational need: large sheets, charts-packs, local series charts. The Yachtsman's allweather charts.

TODD CHART AGENCY LTD
Navigation House, 85 High Street, Bangor, County Down, Northern Ireland BT20 5BD
Tel: 028 9146 6640
Fax: 028 9147 1070
e-mail:admiralty@toddchart.co.uk
www.nautical-charts.com
International Admiralty Chart Agent, chart correction service and nautical booksellers. Programming Centre for C-MAP NT and Navionics electronic charts. Stockist of Imray charts and books, navigation and chartroom instruments, binoculars, clocks etc. UK agent for Icelandic Hydrographic Service. Mail order - Visa, Mastercard, American Express and Switch/Delta accepted.

UK HYDROGRAPHICS OFFICE
Admiralty Way, Taunton,
Somerset TA1 2DN
Tel: (01823) 337900
e-mail:
generalenquiries@ukho.gov.uk
www.ukho.gov.uk
Suppliers of navigational charts and publications, including the Admiralty Leisure series.

Warsash Nautical Bookshop
Southampton..........01489 572384

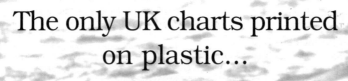
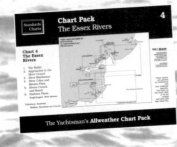 
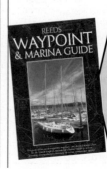

The logo of the CHART AND NAUTICAL INSTRUMENT TRADE ASSOCIATION, founded in 1918. With the full support of the Hydrographer of the Navy and leading manufacturers of nautical instruments, members of the Association are able to place their experience and service at the disposal of the shipping industry and all navigators

CHART SUPPLY AND CORRECTION SERVICES

The CNITA counts among its members many of the leading Admiralty Chart Agents who can supply your requirements from a single chart or publication to a world-wide outfit and special folio requirements from comprehensive stocks in all the major ports. Carefully trained chart correctors are available to examine and correct all Admiralty charts.

THE CNITA TRACING SERVICE

Although tracings have been in use by the Royal Navy and Admiralty Chart Agents for many years, it was the Chart Committee of the Chart and Nautical Instrument Trade Association that successfully negotiated with the Hydrographer of the Navy for them to become available to the merchant navigator and private user.

The CNITA tracing overlay correction service is available from all Admiralty Chart Agents who are members of the Association, and is now supplied to more than 5,000 vessels each week. Each tracing wallet contains the weekly "Notices to Mariners" and tracings printed with the relevant details of the area surrounding the correction, making the correction of each chart a simpler operation. All that the user has to do is match the tracing to the chart, pierce through the small circle showing the exact position of the correction and, in conjunction with the "Notices to Mariners", transfer the information onto the chart. Navigating Officers welcome the tracings system for its accuracy and speed. Onboard chart correction time can be cut by 80% and Masters can now rest assured that their charts are kept continually up to date. Reasonably priced, these tracings are economical and an invaluable contribution to safety at sea.

COMPASS ADJUSTING AND NAUTICAL INSTRUMENTS

CNITA Members who provide Compass Adjusting services use Compass Adjusters having professional qualifications recognised in the locality in which they operate. The relevant qualification for the United Kingdom is the Certificate of Competency as Compass Adjuster, the examination for which is conducted by the Maritime and Coastguard Agency with the assistance of the CNITA in assessing the evidence of practical adjusting skills submitted by the Candidate. CNITA Members can provide Compass Adjusters, who are available day and night to "swing" ships, in most major ports and elsewhere by arrangement.

Members of the CNITA, many with life long experience in this field, can advise you when buying all your nautical instruments. Most suppliers provide an instrument repair service combining traditional craftsmanship with modern methods to ensure that instruments are serviced and tested to a high standard.

ARE YOU COMPLYING WITH THE LATEST INTERNATIONAL REGULATIONS?

Chart and Nautical Instrument Trade Association members established in most U.K. ports and overseas are able to advise you. For full details of the Association, its activities and its services to the Navigator, write to:- The Secretaries, CHART AND NAUTICAL INSTRUMENT TRADE ASSOCIATION, Dalmore House, 310 St. Vincent Street, Glasgow G2 5QR, United Kingdom, Email: cnita@biggartbaillie.co.uk, Web: www.cnita.com

■■■■■ PORTS WHERE SHIPS' COMPASSES ARE ADJUSTED AND BRITISH ADMIRALTY CHARTS ARE AVAILABLE ■■■■■

AMI-GFV Marine Ltd, 18 Canute Road, SOUTHAMPTON, Hants SO14 3FJ Tel: 0238 048 0450, Fax: 0238 048 0451, Email: ami-gfv.marine@dial.pipex.com

A/S Navicharts, Industrivelen 28, 1483 SKYTTA, NORWAY, Tel: 00 47 6 7062020, Fax: 00 47 6 7060015,

Bade & Hornig GmbH, Herrengraben 31, 20459, HAMBURG, Tel: 00 49 40 3748110, Fax: 00 49 40 366400

Bogerd NV, Oude Leeuwenrui 37, ANTWERP 2000, BELGIUM Tel: 00 32 3 2328532 Fax: 00 32 3 2272959, Email: Sales@martin.be

Brown Son & Ferguson Ltd, 4-10 Darnley Street, GLASGOW, G41 2SD Tel: 0141-429 1234, Fax: 0141-420 1694,

Carmichael & Clarke Co Ltd, 1202 Unicorn Trade Centre, 131 Des Voeux Road, Central, HONG KONG Tel: 00 852 2581 2678, Fax: 00 852 2582 2722, Email: carmi@hkstar.com

B Cooke & Son Ltd*, Kingston Observatory, 58/59 Market Place, HULL HU1 1RH Tel: 01482 224412/223454, Fax: 01482 219793,

D.P.M. Singapore Pte Ltd, 1 Maritime Square #13-03, World Trade Centre, SINGAPORE 099253 Tel: 00 65 2704060, Fax: 00 65 2763858, Email: dpmspore@mbox3.singnet.com.sg

DPM (UK) Ltd, Mersey Chambers, Covent Garden, LIVERPOOL L2 8UF Tel: 0151 236 2776 Fax: 0151 236 4577, Email: iaca@dpm.co.uk

George Falconer (Nautical) Ltd, 1/Floor, Hong Kong Jewellery Bldg, 178-180 Queen's Road, Central, HONG KONG Tel: 00 852 28542882 Fax: 00 852 28158056

J Garraio & Co Lda, Avenida 24 De Julho, 2-1 D.1200 LISBON, PORTUGAL Tel: 00 3511 3473081, Fax: 00 3511 3428950

Thomas Gunn Navigation Services Ltd*, Anchor House, 62 Regents Quay, ABERDEEN AB11 5AR Tel: 01224 595045, Fax: 01224 584702, Email: tgns@globalnet.co.uk, www.thomasgunn.globalnet.co.uk

Hong Kong Ships Supplies Co, Room 1614, Melbourne Plaza, 33 Queen's Road, Central, HONG KONG Tel: 00 852 25225963, 00 852 25231205, Fax: 00 852 28681748

Kelvin Hughes Charts & Maritime Supplies*, New North Road, Hainault, ILFORD, Essex IG6 2UR Tel: 0208 500 1020 Fax: 0208 559 8535,

Kelvin Hughes Observator bv*, Nieuwe Langeweg 41, 3194 DC, HOOGVLIET, The Netherlands Tel: 00 31 10 4167622, Fax: 00 31 10 4167218, Email: kelvin.hughes@wxs.nl

Captain L N Jordanov, 13-A Han Omurtag Str., P.O.B. 14, VARNA 9001, BULGARIA Tel: 00 359 52 242018 Fax: 00 359 52 242018

John Lilley & Gillie Ltd* Clive Street NORTH SHIELDS, Tyne & Wear NE29 6LF Tel: 0191 257 2217, Fax: 0191-257 1521, Email: sales@lilleyandgillie.co.uk

"Magnetico" D.A. Dedegikas 100 Colocotroni Str. PIRAEUS 185 35, GREECE Tel: 00 30 1 4178976, Fax: 00 30 1 4178206

Marine Instruments* The Wheelhouse,, Upton Slip, FALMOUTH, Cornwall TR11 3DQ Tel: 01326 312414, Fax: 01326 211414, Email: info@marineinstruments.co.uk

Maritime Services, 3440 Bridgeway Street VANCOUVER, BC V5K 1B6, CANADA Tel: 00 1 604 294444, Fax: 00 1 604 2945879

Martin & Company* Oude Leeuwenrui 37, ANTWERP 2000, BELGIUM Tel: 00 32 3 2134170, Fax: 00 32 3 2326167 Email: sales@martin.be

Maryland Nautical Sales, Inc, 1400 E. Clement Street, BALTIMORE, Maryland 21230, USA, Tel: 00 1 410 752 4268, Fax: 00 1 410 685 5068, E-mail: sales@mdnautical.com, www.mdnautical.com

Motion Smith 78 Shenton Way #01-03, SINGAPORE 079120 Tel: 00 65 2205098 Fax: 00 65 2254902

R J Muir Esq* 22 Seymour Close, Chandlers Ford, EASTLEIGH, Hants SO53 2JE Tel: 0238 026 1042, Fax: 0238 026 1042

Nautisk Forlag A/S, Dronningensgate 8B, PO Box 68 Sentrum, N-0101 OSLO, NORWAY Tel: 00 47 2200 1281, Fax: 00 47 2200 1280, E-mail: sales@nautisk.com, http: www.nautisk.com

Captain Stephan Nedelchev Soc. Co. J.C. Gomez 1445, esc.301, 11000 MONTEVIDEO, URUGUAY Tel: 00 5982 9167988 Fax: 00 5982 9167990

W F Price & Co Ltd Wapping Wharf, BRISTOL BS1 6UD Tel: 0117 9292229, Fax: 0117 9304403

Riviera-Charts, Galerie du Port, 26-30 Rue Lacan, 06600 ANTIBES, France Tel: 00 33 493 344566, Fax: 00 33 493 344336, Email: admiralty@riviera.fr, www.riviera-charts.com

The Sea Chest Nautical Bookshop, Dolphin Building, Queen Anne's Battery Marina, PLYMOUTH, Devon PL4 0LP, Tel: 01752 222012, Fax: 01752 252679, E-mail: sales@seachest.co.uk, www.seachest.co.uk

Seath Instruments (1992) Ltd* Unit 30, Colville Rd Works, Colville Road, LOWESTOFT, Suffolk NR33 9QS Tel: 01502 573811, Fax: 01502 514173

Small Craft Deliveries Ltd Navigation House, 4 Wilford Bridge Road, MELTON, Woodbridge IP12 1RJ Tel: 01394 382600, Fax: 01394 387672, Telex: 51 317210, Email: sales@scd-charts.co.uk

A M Smith (Marine) Ltd 33 Epping Way, Chingford, LONDON E4 7PB Tel: 0208-529 6988 Fax: 0208-524 4498

Tai Seng Trading Co Ltd 198-1 Ta Tong 1st Road, Kaohsiung 800, TAIWAN, R.O.C. Tel: 00 86 7 2217367, Fax: 00 86 7 2818180, Email: taisengt@ms22.hinet.net

The Tyneside Shop 5 John Ross House, 22 Victoria Embankment, DURBAN 4001, SOUTH AFRICA Tel: 00 27 31 3377005, Fax: 00 27 31 3328139, Email: tyneside@global.co.za

Todd Chart Agency Ltd Navigation House, 85 High Street, BANGOR, Northern Ireland BT20 5BD Tel: 028 9146 6640, Fax: 028 9147 1070, Email: admiralty@toddchart.co.uk, www.nautical-charts.com

G Undery & Son* PO Box 235 - Unit 31, The New Harbours, GIBRALTAR Tel: 00 350 40402 (B), 00 350 73107, Fax: 00 350 46489

Vanos S.A. 90 Dim. Moutsopoulou Str., 184 41 PIRAEUS, GREECE Tel: 00 30 1 4829911, Fax: 00 30 1 4812313/4817607

Iver C Weilbach & Co A/S, 35 Toldbodgade, Postbox 1560, DK-1253, COPENHAGEN K, DENMARK Tel: 00 45 33 135927, Fax: 00 45 33 935927

Wessex Marine Equipment Ltd, Logistics House, 1 Park Road, Freemantle, Southampton SO15 3US Tel: 0238 063 5215, Fax: 0238 063 6216, Email: wesmarine@aol.com

Zervoudakis Marine Supplies Ltd 31 Milou Str. 185 45 PIRAEUS GREECE Tel: 00 30 1 4623700, Fax: 00 30 1 4627900

*Those marked * have U.K. Maritime, & Coastguard Agency certificated, Compass Adjusters*

MARINE SUPPLIES AND SERVICES

CHART AGENTS

CLOTHING

AQUA TOGS/SHIPMATES GROUP
115 High Street, Cowes, Isle of Wight PO31 7AX
Tel: (01983) 295071
Fax: (01983) 290169
e-mail: sales@chandlery.co.uk
www.chandlery.co.uk
Leading suppliers of brand name technical marine clothing, leisurewear, safety kit and footwear, specialist chandleries in Cowes and Dartmouth, book and chart agents, mail order available. Branches in Cowes, Lymington, Dartmouth, Salcombe, Seaview and Ryde.

CREWSAVER
Mumby Road, Gosport, Hampshire PO12 1AQ
+44 (0)23 9252 8621
+44 (0)23 9251 090
e-mail: sales@crewsaver.co.uk
www.crewsaver.co.uk
Established manufacturer of lifejackets, lifesaving equipment, sailing clothing and accessories. Check out the latest range of products online at www.crewsaver.co.uk.

HARWOODS
St James' Square, Yarmouth, Isle of Wight PO41 0NS
Tel: (01983) 760258
Fax: (01983) 760245
e-mail: help@harwoods-yacht-chandlers.co.uk
www.harwoods-yacht-chandlers.co.uk
Yacht chandlers, marine and country clothing & shoes. Books and charts. Kite surfing & extreme sports equipment. Fishing tackle, dinghys, kitchenware, ironmongers.

PURPLE SAILS & MARINE
137-138 Stafford Street, Walsall WS2 8EA
Tel: (01922) 614787
Fax: (01922) 630766
e-mail: purple-marine@virgin.net
www.teampurple.co.uk
Retailers of all chandlery goods for all types of sailing. For a copy of our latest mail order catalogue, please call now.

YACHT PARTS PLYMOUTH
Victoria Building, Queen Anne's Battery Marina, Plymouth, Devon PL4 0LP.
Tel: (01752) 252489
Fax: (01752) 225899
e-mail: sales@yachtparts.co.uk
www.yachtparts.co.uk
From anchors to zinc anodes – probably the best stocked chandler in the country. Open seven days with free easy parking. Our large clothing department caters for everyone from the dinghy sailor to the ocean going yachtsman.

CODE OF PRACTICE EXAMINERS

DAVID M. CANNELL & ASSOCIATES
River House,
Quay Street,
Wivenhoe,
Essex CO7 9DD.
Tel: +44 (0) 1206 823 337
Fax: +44 (0) 1206 825 939
e-mail: enquiries@dmcmarine.com
www.dmcmarine.com
Design of yachts and commercial craft to 80m. Newbuilding and refit overseeing. condition surveys, valuations, MCA Code of Practice Compliance and Stability, Expert Witness. Members: Royal Institution of Naval Architects, Yacht Designers and Surveyors Association.

COMPASS ADJUSTERS/ MANUFACTURERS

B P S C MARINE SERVICES
Unit 4 Part Business Centre,
1 Park Road, Freemantle,
Southampton,
Hampshire
SO15 3US
Tel: 023 8023 0045
BPSC offer a fast efficient repair service on a wide range of nautical and survey instruments. Free estimates and advice. A comprehensive range of spares are carried, most of which can be despatched same day. Instruments commissioned. Compass adjusting service.

COMPUTERS & SOFTWARE

MAPTECH UK LTD
The Book Barn,
White Chimney Row,
Westbourne,
Hamphire PO10 8RS
Tel: (01243) 389352
Fax: (01243) 379136
e-mail: sales@maptech.co.uk
www.maptech.co.uk
Navigational software and navigational digital chart supplier.

CORPORATE PROMOTIONS

407 RACING (YACHT CHARTER)
6 Conference Place, Old Orchards, Lymington, Hampshire SO41 3TQ.
Tel: (01590) 688407
Fax: (01590) 610407
e-mail: 407Racing@407YachtCharter.co.uk
www.407yachtcharter.co.uk
Beneteau 40.7 *firsts* for 100 guests or more for corporate outings. Numerous Sunseekers from 34' to 68'. 5 Luxury Swans from 48' to 60'. Where the best yachts just get better.

INDULGENCE CHARTERS
20 High Street, Wendover, Buckinghamshire HP22 6EA
Tel: (01296) 696006
Fax: (01296) 624219
e-mail: paul@indulgencecharters.com
www.indulgencecharters.com
Our luxury fleet of MCA coded Sunseekers offers charters with the privileges of a hotel suite combined with the excitement offered by a performance motor yacht that is yours to plan and play with.

CORPORATE YACHT OWNERSHIP

CUSTOMS

Arklow Customs	00353 402 32553
Bantry Customs	00353 27 50061
Bantry Customs	00353 27 50061
Carlingford Lough Customs	00353 42 34248
Cork Customs	00353 21 311024
Dingle Customs	00353 66 7121480
Dublin Customs	00353 1 679 2777
Dun Laoghaire Customs	00353 1 280 3992
Dunmore East Customs	00353 51 875391
Fenit Harbour Customs	00353 66 36115

Galway Customs	00353 91 567191
Killybegs Customs	00353 73 31070
Kilmore Customs	00353 53 33741
Kilrush Customs	00353 61 415366
Kinsale Customs	00353 21 311044
Lough Swilly Customs	00353 74 21611
Malahide Customs	00353 1 874 6571
Prest Customs	00353 94 21131
Rathmullan Customs	00353 74 26324
Rosslare Customs	00353 53 33116
Schull Customs	00353 27 51562
Shannon Customs	00353 61 471076
Shannon Estuary Customs	00353 69 415366
Sligo Customs	00353 71 61064
UK Customs Nationwide	0845 0109000
Waterford Customs	00353 51 875391
Wexford Customs	00353 53 331116
Wexford Customs	00353 53 33292
Wicklow Customs	00353 404 67222

DECK EQUIPMENT

KENNETH RYLAND
Charity Farm, Stanton,
Nr Broadway, Worcs WR12 7NE
Tel: (01386) 584270
Fax: (01386) 584270
Mobile: 07802 261 931
e-mail:
kennethryland@ukonline.co.uk
www.sanshin.co.uk
Manufacturer of crane davits - the revolutionary lightweight composite davit, UK distrbutor for Goiot deck equipment - CLD air conditioning and refrigeration - Sanshim spotlights - Lagum cockpit tables and Duralac anti corrosive join timp compound.

PRO-BOAT LTD
Burnham Business Park,
Burnham-On-Crouch, Essex
CM0 8TE
Tel: (01621) 785455
Fax: (01621) 785467
e-mail: sales@proboat.co.uk
www.proboat.co.uk
Hardware distributors - catalogue available on request.

VETUS DEN OUDEN LTD
39 South Hants Ind. Park, Totton,
Southampton SO40 3SA
Tel: 023 8086 1033
Fax: 023 8066 3142
e-mail: sales@vetus.co.uk
www.vetus.co.uk
Wholesalers of diesel engines, generators, exhaust systems, propellers, shafts, bow thrusters, hatches, portlights, windlasses, ventilators, fuel and water tanks, hydraulics systems, air conditioning, wipers, pumps, seats, hoses and much much more.

DIESEL MARINE FUEL ADDITIVES

QUAYSIDE FUEL
21 Marsh Road, Weymouth,
Dorset DT4 8JD
Tel: (07747) 182181
Mobile diesel fuel service. Pre-booking welcome. Out of hours service provided. Normal hours 7am - 8pm.

DIVERS

Abco Divers Belfast 028 90610492
Alex Murray Stornoway 01851 704978
Andark Diving
Southampton 01489 581755
Aquatech Diving Services
Port of St Mary 01624 833037
Argonaut Marine
Aberdeen 01224 706526
Baltimore Diving and Watersports Centre West Cork 00353 28 20300
C & C Marine Services
Largs 01475 687180
C I Diving Services Ltd
Invergordon 01349 852500
D MacDonald Nairn 01667 455661
D Purcell - Crouch Sailing School
Burnham 01621 784140/0585 33
Dave Hudson
Trearddur Bay 01407 860628
Divesafe Sunderland 0191 567 8423
Divetech UK King's Lynn 01485 572323
Diving & Marine Engineering
Barry 01446 721553
DV Diving 028 91 464671
Falmouth Divers Ltd
Penryn 01326 374736
Fathom Diving (Chislehurst)
Chislehurst 020 8289 8237
Fathoms Ltd Wick 01955 605956
Felixarc Marine Ltd
Felixstowe 01394 676497
Grampian Diving Services
New Deer 01771 644206
Hilary Keller
Buncrana 00353 77 62146
Inverkip Diving Services

Inverkip 01475 521281
J Parkinson (Sinbad Marine Services)
Killybegs 00353 73 31417
Kaymac Diving Services
Swansea 01792 793316
Kevin Hunt Tralee 00353 6671 25979
Kilkee Diving Centre
Kilkee 00353 6590 56707
Leask Marine Kirkwall 01856 874725
Looe Divers Hannafore 01503 262727
Medway Diving Contractors Ltd
Gillingham 01634 851902
Mojo Maritime
Penzance 01736 762771
New Dawn Dive Centre
Lymington 01590 675656
New Tec Diving Services
Blackpool 01253 691665
Noel Higgins 00353 872027650
Norman Thorpe Portree 01478 612274
Northern Divers (Engineering) Ltd
Hull 01482 227276
Offshore Marine Services Ltd
Bembridge 01983 873125
Old Harbour Dive School
Portland 01305 861000
Port of London Authority
Gravesend 01474 560311
R Donnelly South Shields 07973119455
Salvesen UK Ltd
Liverpool 0151 933 6038
Sea Technical Services Ltd
Denmead 023 92255200
Seaguard Marine Engineering Ltd
Goodwick 01348 872976
Sea-Lift Ltd Dover 01304 201112
Southern Cylinder Services
Fareham 01329 221125
Stealaway Diving Oban 01631 566349
Sub Aqua Services
North Ormesby 01642 230209
Teign Diving Centre
Teignmouth 01626 773965
Tuskar Rock Marine
Rosslare 00353 53 33376
Underwater Services
Dyffryn Arbwy 01341 247702
William Woolford
Bridlington 01262 671710
Wilson Alan c/o Portrush Yacht
Club Portrush 028 2076 2225

NAVIGATIONAL SOFTWARE
• Chart Navigator • Cruising Navigator • Offshore Navigator

NAVIGATIONAL DIGITAL CHARTS

Maptech UK Ltd
Telephone: 01243 389352 • Fax: 01243 379136

www.maptech.co.uk

ELECTRICAL AND ELECTRONIC ENGINEERS

INDEX MARINE
48 Harewood Avenue,
Bounemouth, Dorset
BH7 6NM
Tel: (01202) 470149
Fax: (01202) 430150
e-mail: sales@indexmarine.co.uk
www.indexmarine.co.uk
Manufacturers/suppliers of marine
electrical equipment.

**LANGLEY MARINE
SERVICES LTD**
Sovereign Harbour Marina,
Pevensey Bay Road, Eastbourne,
East Sussex BN23 6JH
Tel: (01323) 470244
Fax: (01323) 470255
Offering a complete service to the boat
owner, engineering, GRP repairs,
shipwrighting, electronics, rigging,
cleaning, etc. We specialise in the refit
and repair of large pleasurecraft and
commercial vessels and are contractors
to the RNLI.

NICK BELSON DESIGN LTD
The Woodlands, Frost Lane,
Hythe, Southampton,
Hampshire SO45 3NB
Tel: (077) 6835 1330
Fax: (023) 8087 9841
e-mail: nbelson@iee.org
Design and manufacture of bespoke
marine electronics for custom
applications. New build and racing data
logging including three axis accelerations.
Manufacture and installation of onboard
and free floating wave height sensors.

REDCAR FISH COMPANY
Cherry Cottage,
The Barns,
Blakeston Lane,
Stockton-on-Tees
TS21 3LE
Tel: (01642) 633638
Fax: (01642) 633639

e-mail:
enquiries@redcar-fish.co.uk
www.redcar-fish.co.uk
We offer expert advice and competitive
prices on a full range of marine
electronics for your boat or outdoor
pursuit. Friendly help and advice is always
available. Mail order hotline 01642
633638.

ELECTRONIC DEVICES AND EQUIPMENT

ANCHORWATCH UK
67 Morningside Park, Edinburgh
EH10 5EZ
Tel: (0131) 447 5057
e-mail: anchorwatch@aol.com
www.anchorwatch.co.uk
Electronic anchor monitoring equipment.
Anchorwatch measures the loading on an
anchor cable up to 1000kg. Records
peak loading and includes alarm facility.

GARMIN (EUROPE) LTD
Unit 5, The quadrangle, Abbey
Park Industrial Estate, Romsey
SO51 9AG
Tel: (01794) 579944
Fax: (01794) 514222
www.garmin.com
GARMIN is a leader in Global Positioning
System (GPS) technology and an
innovator in consumer electronics. We
serve both the aviation and consumer
markets. Our products are used in flying,
boating, driving, hiking and many other
activities. We're customer focused and
committed to producing quality products
and improving people's everyday lives.

**GREENHAM REGIS MARINE
ELECTRONICS**
Shamrock Quay, William Street,
Southampton SO14 5QL
Tel: 023 8063 6555
Fax: 023 8023 1426
e-mail:
sales@greenham-regis.co.uk
www.greenham-regis.co.uk
Sales & service + installation of top
quality marine electronic equipment via
our waterfront sales & service centres in
Poole, Lymington, Cowes, Southampton,
Emsworth and Itchenor. Contact us for a
competitive quotation - you could be
surprised.

MARATHON LEISURE
Teal Building,
Northney Marina,
Hayling Island,
Portsmouth PO11 0NH
Tel: (02392) 637711
Fax: (02392) 937722
e-mail:
sales@marathonleisure.co.uk
General marine wholesalers. Products include Whale Spinlock, Isotherm,, Sterling, Ritchie, Tacktick, Treadmaster, Glomex, English Braids, Eberspacher, Exide, Ongaro, Seafire, Perko, Sharp LCD screens, JVC, Sony.

OCEAN LEISURE LTD
11-14 Northumberland Avenue,
London WC2N 5AQ
Tel: (020) 7930 5050
Fax: (020) 7930 3032
e-mail: info@oceanleisure.co.uk
www.oceanleisure.co.uk
Situated right in the heart of the capital, Ocean Leisure is London's premier watersports store. We stock everything from foul weather gear to marine electronics, and we have expert staff on site to assist you.

RAYMARINE LIMITED
Anchorage Park,
Portsmouth, Hampshire
PO3 5TD.
Tel: (02392) 693611
Fax: (02392) 694642
e-mail: info@raymarine.com
www.raymarine.com
Raymarine Limited provide the complete marine electronics package, including instrumentation, autopilots, radar chartplotters, fishfinders, communications and PC charting software available through a global network of dealers and distributors.

REDCAR FISH COMPANY
Cherry Cottage, The Barns,
Blakeston Lane,
Stockton-on-Tees
TS21 3LE
Tel: (01642) 633638
Fax: (01642) 633639
e-mail: enquiries@redcar-fish.co.uk
www.redcar-fish.co.uk
We offer expert advice and competitive prices on a full range of marine electronics for your boat or outdoor pursuit. Friendly help and advice is always available. Mail order hotline 01642 633638.

SEAQUEST MARINA LTD
16 Fountain Street, St. Peter Port, Guernsey GY1 1BX
Tel: (01481) 721773
Fax: (01481) 716738
e-mail: seaquk@yahoo.co.uk
We are a general chandlery specialising in marine electronics, admirality charts and books, water sports equipment and inflatable dinghys. We are main agents for Avon Inflatables and Garmin Electronics. Lowest prices on the Island.

ENGINES AND ACCESSORIES

RILEY MARINE
Cinque Ports Arms. Western Docks, Dover CT17 9DQ
Tel: (01304) 214544
Fax: (01304) 214544
e-mail: riley.marine@virgin.net
Modern and traditional boat skills and repairs. Wood steel GRP painting, varnishing, osmosis repairs, marine engineering, engine installations, repairs & servicing, most known marine engines, main dealer for Epifan, Awlgrip, Rockoil, Tahatsu outboard motors.

SILLETTE SONIC LTD
182 Church Hill Road,
North Cheam, Sutton,
Surrey SM3 8NF
Tel: (020) 8715 0100
Fax: (020) 8286 0742
Mobile: 0410 270107
e-mail: sales@sillette.co.uk
www.sillette.co.uk
Sillette manufactures a range of propulsion systems - stern drive, saledrives etc and stern gear. Markets Radice & Gori fixed and folding propellors. Acts as agents for Morse controls, Yanmar and Lombardini marine engines, and Fuji Robin generators.

VETUS DEN OUDEN LTD
39 South Hants Ind. Park, Totton, Southampton SO40 3SA
Tel: 023 8086 1033
Fax: 023 8066 3142
e-mail: sales@vetus.co.uk
www.vetus.co.uk
Wholesalers of diesel engines, generators, exhaust systems, propellers, shafts, bow thrusters, hatches, portlights, windlasses, ventilators, fuel and water tanks, hydraulics systems, air conditioning, wipers, pumps, seats, hoses and much much more.

WHITSTABLE MARINE
The Sea Wall, Whitstable,
Kent CT5 1BX
Tel: (01227) 262525
Fax: (01227) 772750
e-mail:
sales@thedinghystore.co.uk
www.thedinghystore.co.uk
Main Mercury outboard dealer. Sales & service. Quicksilver GRP boats and new inflatables. O'Brien waterskiing equipment. Quicksilver oils and lubes.

FABRICATION

SAILSPAR LTD
Tower Street, Brightlingsea,
Essex CO7 0AW.
Tel: (01206) 302679
Fax: (01206) 303796
e-mail:
davidbeech@sailspar.co.uk
www.sailspar.co.uk
Quality masts and spars, ready-made or kit form. Headsail continuous line roller reefing system. Standing and running rigging. Stainless steel and alloy fabrications. Stainless steel polishing service. RDM Sparecraft and Facron agents.

FIRST AID

LYMINGTON CRUISING SCHOOL
24 Waterloo Road, Lymington, Hampshire SO41 9DB
Tel: (01590) 677478
Fax: (01590) 689210
e-mail:
lymingtoncruisin@aol.com
www.lymingtoncruising.co.uk
All RYA practical and shorebased courses including: Yachtmaster preparation, Coastal Skipper, Day Skipper, Competant Crew, SRC and First Aid. Relaxed, friendly, caring service. Courses structured to suit the individuals needs. Adventure and fun but safety paramount.

FOUL-WEATHER GEAR

DUNCAN YACHT CHANDLERS
7 Scotland St, Glasgow
G5 8NL
Tel: (0141) 429 6044
Fax: (0141) 429 3078
e-mail:
duncanyacht@aol.com
www.duncanyacht.com
Scotland's largest independant chandlery and clothing store stocking everything from a needle to an anchor including a large range of electronics.

THE DINGHY STORE
The Sea Wall, Whitstable, Kent CT5 1BX
Tel: (01227) 274168
Fax: (01227) 772750
e-mail:
sales@thedinghystore.co.uk
www.thedinghystore.co.uk
One of the largest marine chandlers in Kent. 1st floor: Harken, Holt, RWO, Marlow, International Paints, charts, books. 2nd floor: Musto, Henri Lloyd, Gill, Crewsaver, Chatham, Icom radios. Open seven days a week in summer months.

GENERAL MARINE EQUIPMENT & SPARES

ARIES VANE GEAR SPARES
48 Saint Thomas Street, Penryn, Cornwall TR10 8JW
Tel: (01326) 377467
Fax: (01326) 378117
e-mail: enquiries@ariesvane.com
www.ariesvane.com
Spare parts for original Aries gears.

C.J. DEEVY & CO LTD
48 Pomoell St, Waterford,
Ireland.
Tel: 00 353 (51) 855717
Fax: 00 353 (51) 855710
e-mail: sales@deevys.com
www.deevys.com
Motor & marine supplies for the South
East region of Ireland. Est 1935. Offering
a comprehensive range of products to
both marine enthusiasts and motor
enthusiasts. Branches in Waterford and
Clonmell.

**CHRIS HORNSEY
(CHANDLERY) LTD**
152/154 Eastern Rd,
Southsea, Hants
PO4 8DY
Tel: (02392) 734728
Fax: (02392) 611500
e-mail: sales@chrishornsey.com
www.chrishornsey.com
Established 1970. Close to Southsea
Marina.

CTC MARINE & LEISURE
Saltwater House, Longlands
Road, Middlesbrough TS4 2JR
Tel: (01642) 230123
Fax: (01642) 232007
www.clevelandtrailers.co.uk
Chandlers & general marine equipment &
spares.

**HARDWARE & MARINE
SUPPLIES**
Kilmore Quay, Co. Wexford,
Ireland.
Tel: 00 353 (53) 29791
Fax: 00 353 (53) 29803
We are a commercial fishing supplier, with
a good selection of leisure boating supplies
and general hardware. Diving service to
inspect damage also available. Camping
Gas, batteries, ropes, shackles, safety
equipment, flags and stays made to order.

INDEX MARINE
48 Harewood Avenue,
Bounemouth, Dorset BH7 6NM
Tel: (01202) 470149
Fax: (01202) 430150
e-mail:
sales@indexmarine.co.uk
www.indexmarine.co.uk
Manufacturers/suppliers of marine
electrical equipment.

KENNETH RYLAND
Charity Farm, Stanton, Nr
Broadway, Worcs WR12 7NE
Tel: (01386) 584270
Fax: (01386) 584270
Mobile: 07802 261 931
e-mail:
kennethryland@ukonline.co.uk
www.sanshin.co.uk
Manufacturer of crane davits - the
revolutionary lightweight composite davit,
UK distrbutor for Goiot deck equipment -
CLD air conditioning and refrigeration -
Sanshim spotlights - Lagum cockpit

tables and Duralac anti corrosive join timp
compound.

MARATHON LEISURE
Teal Building, Northney Marina,
Hayling Island, Portsmouth
PO11 0NH
Tel: (02392) 637711
Fax: (02392) 937722
e-mail:
sales@marathonleisure.co.uk
General marine wholesalers. Products
include Whale Spinlock, Isotherm,,
Sterling, Ritchie, Tacktick, Treadmaster,
Glomex, English Braids, Eberspacher,
Exide, Ongaro, Seafire, Perko, Sharp LCD
screens, JVC, Sony.

NICK COX YACHT CHARTER LTD
Kings Saltern Road, Lymington,
Hampshire SO41 3QD
Tel: (01590) 673489
Fax: (01590) 673489
Lymington's hardware & technical
specialist.

PIRATES CAVE LTD
Unit 14, Northpoint Business
Estate, Enterprise Close,
Medway City Estate, Frindsbury,
Rochester ME2 4LX
Tel: (01634) 295233
Fax: (01634) 722326
e-mail:
piratescaveuk@yahoo.co.uk
We hold a very large stock of general
chandlery as well as being main dealers
for XM, Silva, Raymarine, Whale, Jabsco,
Barton, Spincock and ECS products.
Staffed by people with boating
experience.

PRO-BOAT LTD
Burnham Business Park,
Burnham-On-Crouch, Essex
CM0 8TE
Tel: (01621) 785455
Fax: (01621) 785467
e-mail: sales@proboat.co.uk
www.proboat.co.uk
Hardware distributors - catalogue
available on request.

QUAY WEST CHANDLERS
Mitchells Boatyard, Turks Lane,
Parkstone, Poole, Dorset
BH14 8EW
Tel: (01202) 742488
Fax: (01202) 742489
General yacht chandlers, covering all
aspects of water useage, with practical
hands on experience and loads of
patience!!

R. ARTHURS CHANDLERY
59-61 Forton Road, Gosport,
Hampshire PO12 4TD
Tel: (023) 9252 6522
Fax: (023) 9252 6522
e-mail:
arthurschandlery@aol.com
For all your marine chandlery.
International, Blakes, XM, Coopers,
Sikkens, Epifanes, Jabsco, Rule, Whale,

Attwood, Aquasignal, Hella, Stanfords,
Imray, Admiralty, Liros Ropes. Ocean
Safety Rigging Service.

SHERATON MARINE CABINET
White Oak Green, Hailey, Witney,
Oxfordshire OX8 5XP
Tel/Fax: (01993) 868275
Manufacturers of quality teak and
mahogany marine fittings, louvre doors,
grating and tables. Special fitting-out
items to customer specification. Colour
catalgoue available on request.

WHITSTABLE MARINE
The Sea Wall, Whitstable,
Kent CT5 1BX
Tel: (01227) 262525
Fax: (01227) 772750
e-mail:
sales@thedinghystore.co.uk
www.thedinghystore.co.uk
Main Mercury outboard dealer. Sales &
service. Quicksilver GRP boats and new
inflatables. O'Brien waterskiing
equipment. Quicksilver oils and lubes.

YACHT PARTS PLYMOUTH
Victoria Building, Queen Anne's
Battery Marina, Plymouth,
Devon PL4 0LP.
Tel: (01752) 252489
Fax: (01752) 225899
e-mail:
sales@yachtparts.co.uk
www.yachtparts.co.uk
From anchors to zinc anodes – probably
the best stocked chandler in the country.
Open seven days with free easy parking.
Our large clothing department caters for
everyone from the dinghy sailor to the
ocean going yachtsman.

GENERATORS

GENACIS
Dolphin House, 2 Allens Lane,
Hamworthy, Poole Dorset,
BH16 5DA
Tel: (01202) 624356
Fax: (01202) 625842
e-mail:
enquiries@genacis.com
www.genacis.com
Dolphin water-cooled diesel generators
3-16 CVA.

WESTERN MARINE POWER LTD
Western Hangar,
Mount Batten,
Plymouth, Devon PL9 9SJ.
Tel: (01752) 408804
Fax: (01752) 408807
e-mail: info@wmp.co.uk
www.wmp.co.uk
Suppliers and installers of:- Watermakers,
Air Conditioning, Generators, Electrical
Systems, Electronic Engine Controls,
Bow and Stern Thrusters, Teak Decks,
Davits, Passarelles and Cranes, Galley
and Sanitation Equipment. ISO 9002
Quality Assurance.

HARBOUR MASTERS

Aberaeron HM	01545 571645
Aberdeen HM	01224 597000
Aberdovey HM	01654 767626
Aberystwyth HM	01970 611433
Aldeburgh HM	
Alderney & Burhou HM	01481 822620
Amble HM	01665 710306
Anstruther HM	01333 310836
Appledore HM	01237 474569
Arbroath HM	01241 872166
Ardglass HM	028 4484 1291
Ardrossan Control Tower HM	01294 463972
Arinagour Piermaster	01879 230347
Arklow HM	00353 402 32466
Baltimore HM	00353 28 22145
Banff HM	01261 815544
Bantry Bay HM	00353 27 53277
Barmouth HM	01341 280671
Barry HM	01446 732665
Beaucette HM	01481 245000
Beaulieu River HM	01590 616200
Belfast Lough HM	028 90 553012
Belfast River Manager	028 90 328507
Bembridge HM	01983 872828
Berwick-upon-Tweed HM	01289 307404
Bideford HM	01237 346131
Blakeney HM	
Blyth HM	01670 352678
Boston HM	01205 362328
Bridlington HM	01262 670148/9
Bridport HM	01308 423222
Brighton HM	01273 819919
Bristol HM	0117 9031484
Brixham HM	01803 853321
Buckie HM	01542 831700
Bude HM	01288 353111
Burghead HM	01343 835337
Burnham-on-Crouch HM	01621 783602
Burnham-on-Sea HM	01278 782180
Burtonport HM	00353 075 42155
Caernarfon HM	01286 672118
Camber Berthing Offices - Portsmouth	023 92297395
Campbeltown HM	01586 552552
Canal Office (Inverness) HM	01463 233140
Cardiff HM	029 20400500
Carnlough Harbour HM	07703 606763
Castletown Bay HM	01624 823549
Charlestown HM	01726 67526
Chichester Harbour HM	01243 512301

Christchurch HM	01202 495061
Conwy HM	01492 596253
Cork HM	00353 21 4273125
Corpach Canal Sea Lock HM	01397 772249
Courtmacsherry HM	00353 23 46311/46600
Coverack HM	01326 280545
Cowes HM	01983 293952
Crail HM	01333 450820
Craobh Haven HM	01852 502222
Crinan Canal Office HM	01546 603210
Cromarty Firth HM	01381 600479
Crookhaven HM	00353 28 35319
Cullen HM	01261 842477
Dingle HM	00353 66 9151629
Douglas HM	01624 686628
Dover HM	01304 240400 Ext 4520
Dublin HM	00353 1 874871
Dun Laoghaire HM	00353 1280 1130/8074
Dunbar HM	01368 863206
Dundee HM	01382 224121
Dunmore East HM	00353 51 383166
East Loch Tarbert HM	01859 502444
Eastbourne HM	01323 470099
Eigg Harbour HM	01687 482428
Elie HM	01333 330051
Estuary Control - Dumbarton HM	01389 726211
Eyemouth HM	01890 750223
Falmouth HM	01326 312285
Findochty HM	01542 831466
Fisherrow HM	0131 665 5900
Fishguard (Lower Harbour) HM	01348 874726
Fishguard HM	01348 404425
Fleetwood HM	01253 872323
Flotta HM	01856 701411
Folkestone HM	01303 715354
Fowey HM	01726 832471/2.
Fraserburgh HM	01346 515858
Galway Bay HM	00353 91 561874
Garlieston HM	01988 600274
Glasson Dock HM	01524 751724
Gorey HM	01534 853616
Gourdon HM	01569 762741
Great Yarmouth HM	01493 335501
Groomsport Bay HM	028 91 278040
Hamble River HM	01489 576387
Hayle HM	01736 754043
Helford River HM	01326 250749
Helmsdale HM	01431 821692
Holy Island HM	01289 389217
Holyhead HM	01407 763071
Hopeman HM	01343 835337
Howth HM	00353 1 832 2252

Ilfracombe HM	01271 862108
Inverness HM	01463 715715
Irvine HM	01294 487286
Johnshaven HM	01561 362262
Kettletoft Bay HM	01857 600227
Killybegs HM	00353 73 31032
Kilmore Quay HM	00353 53 29955
Kinlochbervie HM	01971 521235
Kinsale HM	00353 21 4772503
Kirkcudbright HM	01557 331135
Kirkwall HM	01856 872292
Langstone Harbour HM	023 9246 3419
Larne HM	02828 872100
Lerwick HM	01595 692991
Littlehampton HM	01903 721215
Liverpool HM	0151 949 6134/5
Loch Gairloch HM	01445 712140
Loch Inver HM	01571 844265
Looe HM	01503 262839
Lossiemouth HM	01343 813066
Lough Foyle HM	028 7186 0555
Lowestoft HM	01502 572286
Lyme Regis HM	01297 442137
Lymington HM	01590 672014
Lyness HM	01856 791387
Macduff HM	01261 832236
Maryport HM	01900 814431
Menai Strait HM	01248 712312
Methil HM	01333 462725
Mevagissey HM	01726 843305
Milford Haven HM	01646 696100
Minehead HM	01643 702566
Montrose HM	01674 672302
Mousehole HM	01736 731511
Mullion Cove HM	01326 240222
Newhaven HM	01273 612868
Newlyn HM	01736 362523
Newquay HM	01637 872809
Newtown Creek HM	01983 525994
Oban HM	01631 562892
Padstow HM	01841 532239
Par HM	01726 818337
Peel HM	01624 842338
Penrhyn Bangor HM	01248 352525
Penzance HM	01736 366113
Peterhead HM	01779 483630
Pierowall HM	01857 677216
Pittenweem HM	01333 312591
Plockton HM	01599 534589
Poole HM	01202 440233
Port St Mary HM	01624 833205
Porth Dinllaen HM	01758 720276
Porthleven HM	01326 574207
Porthmadog HM	01766 512927
Portknockie HM	01542 840833
Portland HM	01305 824044

Portpatrick HM	01776 810355
Portree HM	01478 612926
Portrush HM	028 70822307
Portsmouth Harbour Commercial Docks HM	023 92297395
Portsmouth Harbour Control	023 92723694
Portsmouth Harbour HM	023 92723124
Preston HM	01772 726711
Pwllheli HM	01758 704081
Queenborough HM	01795 662051
Queens Gareloch/Rhu HM	01436 674321
Ramsey HM	01624 812245
Ramsgate HM	01843 572100
River Bann & Coleraine HM	028 7034 2012
River Blackwater HM	01621 856487
River Colne (Brightlingsea) HM	01206 302200
River Dart HM	01803 832337
River Deben HM	01394 270106
River Exe Dockmaster	01392 274306
River Humber (Grimsby) HM	01472 327171
River Medway HM	01795 596593
River Orwell HM	01473 231010
River Roach HM	01621 783602
River Stour HM	01255 243000
River Tyne/North Shields HM	0191 257 2080
River Yealm HM	01752 872533
Rivers Alde & Ore HM	01473 450481
Rosslare Harbour HM	00353 53 57921
Rothesay HM	01700 503842
Ryde HM	01983 613879
Salcombe HM	01548 843791
Sark HM	01481 832323
Scalloway HM	01595 880574
Scarborough HM	01723 373530
Scrabster HM	01847 892779
Seaham HM	0191 581 3246
Sharpness HM	01453 811862/64
Shoreham HM	01273 598100
Silloth HM	016973 31358
Sligo HM	00353 71 61197
Southampton HM	023 8033 9733
Southend-on-Sea HM	01702 611889
Southwold HM	01502 724712
St Helier HM	01534 885588
St Ives HM	01736 795018
St Margaret's Hope HM	01856 831454
St Mary's HM	01720 422768
St Monans HM	01333 350055
St Peter Port HM	01481 720229
Stonehaven HM	01569 762741
Stornoway HM	01851 702688
Strangford Lough HM	028 44 881637
Stromness HM	01856 850744

Stronsay HM	01857 616317
Sullom Voe HM	01806 242551
Sunderland HM	0191 567 2626
Swale HM	01795 561234
Swansea HM	01792 653787
Tees & Hartlepool Port Authority	01429 277205
Teignmouth HM	01626 773165
Tenby HM	01834 842717
Thames Estuary HM	01474 562200
Tobermory Port Manager HM	01688 302017
Torquay HM	01803 292429
Troon HM	01292 281687
Ullapool HM	01854 612091
Walton-on-the-Naze HM	01255 851899
Watchet HM	01984 631264
Waterford HM	00353 51 874907
Wells-next-the-Sea HM	01328 711646
Weymouth HM	01305 206423
Whitby HM	01947 602354
Whitehaven HM	01946 692435
Whitehills HM	01261 861291
Whitstable HM	01227 274086
Wick HM	01955 602030
Wicklow HM	00353 404 67455
Workington HM	01900 602301
Yarmouth HM	01983 760321
Youghal HM	00353 24 92626

HARBOURS

Serviced berths available throughout Bristol Harbour for all types of leisure craft
Harbour Office
Underfall Yard, Cumberland Road, Bristol BS1 6XG
Website
www.bristol-city.gov.uk

2003/MD31/e

CLYDE MARINA – ARDROSSAN
The Harbour, Ardossan, Ayrshire KA22 8DB.
Tel: (01294) 607077
Fax: (01294) 607076
e-mail: info@clydemarina.com
www.clydemarina.com
Located on the North Ayrshire coast within easy cruising reach of Arran, the Cumbrae Islands, Bute and the Kintyre Peninsula. Deep draught harbour with 200 pontoon berths and quayside for vessels up to 120'. 50-ton hoist, undercover storage and most services and facilities. Ancasta Scotland brokerage, also Beneteau and Wauquiez.

HAFAN PWLLHELI
Glan Don, Pwllheli, Gwynedd LL53 5YT
Tel: (01758) 701219
Fax: (01758) 701443 VHF Ch80
Hafan Pwllheli has over 400 pontoon berths and offers access at virtually all states of the tide. Ashore, its modern purpose-built facilities include luxury toilets, showers, launderette, a secure boat park for winter storage, 40-ton travel hoist, mobile crane and plenty of space for car parking. Open 24-hours a day, 7 days a week.

JERSEY HARBOURS
Maritime House, La Route du Port Elizabeth, St Helier, Jersey JE1 1HB.
Tel: (01534) 885588
Fax: (01534) 885599
e-mail: jsyhbr@itl.net
www.jersey-harbours.com
A warm welcome to visiting yachts! Come and enjoy our 5 Gold anchor facilities. Visiting yachts can stay at La Collette Yacht Basin, which is open 24 hours, or closer to town at St Helier Marina, which is open 3 hours ± HW.

MARYPORT HARBOUR AND MARINA
Bridge Street, Maryport, Cumbria CA15 8AE
Tel: (01900) 818447/4431
Fax: (01900) 818672
e-mail: enquiries@maryportmarina.com
www.maryportmarina.com
Located on the beautiful Lake District coast. Awarded the European 'Blue Flag' Award in 2000 and 2001. Pontoon berths, chandlery, boat repair facility, 12-ton hoist, hardstanding, shower facilities and laundery room.

PADSTOW HARBOUR COMMISSIONERS
Harbour House, Padstow, Cornwall PL28 8AQ
Tel: (01841) 532239
Fax: (01841) 533346
e-mail: padstowharbour@compuserve.com
www.padstow-harbour.co.uk
Inner harbour controlled by tidal gate - opens HW±2 hours. Minimum depth 3 metres at all times. Yachtsmen must be friendly as vessels raft together. Services include showers, toilets, diesel, water and ice. Security by CCTV.

PETERHEAD BAY AUTHORITY
Bath House, Bath Street, Peterhead AB42 1DX
Tel: (01779) 474020
Fax: (01779) 475712
www.peterhead-bay.co.uk
Contact Ken Bennions. Peterhead Bay Marina offers fully serviced pontoon berthing for local and visiting boat owners. Local companies provide a comprehensive range of supporting services. Ideal stopover for vesels heading to/from Scandinavia or the Caledonian Canal.

**SARK MOORINGS -
Channel Islands
Tel: (01481) 832260
Fax: (01481) 832364
Mobile: 07781 106065 Channel
10
e-mail: simon@sarkci.com
www.sarkmoorings.com**
Visitors' moorings now available at Havre
Gosselin (West Coast), and La Grève de
la Ville (East Coast by Point Robert
lighthouse). Call up Ch 10 or mobile
07781 106065. Look for the yellow
buoys and experience the charm and
beauty of Sark.

INSTRUMENTATION &
POSITION FIXING

**NICK BELSON DESIGN LTD
The Woodlands, Frost Lane,
Hythe, Southampton, Hampshire
SO45 3NB
Tel: (077) 6835 1330
Fax: (023) 8087 9841
e-mail: nbelson@iee.org**
Design and manufacture of bespoke
marine electronics for custom
applications. New build and racing data
logging including three axis accelerations.
Manufacture and installation of onboard
and free floating wave height sensors.

INSURANCE/FINANCE

**ST MARGARETS INSURANCES
153-155 High Street, Penge,
London SE20 7DL
Tel: (020) 8778 6161
Fax: (020) 8659 1968
e-mail:
yachts@stminsurance.co.uk
www.stminsurance.co.uk**
Over 30 years dedicated to insuring
yachts and pleasurecraft. Many unique
policies available only through St
Margarets. Immediate quotations
available.

**WEYSURE LTD
First Floor, 82 The Esplanade,
Weymouth, Dorset DT4 7AA
Tel: (07000) 939787
Fax: (07002) 939787**

e-mail: admin@weysure.co.uk
Commercial and marine registered
brokers. Hull and liability for all
commercial and private craft worldwide.
Unique mechanical breakdown insurance
on inboard and outboard.

LIFERAFTS &
INFLATABLES

**A B MARINE LTD
Castle Walk, St Peter Port,
Guernsey, Channel Islands
GY1 1AU.
Tel: (01481) 722378
Fax: (01481) 711080**
We specialise in safety and survival
equipment and are a M.C.A. approved
service station for liferafts including
R.F.D., Beaufort/Dunlop, Zodiac, Avon,
Plastimo and Lifeguard. We also carry a
full range of new liferafts, dinghies and
lifejackets and distress flares.

**ADEC MARINE LTD
4 Masons Avenue, Croydon,
Surrey
CR0 9XS.
TEL: 020 8686 9717
FAX: 020 8680 9912
e-mail: sales@adecmarine.co.uk
www.adecmarine.co.uk**
Approved liferaft service station for south
east UK. Additionally we hire and sell new
rafts and sell a complete range of safety
equipment for yachts including
pyrotechnics, fire extinguishers, lifejackets,
lifebuoys & lights.

**NATIONWIDE MARINE HIRE
Units 4 & 5 Clarendon Court,
Winwick Quay,
Warrington,Cheshire WA2 8QP
Tel: (01925) 245788
Fax: (01925) 245788
e-mail:
sales@zodiacliferafts.co.uk**
The company is an approved liferaft
service station and is the leading supplier
of Zodiac leisure liferafts in the UK.
Zodiac liferafts to RORC/ORC/SOLAS B
specifications are available for hire. Also
EPIRB's, inflatable tenders and
lifejackets.

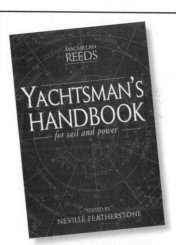

OCEAN SAFETY
Saxon Whart, Lower York Street,
Southampton, Hampshire
SO14 5QF
Tel: (023) 8072 0800
Fax: (023) 8072 0801
e-mail: mail@oceansafety.com
Your Life Saving Supplier: Liferafts,
lifejackets, MOB, flares, fire fighting,
medical, EPIRBS. In addition to our
extensive product range, we also boast
two of the largest liferaft, lifejacket and
inflatable service stations in Europe with
the continued growth of our facility in
Palma de Mallorca, Spain.

PREMIUM LIFERAFT SERVICES
Head Office: Liferaft House,
Burnham Business Park,
Burnham-on-Crouch, Essex
CM0 8TE.
Freephone: 0800 243673
Fax: (01621) 785934
e-mail: info@liferafts.com
www.liferafts.com
Hire, servicing and sales of DoT and
RORC approved liferafts and other safety
equipment. Long and short-term hire from
26 depots nationwide – see Area by Area
section for regional units.

LIFERAFT AND EPIRB HIRE

Send for our FREE info pack and depot list
0800 243673
www.liferafts.com
info@liferafts.com
Fax: 01621 785934
Liferaft House Burnham-on-Crouch
Essex, CM0 8TE
PREMIUM LIFERAFT SERVICES
THE LIFERAFT COMPANY
THE WORLD'S LARGEST DEDICATED LIFERAFT HIRE COMPANY
Hire, servicing & sales of DoT and RORC approved
liferafts and other safety equipment.
Long & short-term hire from 26 depots nationwide.
See Area by Area section for regional units.

MAIL ORDER

A.S.A.P. SUPPLIES - EQUIPMENT & SPARES WORLDWIDE
Beccles, Suffolk England
NR34 7TD
Tel: (0845) 1300 870
Fax: (0800) 316 2727
e-mail:
mma@asap-supplies.com
www.asap-supplies.com
Catalogue sales of quality marine
equipment.

DUNCAN YACHT CHANDLERS
7 Scotland St, Glasgow G5 8NL
Tel: (0141) 429 6044
Fax: (0141) 429 3078
e-mail: duncanyacht@aol.com
www.duncanyacht.com
Scotland's largest independant chandlery
and clothing store stocking everything
from a needle to an anchor including a
large range of electronics.

INSPIRATIONS EVERYTHING
45, Gilders Way,
Clacton-on-Sea,
Essex CO16 8UB
Tel: (01255) 428113
Model A Games manufacturers, also
customised model making, moulding and
casting services, all subject topics
catered for including yachting and sailing.
marine and Nautical in general.

MARINEFORCE LTD
Unit 6, Waterloo Industrial
Estate, Flanders Rd,
Hedge End,
Hampshire SO30 2QT
Tel: (0870) 010 4877
Fax: (0870) 010 4885
e-mail:
enquiries@marineforce.com
www.marineforce.com
The UK's leading marine retailer,
featuring 10 retail outlets, a huge mail
order catalogue and a full trading
website. Thousands of stock lines
available across clothing, electronics,
general chandlery, boats and engines,
books and charts.

MARINESTORE CHANDLERS
Shipways, North St.,
Maldon, Essex CM9 5HN
Tel: (01621) 854380
Fax: (01621) 843849
e-mail:
chandler@marinestore.co.uk
www.marinestore.co.uk
East coast chandlers. Specialists in
traditional chandlery. Mail order service
available worldwide. Privately owned boat
company.

PURPLE SAILS & MARINE
137-138 Stafford Street,
Walsall WS2 8EA
Tel: (01922) 614787
Fax: (01922) 630766
e-mail:
purple-marine@virgin.net
www.teampurple.co.uk
Retailers of all chandlery goods for all
types of sailing. For a copy of our latest
mail order catalogue, please call now.

MARINA DEVELOPMENT CONSULTANTS

Crest Nicholson Marinas Ltd
Avon House, Newbrick Road,
Stokegifford,
Bristol BS34 8RA
Tel: (01179) 236466
Fax: (01179) 236508
e-mail:
sriggs@crestnicholson.com
A wholly owned subsidiary of Crest
Nicholson plc, operate comprehensive
yachting facilities at 5 locations in the UK
and are marketing agents for Malahide
Marina in Dublin Bay.

MARINAS

ABERYSTWYTH MARINA - IMP DEVELOPMENTS
Y Lanfa-Aberystwyth Marina,
Trefechan, Aberystwyth
SY23 1AS
Tel: (01970) 611422
Fax: (01970) 624122
e-mail: abermarina@aol.com
www.abermarina.co.uk
NEW fully serviced marina. Diesel, gas,
water, toilets and hot showers.

Albert Dock Liverpool   0151 709 6558

Allington Marina
Maidstone   01622 752057

Amble Marina Amble   01665 712168

ARDFERN YACHT CENTRE LTD
Ardfern by Lochgilphead, Argyll,
Scotland PA31 8QN
Tel: (01852) 500247
Fax: (01852) 500624
e-mail: office@ardfernyacht.co.uk
www.ardfernyacht.co.uk
Boatyard and marina facilities in a
picturesque natural harbour,
comprehensive workshop facilities,
extensive chandlery, diesel, gas.

Ardglass Marina   028 4484 2332

Ardminish Port
Port Ellen   01583 505254

ARDORAN MARINE
Lerags, Oban, Argyll,
Scotland PA34 4SE
Tel: (01631) 566123
Fax: (01631) 566611
e-mail: colin@ardoran.co.uk
www.ardoran.co.uk
West coast Scotland. All marine facilities.

Arisaig Marine Mallaig 01687 450224

Arklow Marina
Arklow   00353 402 39901

Ballycastle Marina
Ballycastle   028 2076 8525

Bangor Marina Bangor 028 91 453297

Bantry Pier Bantry Bay

Beaucette Marina Vale 01481 245000

Bellanoch Marina
Ardrishaig   01546 603210

Bembridge Marina
Bembridge   01983 872828

Birdham Shipyard Ltd
Birdham   01243 512310

Blackwater Marina
Maylandsea   01621 740264

Blyth Marina Blyth   01679 353636

Boston Marina Boston 01205 364420

Bowling Basin (Dumbarton)
Dumbarton   01389 877969

Bradwell Marina
Bradwell-on-Sea   01621 776235

BRAY MARINA
**Monkey Island Lane, Bray,
Berkshire SL6 2EB
Tel: (01628) 623654
Fax: (01628) 773485
e-mail: bray@mdlmarinas.co.uk
www.marinas.co.uk**
400 berths with fully serviced pontoons for boats up to 18 metres. 24 hour security. Shower and toilet facilities. Licensed restaurant. Chandlery, car park, fuel and Calor gas. Yacht brokerage, engineering and repair services. Boat lifting and hard standing area.

Brentford Dock Marina
Brentford   020 8298 8941

Bridge Marsh Marina
Althorpe   01621 740414

Brighton Marina
Brighton   01273 819919

Bristol Marina Bristol   0117 9213198

BRITISH WATERWAYS
**Crinal Canal Office, Pier Square,
Aedrishaig, Argyll PA30 8DZ
Tel: (01546) 603210
Fax: (01546) 603941
e-mail:
alec.howie@britishways.co.uk
www.scottishcanals.co.uk**
The Scottish canals offer the ideal coast to coast cruising links complemented by excellent marina berthing, ideal for both visitor and long term moorings.

BRIXHAM MARINA
**Berry Head Road, Brixham,
Devon TQ5 9BW
Tel: (01803) 882929
Fax: (01803) 882737
e-mail:
brixham@mdlmarinas.co.uk
www.marinas.co.uk**
480 berth marina with fully serviced pontoons and a special events pontoon. Berths for boats up to 18 metres. Larger vessels by arrangement. 24 hour security. Shower, toilet and laundry facilities. Bar, restaurant and provisions shop. Chandlery, car park and diesel fuel. Yacht and power boat brokerage. Sea school and yacht charter.

Bucklers Hard Marina
Brockenhurst   01590 616200

BURGH CASTLE MARINA
**Butt Lane, Burgh Castle,
Norfolk NR31 9PZ
Tel: (01493) 780331
Fax: (01493) 780163
e-mail:
burghcastlemarina@aol.com**
Safe pontoon moorings with full tidal access on river Waveney and Bellamy Goldaways Holiday Park. One hour sail from sea. Central for Broadland cruising. Amenities include pub-restaurant, pool, showers, laundery & exhibition centre.

Burnham Yacht Harbour Marina Ltd
Burnham-on-Crouch   01621 782150

Caernarfon Dock (Menai Strait)
Caernarfon

Cahersiveen Marina
Cahersiveen   00353 669 473214

CALEY MARINA
**Canal Road, Inverness IV3 8NF
Tel: (01463) 233437
Fax: (01463) 238323
e-mail:
info@caleymarina.co.uk
www.caleymarina.co.uk**
Marina with all usual facilities. Engine workshops & new & used engine sales & parts etc. Chandlery - largest in Scotland. Boat sales - new & used. Also canoe department.

CARLINGFORD MARINA - IRELAND
**Carlingford, Co Louth, Ireland.
Tel/Fax: +353 42 9373073
www.carlingfordmarina.com
VHF Ch16 and 37**
Superb location in beautiful setting close to historic village of Carlingford, our friendly marina provides a top class service for all boat users. Waterside bar and restaurant, chandlery, slipway, 50-ton cranage, power, diesel, water, laundry and showers. Visitors are always welcome.

Carrickfergus Marina
Carrickgergus   028 93 366666

Castlepark Marina
Kinsale   00353 21 4774959

Challenger Marine
Penryn   01326 377222

CHATHAM MARITIME MARINA
**The Lock Building, Leviathan
Way, Chatham Maritime,
Chatham, Medway ME4 4LP
Tel: (01634) 899200
Fax: (01634) 899201
e-mail:
chatham@mdlmarinas.co.uk
www.marinas.co.uk**
New marina on the River Medway in Kent. Accessible from the river at all states of the tide through a lock entrance (restrictions may apply). 300 berth capacity with fully serviced pontoons for boats up to 24 metres. Shower, toilet and laundry facilities. Diesel and petrol fuel. Boat lifting and hard standing area with 20 ton crane.

CHELSEA HARBOUR LTD
The Chambers, Chelsea Harbour,
London SW10 0XF.
TEL: 020 7225 9108
FAX: 020 7352 7868

A tranquil and intimate marina of 55 berths close to the heart of the West End of London. 5-Star hotel, restaurants and bars. Overnight pontoon and amenities. 24-hour security patrols and CCTV.

Chichester Marina
Chichester   01243 512731

Chiswick Quay Marina
London   020 8994 8743

CLYDE MARINA – ARDROSSAN
The Harbour, Ardossan,
Ayrshire KA22 8DB.
Tel: (01294) 607077
Fax: (01294) 607076
e-mail: info@clydemarina.com
www.clydemarina.com

Located on the North Ayrshire coast within easy cruising reach of Arran, the Cumbrae Islands, Bute and the Kintyre Peninsula. Deep draught harbour with 200 pontoon berths and quayside for vessels up to 120'. 50-ton hoist, undercover storage and most services and facilities. Ancasta Scotland brokerage, also Beneteau and Wauquiez.

COBB'S QUAY MARINA
Hamworthy, Poole,
Dorset BH15 4EL

Tel: (01202) 674299
Fax: (01202) 665217
e-mail:
cobbsquay@mdlmarinas.co.uk
www.marinas.co.uk

850 berth marina with fully serviced pontoons for boats up to 25 metres. 24 hour security. Shower, toilet and laundry facilities. Yacht club and restaurant. Chandlery, car park and fuel. Boat lifting and hard standing area for maintenance and storage ashore. Slipping & boat repairs. Dry stack facility and under cover storage. Brokerage and new boat sales.

Coleraine Marina
Coleraine   028 7034 4768

Conwy Marina Conwy   01492 593000

COWES YACHT HAVEN
Vectis Yard, High Street,
Cowes, Isle of Wight
PO31 7BD
Tel: (01983) 299975
Fax: (01983) 200332
e-mail:
info@cowesyachthaven.com
www.cowesyachthaven.com

Marina and yachting event centre.

CRAOBH MARINA
A member of the Holt Leisure Group
By Lochgilphead, Argyll
PA31 8UA.

Tel: (01852) 500222
Fax: (01852) 500252
VHF Ch37 and 80 (M).

250-berth marina on Loch Shuna. Water, electricity, diesel and gas. Full boatyard services. Chandlery. Brokerage. Insurance. Shops, bar, restaurant, car hire, 24-hour access.

CREST NICHOLSON MARINAS LTD
Avon House, Newbrick Road,
Stokegifford, Bristol BS34 8RA
Tel: (01179) 236466
Fax: (01179) 236508
e-mail:
sriggs@crestnicholson.com

A wholly owned subsidiary of Crest Nicholson plc, operate comprehensive yachting facilities at 5 locations in the UK and are marketing agents for Malahide Marina in Dublin Bay.

CROSSHAVEN BOATYARD MARINA - IRELAND
Crosshaven, Co. Cork, Ireland
Tel: 00 353 (21) 48 31161
Fax: 00 353 (21) 48 31603
e-mail: cby@eircom.net

All facilities at this 100-berth marina situated 12 miles from Cork City and close to ferryport and airport. Travel lift - 40 tons, full repair and maintenance services, spray painting and approved International Gelshield centre. Storage undercover and outside for 400 boats. Brokerage. Irish agents for Dufour and Oyster yacths, & Kelt White Shark. RNLI and Defence contractors.

Cuxton Marina Ltd
Rochester   01634 721941

Dart Marina Dartmouth   01803 833351

DARTHAVEN MARINA LTD
Brixham Road, Kingswear, Devon TQ6 0SG
Tel: (01803) 752242
Fax: (01803) 752722
www.darthaven.co.uk
Darthaven provides "one stop shop" for all repairs/maintenance. Experienced staff. Extensive Chandlery stocks, all leading brands, Volvo Penta, Yanmar, Raymarine, B&G, etc. 7 days, 35 tonne mobile hoist. Visitors pontoon - Channel 80.
Engineering Emergency - 07973 280584.

DARTSIDE QUAY
Galmpton Creek, Galmpton, Brixham, Devon TQ5 0EH
Tel: (01803) 845445
Fax: (01803) 843558
e-mail:
dartsidequay@mdlmarinas.co.uk
www.marinas.co.uk
9 acre boat storage facility. Mud moorings. Fully serviced with power and water. Chandlery, 65 ton hoist, 16 ton trailer hoist and 25 ton crane. Pressure washing service. Various marine trades.

DINGLE MARINA - IRELAND
Harbour Master, Strand Street, Dingle, Co Kerry, Ireland.
Tel: 353 66 (91) 51629
Fax: 353 42 (91) 52629
e-mail:
dinglemarina@eircom.net
Europe's most westerly marina on the beautiful south west coast of Ireland in the heart of the old sheltered fishing port of Dingle. Visitor berths, fuel and water. Shops, 52 pubs and many restaurants with traditional music and hospitality. Harbour easily navigable day or night.

Dolphin Haven Poole   01202 649488

Doune Marine Loch Alsh 01687 462667

Dove Marina London   020 8748 9474

Dover Marina Dover   01304 241663

DUN LAOGHAIRE MARINA
Harbour Road, Dun Laoghaire, Co. Dublin
Tel: ++353 1 2020040
Fax: ++353 1 2020043
e-mail: dlmarina@indigo.ie
www.dlharbour.ie
Located within Dun Laoghaire - 8 miles from Dublin City centre adjacent suburban rail station and all amenities. Facilities include shore power, portable water, showers, laundry, fuel - petrol & diesel, gas, sewage pump out.

Dunstaffnage Marina Ltd
By Oban   01631 566555

East Cowes Marina
Isle of Wight   01983 293983

East Ferry Marina
Cobh   00353 21 481 1342

Elizabeth Marina
St Helier   01534 885530

Elmhaven Marina
Halling   01634 240489

EMSWORTH YACHT HARBOUR LTD
Thorney Road, Emsworth, Hampshire PO10 8BP.
Tel: (01243) 377727
Fax: (01243) 373432
www.emsworth-marina.co.uk
Friendly marina in Chichester harbour. Water, electricity, diesel, Calor gas, 40-tonne mobile crane, slipways, hard-standing and storage areas. Showers and toilets, car parking, chandlery, engineers and boat repairs.

Essex Marina Rochford 01702 258531

Falmouth Marina
Falmouth   01326 316620

Falmouth Yacht Haven
Falmouth   01326 312285

Fareham Marina
Fareham   01329 822445

FENIT MARINA, TRALEE & FENIT HARBOUR COMMISSIONERS
Fenit, County Kerry, Ireland
Tel: 353 66 (71) 36231
Fax: 353 66 (71) 36473
e-mail: fenitmarina@eircom.net
Marina operators.

Fleetwood Harbour Village Marina
Fleetwood   01253 872323

Fox's Marina Ipswich Ltd
Ipswich   01473 689111

Gallions Point Marina
London   020 7476 7054

Gillingham Marina
Gillingham   01634 280022

Glasson Dock Marina
Lancaster   01524 751491

HAFAN PWLLHELI
Glan Don, Pwllheli, Gwynedd LL53 5YT
Tel: (01758) 701219
Fax: (01758) 701443 VHF Ch80
Hafan Pwllheli has over 400 pontoon berths and offers access at virtually all states of the tide. Ashore, its modern purpose-built facilities include luxury toilets, showers, launderette, a secure boat park for winter storage, 40-ton travel hoist, mobile crane and plenty of space for car parking. Open 24-hours a day, 7 days a week.

Halcon Marine Ltd
Canvey Island   01268 511611

HAMBLE POINT MARINA
School Lane, Hamble, Southampton, Hampshire SO31 4NB
Tel: (023) 8045 2464
Fax: (023) 8045 6440
e-mail:
hamblepoint@mdlmarinas.co.uk
www.marinas.co.uk
Situated at the mouth of the River Hamble. 229 berth marina with fully serviced pontoons for boats up to 20 metres. 24 hour security. Shower, toilet and laundry facilities. Bar and restaurant. Chandlery, car park and ice. Lifting for boats up to 62 tons, hard standing area and slipway. Boat repairs and electronic services. Boat storage and winter lay-up. 4 ton crane for masts/engines. Yacht brokerage, new boat sales and dry sailing facility.

Hartlepool Marina
Hartlepool   01429 865744

Haslar Marina Gosport 023 9260 1201

Heybridge Basin Maldon   01621 853506

Holy Loch Marina
Dunoon   01369 701800

HOLYHEAD MARINA & TRINITY MARINE LTD
**Newry Beach,
Holyhead LL65 1YA.
Tel: (01407) 764242
Fax: (01407) 769152
e-mail:
info@holyhead-marina.co.uk**
Marine engineering and comprehensive boatyard facilities for all types of craft up to 100 tonnes. 500-berth pontoon marina under construction Summer 2001, including all shoreside amenities, exclusive apartments and chandlery. Access at all tides. Berths now available.

Hoo Marina Rochester 01634 250311

HOWTH MARINA - IRELAND
**Howth, Co Dublin, Ireland
TEL: 00 353 (1) 839 2777
FAX: 00 353 (1) 839 2430
e-mail: marina@hyc.ie
www.hyc.ie**
Modern marina in beautiful sheltered location. Fully services berths with every facility and 24-hour security. Very popular marina for traffic in the Irish Sea. Is available at all stages of tide with extremely easy access. Visitors benefit from temporary membership of Howth Yacht Club.

Hull Marina Hull   01482 330505

Humber Cruising Association Marina
Grimsby   01472 268424

HYTHE MARINA VILLAGE
**Shamrock Way, Hythe,
Southampton, Hampshire
SO45 6DY
Tel: (023) 8020 7073
Fax: (023) 8084 2424
e-mail:
hythe@mdlmarinas.co.uk
www.marinas.co.uk**
210 berth marina with fully serviced pontoons for boats up to 20 metres. Access by lock manned 24 hours. 24 hour security. Shower, toilet and laundry facilities. Chandlery, brokerage, shops, hairdresser, bar and restaurants. Car park, petrol and diesel fuel. Boat lifting and hard standing area. Slipway, 30 ton hoist and boat repairs.

IPSWICH HAVEN MARINA
**New Cut East, Ipswich,
Suffolk IP3 0EA
Tel: (01473) 236644
Fax: (01473) 236644
e-mail:
ipswichhaven@abports.co.uk**
5 gold anchor marina, access through

lock manned 24 hours, 70 tonne boat hoist, storage ashore, licenced club house, chronology, new and used boat sales, 5 mins walk from Ipswich town centre, 10 mins to station.

Island Harbour Marina
Newport   01983 822999

Itchen Marina
Southampton   023 8063 1500

JERSEY HARBOURS
**Maritime House,
La Route du Port Elizabeth,
St Helier, Jersey JE1 1HB.
Tel: (01534) 885588
Fax: (01534) 885599
e-mail: jsyhbr@itl.net
www.jersey-harbours.com**
A warm welcome to visiting yachts! Come and enjoy our 5 Gold anchor facilities. Visiting yachts can stay at La Collette Yacht Basin, which is open 24 hours, or closer to town at St Helier Marina, which is open 3 hours ± HW.

Island Harbour Marina
Newport   01983 822999

Itchen Marina
Southampton   023 8063 1500

KILMORE QUAY MARINA - IRELAND
**Kilmore Quay,
Co Wexford, Ireland.
Tel: 353 53 (29) 955
Fax: 353 53 (29) 915**
Kilmore Quay in the south east of Ireland has a new Blue Flag marina with 20 pontoon visitor berths. This friendly fishing port has pleasant hotel facilities, pubs and restaurants offering a traditional Irish welcome. Rosslare ferryport is only 15 miles away.

KILRUSH MARINA & BOATYARD - IRELAND
**Kilrush, Co Clare, Ireland
Tel: 00 353 (65) 9052072
Fax: 00 353 (65) 9051692
Mobile: 00 353 862313870
VHF Ch80
e-mail:
kcm@shannon.dev.ie
www.shannon-dev.ie/kcm**
Marina on Ireland's beautiful west coast, is a new marina with 120 fully serviced berths. The marina has all shore facilities including a modern boatyard with 45-ton hoist. It adjoins the busy market town of Kilrush which has every facility required by the visiting yachtsman.

Kinsale Yacht Club Marina
Kinsale   00353 21 4772196

Kip Marina   01475 521485

Kirkwall Marina
Kirkwall   01856 872292

La Collette Yacht Basin
St Helier   01534 885588

Lady Bee Marina
Brighton   01273 593801

LARGS YACHT HAVEN
**Irvine Road, Largs,
Ayrshire KA30 8EZ.
Tel: (01475) 675333
Fax: (01475) 672245
e-mail: largs@yachthavens.com**
Perfectly located 630-berth marina with full services afloat and ashore. 70-ton travel hoist operational 6 days; fuel (diesel and petrol); gas and ice on sale 24-hours. Bar, coffee shop, dive shop plus usual marine services.

LAWRENCE COVE MARINA - IRELAND
**Bere Island, Bantry Bay,
Co Cork, Ireland.
Tel/Fax: 353 27 (75) 044
e-mail: lcm@iol.ie
www.lawrencecovemarina.com**
Lawrence Cove Marina is situated in Bantry Bay in the south west corner of Ireland in the heart of the best cruising ground in Europe. It is a fairly new marina, personally run by John and Phil Harrington with full facilities and a very safe haven to leave a boat. It is two hours from Cork airport with good connections. The marina now provides winter storage having acquired a hoist and all your boating problems can be solved.

Limehouse Basin Marina
London   020 7537 2828

Littlehampton Marina
Littlehampton   01903 713553

Liverpool Marina
Liverpool   0151 708 5228

Longmans Yacht Haven
Inverness   01463 715715

Lossiemouth Marina
Lossiemouth   01343 813066

Lymington Marina
Lymington   01590 673312

LYMINGTON YACHT HAVEN
**King's Saltern Road, Lymington,
Hampshire SO41 3QD.
Tel: (01590) 677071
Fax: (01590) 678186
e-mail:
lymington@yachthavens.com**
Perfectly situated at the mouth of the Lymington River giving instant access to the Western Solent. Full marina services, boatyard, brokerage, diesel, petrol, gas, restaurant and bar.

MALAHIDE MARINA - IRELAND
**Malahide, Co Dublin, Ireland.
Tel: +353 1 8454129
Fax: +353 1 8454255**
Located next to the picturesque village of Malahide our marina village is the ideal spot to enjoy and relax. There are 350 fully serviced berths, petrol and diesel available. 30-ton hoist with full boatyard facilities with winter storage ashore or afloat. A fine selection of shops, and friendly pubs and restaurants serving good food are close by.

MARINA DEVELOPMENTS LIMITED
Outlook House, Hamble Point, School Lane, Hamble, Southampton, Hampshire SO31 4NB
Tel: (023) 8045 7155
Fax: (023) 8045 7154
e-mail:
enquiries@mdlmarinas.co.uk
www.marinas.co.uk
Marina Developmnets Limited (MDL) is the UK's leading marina group with 18 prime boating locations offering 6,000 berths and 500 on site commercial tenants.

Maryport Harbour and Marina
Maryport   01900 814431

Mayflower International Marina
Plymouth   01752 556633

Medway Bridge Marina
Rochester   01634 843576

Medway Pier Marina
Gillingham   01634 851113

Melfort Pier & Harbour
Kilmelford   01852 200333

MERCURY YACHT HARBOUR
Satchell Lane, Hamble, Southampton, Hampshire SO31 4HQ
Tel: (023) 8045 5994
Fax: (023) 8045 7369

e-mail:
mercury@mdlmarinas.co.uk
www.marinas.co.uk
350 berth marina with fully serviced pontoons for boats up to 24 metres. 24 hour security. Shower, toilet and laundry facilities. Bar and restaurant. Chandlery and car park. Boat lifting and hard standing area. Sailmakers and electronic services. Sailing schools, yacht charters and yacht brokerage.

Meridian Quay Marina
Grimsby   01472 268424

MILFORD MARINA
Milford Haven, Pembrokeshire SA73 3AF
Tel: (01646) 696312/3
Fax: (01646) 696314
e-mail:
marina@milford-docks.co.uk
www.milford-docks.co.uk
Marina berths, boat storage, 16t hoist, diesel, electricity, laundery, chandlery, boat & engine repairs, brokerage, engine sales, restaurants, retail park on site, 24 hour staff, 22 miles of sheltered estuary for all year round sailing.

Mill Bay Village Marina
Plymouth   01752 226785

MYLOR YACHT HARBOUR LTD
Mylor Yacht Harbour, Falmouth, Cornwall TR11 5UF
Tel: (01326) 372121

Fax: (01326) 372120
e-mail: enquiries@mylor.com
www.mylor.com
picturesque, all tide, full service marina.

Naburn Marina   01904 621021
NEPTUNE MARINA LTD
Neptune Quay, Ipswich, Suffolk IP4 1AX
Tel: (01473) 215204
Fax: (01473) 215206
e-mail:
enquiries@neptune-marina.com
www.neptune-marina.com
Accessible through continuously operating lockgates (VHF Channel 68) Neptune Marina (VHF Channels 80 or 37) is located on the north side of Ipswich wet dock immediately adjacent to the town centre and integrated into the rapidly regenerating northern quays.

Newhaven Marina Ltd
Newhaven   01273 513881

NEYLAND YACHT HAVEN LTD
Brunel Quay, Neyland, Pembrokeshire SA73 1PY
Tel: 01646 601601
Fax: 01646 600713
e-mail: neyland@yachthavens.com
www.yachthavens.com
24 hr access, 360 berth marina, visitors berths available, water, electricity, laundry, payphone, gas, diesel, showers, cafe, bar, chandleries, sailmaker, engineers, yard facilities, weather information, all available in a picturesque location.

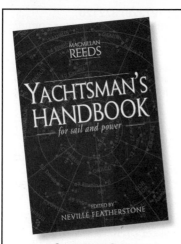

The New Edition
YACHTSMAN'S HANDBOOK

This new edition has been fully revised and updated throughout and provides the boat owner with the latest information on all aspects of yachting.

Illustrated throughout with clear explanatory drawings, diagrams and cross sections. *The Yachtsman's Handbook* is an essential part of any yachtsman's inventory – whether you are a novice or an experienced sailor.

NORTHNEY MARINA
Northney Road, Hayling Island, Hampshire PO11 0NH
Tel: (023) 9246 6321
Fax: (023) 9246 1467
e-mail:
northney@mdlmarinas.co.uk
www.marinas.co.uk
Situated within Chichester Harbour. 228 berth marina with fully serviced pontoons for boats up to 24 metres. 24 hour

security. Shower and toilet facilities. Car park and diesel fuel. Boat lifting and hard standing area with 35 ton hoist. Yacht repair and boatyard services. Yacht brokerage.

Noss-on-Dart Marina
Dartmouth   01803 834582

Ocean Marine (Mayflower Marina)
Plymouth   01752 500121

OCEAN VILLAGE MARINA
2 Channel Way, Southampton, Hampshire SO14 3TG
Tel: (023) 8022 9385
Fax: (023) 8023 3515
e-mail:
oceanvillage@mdlmarinas.co.uk
www.marinas.co.uk
Situated in the centre of Southampton. 450 berth marina with fully serviced pontoons for boats up to 90 metres. 24 hour security. Shower, toilet and laundry facilities. Car park. Yacht brokerage. Adjacent shopping and entertainment complex including cinema and restaurants. Boat lifting and hard standing area at nearby Shamrock Quay and Hamble Point Marina.

ORKNEY MARINAS LIMITED
Scotts Road, Hatston, Kirkwall, Orkney KW15 1GR
www.orkneymarinas.co.uk
Cruise the Okney Islands using our secure, serviced pontoon. Berthing for visitors in three new marinas at Kirkwall, Stromness and Westray for Summer 2003.

Parkstone YC (Haven) Ltd
Poole   01202 743610

Penarth Marina
Penarth   029 20705021

PENTON HOOK MARINA
Staines Road, Chertsey, Surrey KT16 8PY
Tel: (01932) 568681
Fax: (01932) 567423
e-mail:
pentonhook@mdlmarinas.co.uk
www.marinas.co.uk
Britain's largest inland marina. 610 berth marina with fully serviced pontoons for

boats up to 30 metres. 24 hour security. Shower, toilet and laundry facilities. Yacht club. Chandlery, car park, fuel and Calor gas. Engineering and repairs. Boat lifting and hard standing area. Refuse and chemical toilet disposal. Trailer boat storage and yacht brokerage.

Peter Georgeson Marina - Vaila Sound
(Walls) Lerwick   01595 809273

PETERHEAD BAY AUTHORITY
Bath House, Bath Street, Peterhead AB42 1DX
Tel: (01779) 474020
Fax: (01779) 475712
www.peterhead-bay.co.uk
Contact Ken Bennions. Peterhead Bay Marina offers fully serviced pontoon berthing for local and visiting boat owners. Local companies provide a comprehensive range of supporting services. Ideal stopover for vesels heading to/from Scandinavia or the Caledonian Canal.

Phennick Cove Marina
Ardglass   028 44842332

Plymouth Yacht Haven
Plymouth   01752) 404231

Poplar Dock Marina
London   020 7515 1046

Port Dinorwic Marina
Y Felinheli   01248 671500

Port Edgar Marina & Sailing School
South Queensferry   0131 331 3330

PORT HAMBLE MARINA
Satchell Lane, Hamble, Southampton, Hampshire SO31 4QD
Tel: (023) 8045 2741
Fax: (023) 8045 5206
e-mail:
porthamble@mdlmarinas.co.uk
www.marinas.co.uk
Close to Hamble Village. 310 berth marina with fully serviced pontoons for boats up to 24 metres. 24 hour security. Shower, toilet and laundry facilities. Bar and restaurant. Chandlery, car park, petrol and diesel fuel. Boat lifting and hard standing area. Yacht repair yard, brokerage, sailmakers and electronic services. Divers, salvage and towing launch.

Port Medway Marina
Rochester   01634 720033

Port Pendennis Marina
Falmouth   01326 211211

Port Solent Marina
Portsmouth   023 9221 0765

PORTAFERRY MARINA
11 The Strand, Portaferry
BT22 1PF
Tel: 028 427 29598
Fax: 028 427 29784
Portaferry Marina, on the east shore of the
Narrows, the gateway to Strangford-
Lough, a marine nature reserve of
unparalleled beauty. It is a good starting
point on which to explore the Lough and
on-shore activities.s

Portavon Marina
Keynsham   0117 9861626

Portishead Quays Marina
Bristol   01275 841941

PREMIER MARINAS LTD
South Lockside, Port Solent,
Hampshire PO6 4TJ
Tel: (023) 9221 4145
Fax: (023) 9222 1876
e-mail:
office@premiermarinas.com
www.premiermarinas.com
Premier Marinas owner and operator of
5 of the UK's most prestigious marinas in
Beaucette (Guernsey), Brighton,
Chichester, Falmouth and Port Solent.

Preston Marina
Preston   01772 733595

QUEEN ANNE'S BATTERY
Plymouth, Devon PL4 0LP
Tel: (01752) 671142
Fax: (01752) 266297
e-mail: qab@mdlmarinas.co.uk
www.marinas.co.uk
260 berth marina with fully serviced
pontoons for boats up to 19 metres.
24 hour security. Shower, toilet and
laundry facilities. On site restaurant and
bar, café and cycle hire. Chandlery, petrol
and diesel fuel. Boat lifting and hard
standing area. 25 ton boat hoist and boat
repairs. Yacht club, yacht brokerage and
new boat sales.

Queenborough Harbour
Isle of Sheppey   01795 662051

RACECOURSE YACHT BASIN
(WINDSOR) LTD
Maidenhead Road, Windsor,
Berkshire SL4 5HT
Tel: (01753) 851501
Fax: (01753) 868172
e-mail: marina@ryb.co.uk
www.ryb.co.uk
Marina - full facilities - shop - sales -
brokerage.

Ramsgate Royal Harbour Marina
Ramsgate   01843 592277

Rhu Marina Ltd Rhu   01436 820238

Ridge Wharf Yacht Centre
Wareham   01929 552650

Royal Cork Yacht Club Marina
Crosshaven   00353 21 4831023

Royal Harbour Marina Ramsgate
01843 592277

Royal Norfolk and Suffolk Yacht Club
Lowestoft   01502 566726

Royal Quays Marina
North Shields   0191 272 8282

Ryde Leisure Harbour
Ryde   01983 613879

Salterns Marina Boatyard & Hotel
Poole   01202 707321

SALVE MARINE LTD - IRELAND
Crosshaven, Co. Cork, Ireland.
Tel: 353 214 (83) 1145
Fax: 353 214 (83) 1747
e-mail: salvemarine@eircom.net
The marina is just 20 minutes from Cork
City, Cork airport and Ringaskiddy ferry
port. Located yards from Royal Cork yacht
club and Crosshaven village centre.
Facilities for yachts up to 140' x 14'
draught including mains electricity
240/380 volts. Slip, telephone, fax, toilets
and showers. Stainless steel, aluminium
and bronze welding/machining. Repairs
and maintenance to hulls and rigging.

Sandpoint Marina (Dumbarton)
Dumbarton   01389 762396

SAXON WHARF
Lower York Street, Northam,
Southampton,
Hampshire SO14 5QF
Tel: (023) 8033 9490
Fax: (023) 8033 5215
e-mail:
saxonwharf@mdlmarinas.co.uk
www.marinas.co.uk
Marine trade centre with capacity for
lifting boats up to 50 metres. 200 ton
boat hoist and storage ashore. Extensive
marine trades and services. Extra facilities
available at nearby Shamrock Quay.

Seaport Marina
Inverness   01463 233140

Seaton Marina
Coleraine   028 703 832086

SHAMROCK QUAY
William Street, Northam,
Southampton,
Hampshire SO14 5QL
Tel: (023) 8022 9461
Fax: (023) 8021 3808
e-mail:
shamrockquay@mdlmarinas.co.uk
www.marinas.co.uk
250 berth marina with fully serviced
pontoons for boats up to 60 metres. 24
hour security. Shower, toilet and laundry
facilities. Shops, bars and restaurant.
Chandlery. Boat lifting and hard standing
area. 63 ton hoist and 12 ton mobile
crane. Extensive marine trades and
services. Yacht brokerage, new boat sales
and yacht charters.

Sharpness Marine
Berkley   01453 811476

Shepherds Wharf Boatyard Ltd
Cowes   01983 297821

Shepperton Marina
London   01932 247427

South Dock Marina
London   020 7252 2244

South Ferriby Marina
Barton on Humber   01652 635620

Southdown Marina
Millbrook   01752 823084

Southsea Marina
Southsea   023 9282 2719

Sovereign Harbour Marina
Eastbourne   01323 470099

Sparkes Marina
Hayling Island   023 92463572

St Helier Marina
St Helier   01534 885588

St Katharine Haven
London   020 7481 8350

St Peter Port Marinas
St Peter Port   01481 720229

St Peter's Marina
Newcastle upon Tyne   0191 265 4472

Strangford Lough Marina
Portaferry   00353 1247 729598

Stromness Marina
Stromness   01856 850744

Suffolk Yacht Harbour Ltd
Ipswich   01473 659240

Sunderland Marina
Sunderland   0191 5144721

Sunseeker International Marina
Poole   01202 381111

SUTTON HARBOUR MARINA
North Quay House, Sutton
Harbour, Plymouth PL4 0RA
Tel: (01752) 204186
Fax: (01752) 205403
Our historic harbour is a firm favourite
with today's yachtsmen. Our friendly staff
pride themselves on giving our visitors a
warm welcome and offer excellent
facilities including chandlery, boat repairs,
fuel, servicing and car parking.

Swale Marina Ltd
Teynham   01795 521562

Swansea Marina
Swansea   01792 470310

Swanwick Marina
Southampton   01489 885000

Tarquin Marina
Emsworth   01243 377727

Tayport Harbour   01382 553679

The Gosport Marina Ltd
Gosport   023 92524811

Thornham Marina
Emsworth   01243 375335

Tide Mill Yacht Harbour
Woodbridge   01394 385745

TITCHMARSH MARINA
**Coles Lane, Walton-on-the-Naze,
Essex CO14 8SL
Tel: (01255) 672185
Fax: (01255) 851901
www:titchmarshmarina.com**
Friendly service in the peaceful
backwaters. Visiting yachtsmen welcome.
Sheltered marina berths. Full marina
facilities: Travel-lift, cranage, 16-amp
electricity, diesel. Winter storage.
Brokerage. Restaurant and bar (see
Harbour Lights Restaurant.)

TOLLESBURY MARINA
**The Yacht Harbour, Tollesbury,
Maldon, Essex CM9 8SE
Tel: (01621) 869202
Fax: (01621) 868489
e-mail:
brokerage@woodrolfe.demon.co.uk
www.woodrolfe.com
VHF Ch37 and 80**
Dedicated to customer service, this
family-run marina can offer 240 marina
berths with water and electricity on all
pontoons. Cruising club with bar,
restaurant, swimming pool and tennis
courts. Repair workshop, osmosis
treatment centre. Full brokerage service
listing over 200 boats.

Torpoint Yacht Harbour
Plymouth   01752 813658

TORQUAY MARINA
**Torquay, Devon TQ2 5EQ
Tel: (01803) 200210
Fax: (01803) 200225
e-mail:
torquaymarina@mdlmarinas.co.uk**
Situated in the centre of town, a 500

berth marina with fully serviced pontoons
for boats up to 30 metres. 24 hour
security. Shower, toilet and laundry
facilities. Café/bar, restaurant. Chandlery,
car park and boat repair facilities. Yacht
brokerage and new boat sales. Fuel and
lifting facilities on South Pier.
Website: www.marinas.co.uk

Town Quay Marina
Southampton   023 8023 4397

Troon Yacht Haven
Troon   01292 315553

Victoria Marina
St Peter Port   01481 725987

Walton and Frinton Yacht Trust
Walton on the Naze   01255 675873

WATERFORD CITY MARINA - IRELAND
**Waterford City, Irleand.
Tel: 00 353 (51) 309900
Fax: 00 353 (51) 870813
www.waterfordcorp.ie**
Located in the heart of the historic city
centre. There are 100 fully serviced
berths available. Full CCTV in operation.
Showers on-shore nearby in Tower Hotel.
Wide range of shops, restaurants, pubs
and other amenities available on the
doorstep of the marina because of its
unique city-centre location. Open all year
with both winter and summer season
rates available.

West Wick Marina Ltd
Nr Chelmsford   01245 741268

Weymouth Marina
Weymouth   01305 767576

Whitby Marina Whitby   01947 602354

Whitehaven Harbour Marina
Whitehaven   01946 692435

WINDSOR MARINA
**Maidenhead Road, Windsor,
Berkshire SL4 5TZ
Tel: (01753) 853911
Fax: (01753) 868195
e-mail:
windsor@mdlmarinas.co.uk
www.marinas.co.uk**

200 berth marina with fully serviced
pontoons for boats up to 15 metres.
24 hour security. Showers and toilet
facilities. Private yacht club. Chandlery,
yacht brokerage, car park, petrol, diesel
and Calor gas. Engineering and repair
services. Refuse and chemical toilet
disposal and pump-out. Boat lifting and
hard standing area with mobile crane.
Slipway, trailer boat storage.

WISBECH YACHT HARBOUR
**Dock Cottage, Crab Marsh,
Wisbech, Cambs PE13 3JJ
Tel: 01945 588059
Fax: 01945 463207
e-mail: torbeau@btclick.com
www.fenland.gov.uk/harbour**
The finest moorings between the Humber
and Lowestoft! 102 all afloat, fully
serviced pontoon moorings in heart of
historic, Georgian Wisbech. Max. 40m
LOA. Unbeatable rates. Visitors welcome.
Pilot guide and brochure available.

WOOLVERSTONE MARINA
**Woolverstone, Ipswich,
Suffolk IP9 1AS
Tel: (01473) 780206
Fax: (01473) 780273
e-mail:
woolverstone@mdlmarinas.co.uk
www.marinas.co.uk**
210 berth marina with fully serviced
pontoons for boats up to 24 metres.
120 swining moorings with water taxi
service. 24 hour security. Shower, toilet
and laundry facilities. Chandlery,
foodstore, restaurant and bar. Car park,
diesel fuel and Calor gas. Boat lifting and
hard standing area with 20 ton mobile
crane. Repair yard. Storage sheds. Yacht
brokerage, sailing school and caravan
park.

Yarmouth Harbour
Yarmouth   01983 760321

When replying to adverts please mention the Waypoint & Marina Guide

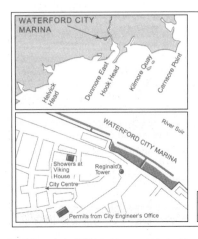

WATERFORD CITY MARINA
IN THE HEART OF HISTORIC WATERFORD
- 100 berths with shorepower and water
- Security / CCTV system
- Showers available nearby in Tower Hotel
- Convenient for all City amenities

For further information contact:
Waterford Corporation, The Mall, Waterford. Tel: 051 309900   Fax: 051 870813

MARINE ACTIVITY CENTRES

COWES YACHT HAVEN
Vectis Yard, High Street, Cowes,
Isle of Wight PO31
Tel: (01983) 299975
Fax: (01983) 200332
e-mail:
info@cowesyachthaven.com
www.cowesyachthaven.com
Marina and yachting event centre.

DOUNE MARINE
Doune, Knoydart, Mallaig,
Inverness-shire PH41 4PL
Tel: (01687) 462667
Fax: (01687) 462667
e-mail: liz@doune-marine.co.uk
www.doune-marine.co.uk
Charter Eda Frandsen our 70ft traditional
gaff cutter. Restaurant meals / showers /
2 free moorings. Shorebased holidays for
walking, wildlife, photography and diving.

TOLLESBURY MARINA
The Yacht Harbour, Tollesbury,
Maldon, Essex CM9 8SE
Tel: (01621) 869202
Fax: (01621) 868489
e-mail:
brokerage@woodrolfe.demon.co.uk
www.woodrolfe.com
VHF Ch37 and 80
Dedicated to customer service, this
family-run marina can offer 240 marina
berths with water and electricity on all
pontoons. Cruising club with bar,
restaurant, swimming pool and tennis
courts. Repair workshop, osmosis
treatment centre. Full brokerage service
listing over 200 boats.

MARINE ARTISTS

MARI LYNCH
The Annex of Keystone House,
Plaistow Road, Dunsfold,
Godalming, Surrey GU8 4PT
Tel: (01483) 201085
www.mariart.co.uk
Yacht portraits and marine art by Mari
Lynch. Visit my virtual gallery at:
www.mariart.co.uk for photo-samples &
commissions phone Mari +44 (0)1483
201085.

MARINE CONSULTANTS AND SURVEYORS

DAVID M. CANNELL & ASSOCIATES
NAVAL ARCHITECTS
CONSULTANTS – SURVEYORS
Yachts & Small Ships Worldwide to 100m
River House, Quay Street, Wivenhoe,
Essex CO7 9DD, England.
Tel: +44 (0) 1206 823 337
Fax: +44 (0) 1206 825 939
E-mail: enquiries@dmcmarine.com
www.dmcmarine.com
2003/M&WMD34/bd

marintec
MARINE CONSULTANCY
2003/M&WMD15/b
Tel: (01590) 683414 Fax: (01590) 683719
Mobile: (07836) 645577
MARINE CONSULTANCY • SURVEYS
PROJECT MANAGEMENT
SYSTEMS DESIGN
ESTABLISHED 1983
Silverton House, Kings Hyde,
Mount Pleasant Lane,
Lymington,
Hants SO41 8LT.

**GRAHAM BOOTH MARINE
SURVEYS**
96 Canterbury Road, Birchington-
on-Sea, Kent CT7 9BB
Tel: (01843) 843793
Fax: (01843) 846860
e-mail: gbma@clare.net
Authorised for MCA Codes of Practice,
most frequently on French and Italian
Riviera - also for certification of Sail
Training vessels and other commercial
craft. Call UK office for further information.
Other expert marine consultancy services
also available.

**JP SERVICES -
MARINE SAFETY & TRAINING**
The Old Police House, Arundel
Road, Tangmere, Chichester,
West Sussex PO18 0DZ
Tel: (01243 537552

Fax: (01243) 531471
e-mail:
training@jpservices.co.uk
www.jpservices.co.uk
RYA and professional training for motor
yachts and work boats. Max 2 students
per practical course. Sea survival courses.
Safety Training and risk awareness to
MCA standards. Consultancy following on
the water accidents.

**SWANWICK YACHT
SURVEYORS**
Swanwick Marina, Lower
Swanwick,
Southampton SO31 12L
Tel: (01489) 564822
Fax: (01489) 564828
e-mail: swanwickys@aol.com
www.swanwickys.co.uk
Pre-purchase surveys. MIIMS & BMF
member.

**WARD & McKENZIE
(NORTH EAST)**
11 Sherbuttage Drive,
Pocklington, East Yorkshire
YO42 2ED
Tel: (01759) 304322
Fax: (01759) 303194
E-mail: surveyor@proworks.co.uk
Professional yacht & powerboat
surveyors, services include damage, pre
purchase, insurance condition surveys &
technical advice. Competitive rates, fast
reliable 24 hour service. Members of the
International Institute of Marine
Surveyors.

MARINE ENGINEERS

**LANGLEY MARINE
SERVICES LTD**
Sovereign Harbour Marina,
Pevensey Bay Road,
Eastbourne,
East Sussex BN23 6JH
Tel: (01323) 470244
Fax: (01323) 470255
Offering a complete service to the boat
owner, engineering, GRP repairs,
shipwrighting, electronics, rigging,
cleaning, etc. We specialise in the refit
and repair of large pleasurecraft and
commercial vessels and are contractors
to the RNLI.

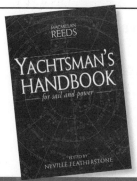

Suppliers of:
- ► New Engines
- ► Reconditioned Engines
- ► Marine installation equipment
- ► Propellers
- ► Stern Tubes
- ► Seacocks
- ► Exhaust hose and mufflers
- ► Fuel systems

2003/M&WM39/a

Full range of chandlery, ropes, paints, Outboard Motors, Clothing, Life jackets, Inflatables...... the list goes on!

Four outlets on the East Coast
Brightlingsea, Head Office
61-63 Waterside, Brightlingsea, Essex, CO7 0AX
Tel :+ 44 (0) 1206 302133 or 305233 Fax: + 44 (0) 1206 305601

Titchmarsh Marina, Coles Lane, Walton-on-Naze, Essex, CO14 8SL.
TEL / Fax: + 44 (0) 1255 850303

Suffolk Yacht Harbour (Stratton Hall), Levington, Ipswich, Suffolk, IP10 0LN.
Tel / Fax: + 44 (0) 1473 659882

Unit 19 Wendover Road, Rackheath, Norwich, Norfolk. NR13 6LR.
Tel :+ 44 (0) 1603 722079 Fax:+44 (0) 1603 721311

Area Dealers for:

VANGUARD VOLVO PENTA SCANIA *vetus* YAMAHA MERCURY *The Water Cars*

and More

ROSSITER YACHTS LTD
**Rossiters Quay, Bridge St,
Christchurch, Dorset BH23 1DZ
Tel: (01202) 483250
Fax: (01202) 490164
e-mail:
rossiteryachts@hotmail.com
www.rossiteryachts.co.uk**
Builders of Curlew and Pontail + repairs & restorations in wood and GRP, osmosure treatment centre. Marine engineering: diesel, petrol, inboard, outboard, marine diesel sales, rigging service, cranage & storage, chandlery, brokerage, moorings.

SEA START LIMITED
**Unit 13, Hamble Point Marina,
Hamble, Southampton SO31 4JD
Tel: (023) 8045 8000
Fax: (023) 8045 2666
e-mail: sales@seastart.co.uk
www.seastart.co.uk**
24 hours a day, 365 days a year - marine breakdown assistance.

MASTS, SPARS & RIGGING

ATLANTIC SPARS LTD
**Hatton House, Bridge Road,
Churston Ferrers, Brixham,
Devon TQ5 0JL
Tel: (01803) 843322
Fax: (01803) 845550
e-mail: atlantic@spars.co.uk
www.spars.co.uk**
Regional centre for SELDEN integrated sailing systems. Services include standing and running rigging, repairs, custom spars and furling systems. Aluminium design and fabrications for industry. Official suppliers to the BT Global Challenge.

BOATWORKS + LTD
**Castle Emplacement,
St Peter Port,
Guernsey, Channel Islands
GY1 1AU.
Tel: (01481) 726071
Fax: (01481) 714224**
Boatwork + provides a comprehensive range of services including boatbuilding

and repairs, chandlery, clothing and fuel supplies.

COATES MARINE LTD
**Northern Spars & rigging
Services, The Marina Boatyard,
Whitby, North Yorkshire
YO21 1EU
Tel: (01947) 604486
Fax: (01947) 600580**
Boat storage and repairs, full rigging services, repairs, clothing, chandlery.

EUROSPARS LTD
**Queen Anne Works, Queen
Anne's Battery, Plymouth PL4 0LT
Tel: (01752) 550550
Fax: (01752) 565005
e-mail: espars@aol.com
www.eurospars.com**
Yacht mast manufacturer & rigging specialist.

FOX's MARINA IPSWICH LTD
**The Strand, Ipswich,
Suffolk IP2 8SA
Tel: (01473) 689111
Fax: (01473) 601737**
Comprehensive boatyard. New 100ft workshop. Specialists in osmosis and spray painting. Marina access 24hrs. Diesel dock, travel hoists to 70 tons, 10 ton crane. Full electronics, rigging, engineering, stainless steel services. Extensive chandlery.

HOLMAN RIGGING
**Chichester Marina, Chichester,
West Sussex PO20 7EJ.
Tel/Fax: (01243) 514000
e-mail:
enquiries@holmanrigging.co.uk
www.holmanrigging.co.uk**
Agent for major suppliers in this field we offer a specialist mast and rigging service. Purpose designed mast trailer for quick and safe transportation. Installation for roller headsail and mainsail reefing systems. Insurance reports and quotations.

SAILSPAR LTD
**Tower Street, Brightlingsea,
Essex CO7 0AW.
Tel: (01206) 302679
Fax: (01206) 303796
e-mail:
davidbeech@sailspar.co.uk
www.sailspar.co.uk**
Quality masts and spars, ready-made or kit form. Headsail continuous line roller reefing system. Standing and running rigging. Stainless steel and alloy fabrications. Stainless steel polishing service. RDM Sparecraft and Facron agents.

T J RIGGING
**9 Vardre Park Deganwy,
Conwy LL31 9YQ
Tel: (07780) 972411
e-mail: tj.rigging@virgin.net**
Specialist mobile rigging service.

NAVIGATION EQUIPMENT - GENERAL

MAPTECH®

Navigational Software
• Chart Navigator • Cruising Navigator
• Offshore Navigator

Navigational Digital Charts

Maptech UK Ltd

Telephone: 01243 389352 • Fax: 01243 379136

w w w . m a p t e c h . c o . u k

**DOLPHIN MARITIME
SOFTWARE LTD**
334 Storey House, White Cross,
South Road, Lancaster
LA1 4XQ.
Tel/Fax: (01524) 841946
e-mail:
sales@dolphinmaritime.com
www.dolphinmaritime.com
Marine computer programs for IBM PC,
Psion and Sharp pocket computers.
Specialists in navigation, tidal prediction
and other programs for both yachting and
commercial uses.

Maptech UK Ltd
Westbourne   01243 389352

RAYMARINE LIMITED
Anchorage Park, Portsmouth,
Hampshire PO3 5TD.
Tel: (02392) 693611
Fax: (02392) 694642
e-mail: info@raymarine.com
www.raymarine.com
Raymarine Limited provide the complete
marine electronics package, including
instrumentation, autopilots, radar
chartplotters, fishfinders, communications
and PC charting software available
through a global network of dealers and
distributors.

**ROYAL INSTITUTE OF
NAVIGATION**
1 Kensington Gore, London
SW7 2AT
Tel: (020) 7591 3130
Fax: (020) 7591 3131
e-mail: info@rin.org.uk
www.rin.org.uk
Forum for all interested in navigation.

PAINT & OSMOSIS

SP SYSTEMS
St. Cross Business Park,
Newport, Isle of Wight
PO30 5WU
Tel: (01983) 828000
Fax: (01983) 828100
Epoxy resins for laminating, bonding,
coating and filling. Usable with wood,
GRP, ferrocement, GRP/FRP materials
including glass, carbon and Kevlar fibres.
Structural engineering of GRP and
composite materials. Technical advice
service.

STONE PIER YACHT SERVICES
Stone Pier Yard, Shore Road,
Warsash, Hampshire SO31 9FR
Tel: (01489) 885400
Fax: (01489) 482049
e-mail: jgale82246@aol.com
High quality workmanship at reasonable
prices, friendly and professional repair,
refit and restoration facilities for GRP and
timber vessels in our spacious workshop.
Call Jon Gale for personal solutions to
your problems, large or small.

POLICE

Aberdeen Police	01224 386000
Aberdovey Police	01286 673333
Abersoch Police	01286 673333
Aberystwyth Police	01970 612791
Alderney and Burhou Police	
	01481 725111
Anstruther Police	01333 592100
Appledore Police	08705 777444
Arbroath Police	01241 872222
Ardglass Police	028 4461501
Ardrishaig Police	01546 603233
Ardrossan Police	01294 468236
Arklow Police	00353 402 32304/5
Baltimore Police	00353 28 20102
Bantry Bay Police	00353 27 50045
Barmouth Police	01286 673333
Barry Police	01446 734451
Beaulieu River Police	023 80335444
Belfast Lough Police	028 91 454444
Berwick-upon-Tweed Police	
	01289 307111
Blyth Police	01661 872555
Boston Police	01205 366222
Bridlington Police	01262 672222
Bridport Police	01308 422266
Brighton Police	01273 606744
Bristol Police	0117 9277777
Brixham Police	0990 777444
Buckie Police	01542 832222
Burnham-on-Crouch Police	
	01621 782121
Burnham-on-Sea Police	01823 337911
Burry Port Police	01554 772222
Caernarfon Police	01286 673333
Campbeltown Police	01586 552253
Cardiff Police	01446 734451
Carlingford Lough Police	
	042 9373102
Castle Haven Police	00353 28 36144
Christchurch Police	01202 486333
Colchester Police	01206 762212
Conwy Police	01492 517171
Corpach Police	01397 702361
Courtmacsherry Police	
	00353 23 46122
Crinan Canal Police	01546 602222
Dartmouth Police	0990 777444
Dingle Police	00353 66 9151522
Douglas Police	01624 631212
Dover Police	01304 216084
Dover Police	01304 240055
Dublin Police	00353 1 6665000
Dunbar Police	01368 862718
Dunmore East Police	
	00353 51 383112

East Loch Tarbert Police	
	01880 820200
Eastbourne Police	01323 722522
Eyemouth Police	01890 750217
Findhorn Police	01309 672224
Fishguard Police	01437 763355
Fleetwood Police	01524 63333
Folkestone Police	01303 850055
Fowey Police	0990 777444
Fraserburgh Police	01346 513121
Galway Bay Police	00353 91 538000
Glandore Police	00353 23 48162
Great Yarmouth Police	01493 336200
Guernsey Police	01481 725111
Hamble River Police	023 80335444
Hartlepool Police	01429 221151
Helmsdale Police	01431 821222
Holyhead Police	01286 673333
Hopeman Police	01343 830222
Howth Police	00353 1 6664900
Ilfracombe Police	08705 777444
Inverkip Police	01475 521222
Inverness Police	01463 715555
Isles of Scilly Police	01721 422444
Kenmare River	
Police	00353 64 41177
Keyhaven Police	01590 615101
Killybegs Police	00353 73 31002
Kilmore Quay Police	00353 53 29642
Kilrush Police	00353 65 51057
Kinlochbervie Police	01971 521222
Kinsale Police	00353 21 4772302
Kirkcudbright Police	01557 330600
Kirkwall Police	01856 872241
Lamlash Police	01770 302573
Largs Police	01475 674651
Larne Police	02828 272266
Lerwick Police	01595 692110
Littlehampton Police	01903 731733
Liverpool Police	0151 709 6010
Loch Melfort Police	01852 562213
Looe Police	01503 262233
Lossiemouth Police	01343 812022
Lough Foyle Police	028 77766797
Lough Swilly Police	00353 72 51102
Lowestoft Police	01986 855321
Lyme Regis Police	01297 442603
Macduff and Banff Police	
	01261 812555
Malahide Police	00353 1 6664600
Mallaig Police	01687 462177
Maryport Police	01900 602422
Medway Police	01634 811281
Menai Strait Police	01286 673333
Methil Police	01592 418888
Mevagissey Police	0990 777444
Milford Haven Police	01437 763355

Minehead Police	01823 337911	Stromness Police	01856 850222	
Montrose Police	01674 672222	Stronsay Police	01857 872241	
Nairn Police	01667 452222	Sunderland Police	0191 4547555	
Newhaven Police	01273 515801	Swanage Police	01929 422004	
Newtown Creek Police	01983 528000	Swansea Police	01792 456999	
Oban Police	01631 562213	Teignmouth Police	01626 772433	
Padstow Police	08705 777444	Tenby Police	01834 842303	
Peel Police	01624 631212	Thames Estuary Police	020 7 754421	
Penzance Police	01736 362395	The Swale Police	01795 536639	
Peterhead Police	01779 472571	Tobermory Police	01688 302016	
Plymouth Police	01752 701188	Torquay Police	0990 777444	
Poole Harbour Police	01202 223954	Troon Police	01292 313100	
Port St Mary Police	01624 631212	Ullapool Police	01854 612017	
Porthmadog Police	01286 673333			

Walton Backwaters Police
01255 241312

Wells-next-the-Sea Police
01493 336200

Portishead Police	01934 638272	West Mersea Police	01206 382930
Portland Police	01305 821205	Westport Police	00353 98 25555
Portpatrick Police	01776 702112	Wexford Police	00353 404 67107
Portree Police	01478 612888	Weymouth Police	01305 250512
Portrush Police	028 70344122	Whitby Police	01947 603443
Preston Police	01772 203203	Whitehaven Police	01946 692616
Pwllheli Police	01286 673333	Whitstable Police	01227 770055
Queenborough Police	01795 477055	Wick Police	01955 603551
Ramsey Police	01624 631212	Wicklow Police	00353 404 67107
Ramsgate Police	01843 231055	Workington Police	01900 602422
Rhu Police	01436 672141	Yarmouth Police	01983 528000
		Youghal Police	00353 24 92200

River Bann and Coleraine Police
028 70344122

River Colne Police	01255 221312
River Deben Police	01394 383377
River Humber Police	01482 359171
River Orwell Police	01473 233000
River Stour Police	01255 241312
River Tyne Police	0191 232 3451
River Yealm Police	0990 777444

Rivers Alde and Ore Police
01394 613500

Rothesay Police	01700 502121
Rye Police	01797 222112
S. Queensferry Police	0131 331 1798
Salcombe Police	01548 842107
Scarborough Police	01723 500300
Schull Police	00353 28 28111
Scrabster Police	01847 893222
Seaham Police	0191 581 2255
Sharpness Police	01452 521201
Shoreham Police	01273 454521
Sligo Police	00353 71 57000
Southampton Police	023 80845511

Southend-on-Sea Police
01702 341212

Southwold Police	01986 855321
St Helier Police	01534 612612
Stonehaven Police	01569 762963
Stornoway Police	01851 702222

Strangford Lough Police
028 44615011

PROPELLORS & STERNGEAR / REPAIRS

ProProtector LTD
74 Abingdon Road, Maidstone,
Kent ME16 9EE
Tel: (01622) 728738
Fax: (01622) 727973
e-mail:
sails@prop-protector.co.uk
www.prop-protector.co.uk
Prevention is better than cure when it comes to fouled propellers. ProProtectors are now welcome and used worldwide as the most economical and simplest way to combat stray rope, netting, weed and plastic bags. Fit one before it is too late.

RADIO COURSES / SCHOOLS

BISHAM ABBEY SAILING & NAVIGATION SCHOOL
National Sports Centre,
Bisham, Nr. Marlow,
Bucks SL7 1RT
Tel: (01628) 474960
www.bishamabbeysailing.co.uk
RYA recognised establishment. Dinghy Sailing for adults and children. Shore-based navigation, intensive and semi-intensive - Dayskipper, Yachtmaster, YMOcean. One day - 1st aid, VHF-SRC, Radar, Diesel Engine, Electronic Navigation, CEVNI, Boat handling, Powerboat, IWHC, ICC. Boat Safety Scheme.

REEFING SYSTEMS

EUROSPARS LTD
Queen Anne Works,
Queen Anne's Battery,
Plymouth PL4 0LT
Tel: (01752) 550550
Fax: (01752) 565005
e-mail: espars@aol.com
www.eurospars.com
Yacht mast manufacturer & rigging specialist.

HOLMAN RIGGING
Chichester Marina, Chichester,
West Sussex PO20 7EJ.
Tel/Fax: (01243) 514000
e-mail:
enquiries@holmanrigging.co.uk
www.holmanrigging.co.uk
Agent for major suppliers in this field we offer a specialist mast and rigging service. Purpose designed mast trailer for quick and safe transportation. Installation for roller headsail and mainsail reefing systems. Insurance reports and quotations.

REPAIR MATERIALS AND ACCESSORIES

J. B. TIMBER LTD
56 Woodgates Lane,
North Ferriby, Yorks
HU14 3JY
Tel: (01482) 631765
Fax: (01482) 634846
Boatbuilding timbers: Larch, Oak, Iroko, Opepe.

SIKA LTD
Watchmead,
Welwyn Garden City,
Hertfordshire AL7 1BQ
Tel: (01707) 394444
Fax: (01707) 329129
e-mail:
waktins.terry@uk.sika.com
www.sika.com
Sikaflex watertight bonding. Deck caulking and glazing.

SP SYSTEMS
St. Cross Business Park,
Newport, Isle of Wight
PO30 5WU
Tel: (01983) 828000
Fax: (01983) 828100
Epoxy resins for laminating, bonding,
coating and filling. Usable with wood,
GRP, ferrocement, GRP/FRP materials
including glass, carbon and Kevlar fibres.
Structural engineering of GRP and
composite materials. Technical advice
service.

ROPE AND WIRE

ProProtector LTD
74 Abingdon Road,
Maidstone, Kent
ME16 9EE
Tel: (01622) 728738
Fax: (01622) 727973
e-mail:
sails@prop-protector.co.uk
www.prop-protector.co.uk
Prevention is better than cure when it
comes to fouled propellers.
ProProtectors are now welcome and
used worldwide as the most economical
and simplest way to combat stray rope,
netting, weed and plastic bags. Fit one
before it is too late.

T J RIGGING
9 Vardre Park Deganwy,
Conwy LL31 9YQ
Tel: (07780) 972411
e-mail: tj.rigging@virgin.net
Specialist mobile rigging service.

SAFETY EQUIPMENT

A B MARINE LTD
Castle Walk,
St Peter Port, Guernsey,
Channel Islands
GY1 1AU.
Tel: (01481) 722378
Fax: (01481) 711080
We specialise in safety and survival
equipment and are a M.C.A. approved
service station for liferafts including
R.F.D., Beaufort/Dunlop, Zodiac, Avon,
Plastimo and Lifeguard. We also carry a
full range of new liferafts, dinghies and
lifejackets and distress flares.

ADEC Marine Limited
Approved liferaft service station for South East.
Buy or hire new rafts. Complete range of safety
equipment for yachts including pyrotechnics.
Fire extinguishers – Lifejackets – Buoyancy aids
4 Masons Avenue, Croydon,
Surrey CR0 9XS
Tel: 020 8686 9717
Fax: 020 8680 9912
E-mail: sales@adecmarine.co.uk
Website: www.adecmarine.co.uk

ADEC MARINE LTD
4 Masons Avenue, Croydon,
Surrey
CR0 9XS.
TEL: 020 8686 9717
FAX: 020 8680 9912
e-mail: sales@adecmarine.co.uk
www.adecmarine.co.uk
Approved liferaft service station for south
east UK. Additionally we hire and sell new
rafts and sell a complete range of safety
equipment for yachts including
pyrotechnics, fire extinguishers, lifejackets,
lifebuoys & lights.

ANCHORWATCH UK
67 Morningside Park, Edinburgh
EH10 5EZ
Tel: (0131) 447 5057
e-mail: anchorwatch@aol.com
www.anchorwatch.co.uk
Electronic anchor monitoring equipment.
Anchorwatch measures the loading on an
anchor cable up to 1000kg. Records
peak loading and includes alarm facility.

CREWSAVER
Mumby Road, Gosport,
Hampshire PO12 1AQ
+44 (0)23 9252 8621
+44 (0)23 9251 090
e-mail: sales@crewsaver.co.uk
www.crewsaver.co.uk
Established manufacturer of lifejackets,
lifesaving equipment, sailing clothing and
accessories. Check out the latest range of
products online at www.crewsaver.co.uk.

MET OFFICE
London Road, Bracknell,
Berkshire RG12 2SZ
Tel: (0845) 300 0300
Fax: (0845) 300 1300
e-mail: sales@metoffice.com
www.metoffice.com
Need an extra pair of hands on deck?
The Met Office offers accurate weather
information for planning or adapting to
changing conditions at sea. For a free
booklet detailing all our services please
contact us.

OCEAN SAFETY
Saxon Wharf, Lower York Street,
Southampton, Hampshire
SO14 5QF
Tel: (023) 8072 0800
Fax: (023) 8072 0801
e-mail: mail@oceansafety.com
Your Life Saving Supplier: Liferafts,
lifejackets, MOB, flares, fire fighting,
medical, EPIRBS. In addition to our
extensive product range, we also boast
two of the largest liferaft, lifejacket and
inflatable service stations in Europe with
the continued growth of our facility in
Palma de Mallorca, Spain.

PREMIUM LIFERAFT SERVICES
Head Office: Liferaft House,
Burnham Business Park,
Burnham-on-Crouch, Essex
CM0 8TE.
Freephone: 0800 243673

Fax: (01621) 785934
e-mail: info@liferafts.com
www.liferafts.com
Hire, servicing and sales of DoT and
RORC approved liferafts and other safety
equipment. Long and short-term hire from
26 depots nationwide – see Area by Area
section for regional units.

WINTERS MARINE LIMITED
(Lincombe Boatyard)
Lincombe, Salcombe,
Devon TQ8 8NQ.
Tel: (01548) 843580
e-mail:
lincombeboatyard@eclipse.co.uk
Deep water pontoon moorings. Winter
storage for 150 boats. All maintenance
and repair facilities. Slipway capacity 30
tonnes. Short and long-term liferaft hire.

SAILMAKERS & REPAIRS

A Hooper Plymouth		01752 830411
A Mathew Sail Loft (Ocean Blue Chandlery) Penzance		01736 364004
Arthur Duthie Marine Safety Glasgow		0141 429 4553
Arun Sails Chichester		01243 573185
Bissett and Ross Aberdeen		01224 580659
Breaksea Sails Barry		01446 730785
Bristol Sails Bristol		0117 922 5080
Bruce Bank Sails Southampton		01489 582444
Calibra Sails Dartmouth		01803 833094
Canard Sails Swansea		01792 367838
Crusader Sails Poole		01202 670580
Dolphin Sails Harwich		01255 243366
Downer International Sails & Chandlery Dun Laoghaire		00353 1 280 0231
E A Gaw Belfast		028 90451905
East Coast Sails Walton-on-the-Naze		01255 678353
Fylde Coast Sailmaking Co Fleetwood		01253 873476
Goldfinch Sails Whitstable		01227 272295
Gowen Sails Nr Colchester		01206 382922
Graham Scott & Co St Peter Port		01481 728989
Hood Sailmakers Lymington		01590 675011
Hyde Sails (Benfleet) Benfleet		01268 756254
Irish Sea Yachts Maryport		01900 816881

MARINE SUPPLIES AND SERVICES

POLICE – SAILMAKERS

Islands Yachts St Helier 01534 25048

J Dawson (Sails)
Port Dinorwic   01248 670103

J Lawrence Sailmakers
Brightlingsea   01206 302863

J McCready and Co Ltd
Belfast   028 90232842

Jeckells and Son Ltd (Wroxham)
Wroxham   01603 782223

JESSAIL
58 Glasgow Street,
Ardrossan KA22 8EH
Tel: (01294) 467311
Fax: (01294) 467311
e-mail: jessail@btinternet.com
Sails, covers, upholstery.

JKA Sailmakers

Pwllheli   01758 613266

John Alsop Sailmakers
Salcombe   01548 843702

Keith Buchanan
St Mary's   01720 422037

Kemp Sails Ltd
Wareham   01929 554308/554378

Malcolm Sails Fairlie   01475 568500

Margaret Crawford
Kirkwall   01856 875692

McKillop Sails (Sail Locker)
Ipswich   01473 780007

McWilliam Sailmaker (Killinchy)
Killinchy   028 97542345

McWilliam Sailmaker Ltd (Crosshaven)
Crosshaven   00353 21 4831505

McWilliams Sailmakers
Cowes   01983 281100

Mitchell Sails Fowey   01726 833731

Montrose Rope and Sails
Montrose   01674 672657

Mouse Sails Holyhead 01407 763636

Nicholson Hughes Sails
Rosneath   01436 831356

North Sea Sails
Tollesbury   01621 869367

Northrop Sails
Ramsgate   01843 851665

Ocean Sails Plymouth 01752 563666

Owen Sails (Gourock)
Gourock   01475 636196

Owen Sails By Oban   01631 720485

Parker & Kay Sailmakers -
East Ipswich   01473 659878

Parker & Kay Sailmakers -
South Hamble   023 8045 8213

Paul Green Sailmakers
Plymouth   01752 660317

Penrose Sailmakers
Falmouth   01326 312705

Pollard Marine
Port St Mary   01624 835831

**QUANTUM-PARKER & KAY
SAILMAKERS - SOUTH
Hamble Point Marina, School
Lane, Hampshire SO31 4JD
Tel: 023 8045 8213
Fax: 023 8045 8228
e-mail: pkay@quantumsails.com
www.quantumsails.com**
A complete sail making service, from
small repairs to the construction of
custom designed sails for racing or
cruising yachts. Covers constructed for
sail and powercraft, plus the supply of all
forms of sail handling hardware.

Quay Sails (Poole) Ltd
Poole   01202 681128

Ratsey & Lapthorn
Isle of Wight   01983 294051

Richardson Sails
Southampton   023 80403914

Rockall Sails
Chichester   01243 573185

Sails & Canvas Exeter 01392 877527

Saltern Sail Co West Cowes   01983
280014

Saltern Sail Company
Yarmouth   01983 760120

Saturn Sails Largs   01475 689933

South West Sails Penryn   01326
375291

Southern Sails Poole 01202 677000

**STEPHEN RATSEY
SAILMAKERS
8 Brunel Quay, Neyland, Milford
Haven, Pembrokeshire SA73 1PY.
Tel: (01646) 601561
Fax: (01646) 601968
e-mail: info@ratseys.co.uk
www.stephenratsey.co.uk**
Emergency repairs – sails, covers, rigging
and upholstery.

Suffolk Sails
Woodbridge   01394 386323

Sunset Sails Sligo   00353 71 62792

Trident Sails Gateshead 0191 490 1736

Ursula Wilkinson
Brighton   01273 677758

Watson Sails
Dublin 13   00353 1 832 6466

WB Leitch and Son
Tarbert   01880 820287

Wilkinson Sails Teynham   01795
521503

William Leith
Berwick on Tweed   01289 307264

SEA DELIVERIES

PETERS & MAY LTD
18 Canuse Road, Ocean Village,
Southampton SO14 3FJ
Tel: (023) 8048 0480
Fax: (023) 8048 0400
e-mail: sales@petersandmay.com
www.petersandmay.com
Peters & May move marine equipment and
900+ sailboats and motoryachts each
year worldwide. Weekly sailings to US,
Australasia, Far and Middle East; shipping
monthly to Mediterranean and Caribbean;
daily airfreight shipments of urgent
spares/equipment.

SLIPWAYS

WINTERS MARINE LIMITED
(Lincombe Boatyard)
Lincombe, Salcombe,
Devon TQ8 8NQ.
Tel: (01548) 843580
e-mail:
lincombeboatyard@eclipse.co.uk
Deep water pontoon moorings. Winter
storage for 150 boats. All maintenance
and repair facilities. Slipway capacity 30
tonnes. Short and long-term lifecraft hire.

SOLAR POWER

SOLAR PANELS

Flexible, Rigid,
Deckmount
Regulators, Controls
5W-120W

2003/M&WMD53/bd

01425 480780
www.ampair.com

AMPAIR
Tel: (01425) 480780
www.ampair.com
Battery Charging: Ampair specialise in
wind, water and solar powered battery
charging systems for boats of all sizes.
We can also supply inverters, chargers,
regulators and monitors. Technical
information and catalogue.

MARLEC ENGINEERING CO LTD
Rutland House, Trevithick Road,
Corby, Northamptonshire
NN17 5XY
Tel: (01536) 201588
Fax: (01536) 400211
e-mail: sales@marlec.co.uk
www.marlec.co.uk
For wind and solar powered battery
charging on the board talk to Marlec. We
manufacture the Rutland Marine range of
wind windchargers, and import and
distribute Solarex photovoltaic modules.
Manufacturer of Leisurelights - low energy
high efficiency 12v lamps.

SPRAYHOODS & DODGERS

JESSAIL
58 Glasgow Street,
Ardrossan KA22 8EH
Tel: (01294) 467311
Fax: (01294) 467311
e-mail: jessail@btinternet.com
Sails, covers, upholstery.

SURVEYORS & NAVAL ARCHITECTS

ATKIN & ASSOCIATES
2 Pippin Close, Lymington,
Hampshire UK SO41 3TP
Tel: (01590) 688633
Fax: (01590) 677793
e-mail:
mike.atkin@ukonline.co.uk
Sailing & motor yacht surveyors.

DAVID M. CANNELL &
ASSOCIATES
River House, Quay Street,
Wivenhoe,
Essex CO7 9DD.
Tel: +44 (0) 1206 823 337
Fax: +44 (0) 1206 825 939
e-mail:
enquiries@dmcmarine.com
www.dmcmarine.com
Design of yachts and commercial craft
to 80m. Newbuilding and refit
overseeing. condition surveys,
valuations, MCA Code of Practice
Compliance and Stability, Expert
Witness. Members: Royal Institution of
Naval Architects, Yacht Designers and
Surveyors Association.

GRAHAM BOOTH MARINE
SURVEYS
96 Canterbury Road,
Birchington-on-Sea, Kent

CT7 9BB
Tel: (01843) 843793
Fax: (01843) 846860
e-mail: gbma@clare.net
Authorised for MCA Codes of Practice,
most frequently on French and Italian
Riviera - also for certification of Sail Training
vessels and other commercial craft. Call UK
office for further information. Other expert
marine consultancy services also available.

NORWOOD MARINE
65 Royal Esplanade, Margate,
Kent CT9 5ET
Tel: (01843) 835711
Fax: 01843 832044
e-mail: greenfieldgr@aol.com
Marine consultants and advisers.
Specialists in collisions, groundings,
pioltage, yachting and RYA examinations -
Fellows of Nautical Institute and RIN.

OWEN CLARKE DESIGNS LLP
Lower Ridge Barns, PO Box 26,
Dartmouth, Devon TQ6 0YG
Tel: (01803) 770495
e-mail:
info@owenclarkedesign.com
www.owenclarkedesign.com
Yacht design, naval architects, surveyors.

SWANWICK YACHT SURVEYORS
Swanwick Marina,
Lower Swanwick,
Southampton SO31 12L
Tel: (01489) 564822
Fax: (01489) 564828
e-mail: swanwickys@aol.com
www.swanwickys.co.uk
Pre-purchase surveys. MIIMS & BMF
member.

WARD & McKENZIE
(NORTH EAST)
11 Sherbuttage Drive,
Pocklington, East Yorkshire
YO42 2ED
Tel: (01759) 304322
Fax: (01759) 303194
E-mail: surveyor@proworks.co.uk
Professional yacht & powerboat
surveyors, services include damage, pre
purchase, insurance condition surveys &
technical advice. Competitive rates, fast
reliable 24 hour service. Members of the
International Institute of Marine Surveyors.

YDSA YACHT DESIGNERS &
SURVEYORS ASSOC.
Wheel House, Petersfield Road,
Whitehill, Bordon,
Hants GU35 9BU
Tel: (0845) 0900162
Fax: (0845) 0900163
e-mail: info@ybdsa.co.uk
www.ybdsa.co.uk
Professional association for designers and
surveyors.

TAPE TECHNOLOGY

CC MARINE (RUBBAWELD) LTD
P.O. Box 155, Chichester,
W. Sussex PO20 8TS
Tel: (01243) 672606
Fax: (01243) 673703
Manufacturer of marine adhesive tapes.

TRANSPORT / YACHT DELIVERIES

CONVOI EXCEPTIONNEL LTD
Castleton House, High Street,
Hamble, Southampton,
Hampshire SO31 4HA.
Tel: (023) 8045 3045
Fax: (023) 8045 4551
e-mail: info@convoi.co.uk
International marine haulage and abnormal
load consultants. European abnormal load
permits obtained and escort car service.
Capacity for loads up to 100 tons.

FORREST MARINE LTD
Kerswell Grange,
Old Dawlish Road,
Kennford, Exeter,
Devon EX6 7LR
Tel: (01392) 833504
Fax: (01392) 833608
e-mail:
forrest.transport@virgin.net
UK & European specialist yacht and
cruiser overland transport.

PETERS & MAY LTD
18 Canuse Road, Ocean Village,
Southampton SO14 3FJ
Tel: (023) 8048 0480
Fax: (023) 8048 0400
e-mail:
sales@petersandmay.com
www.petersandmay.com
Peters & May move marine equipment and
900+ sailboats and motoryachts each
year worldwide. Weekly sailings to US,
Australasia, Far and Middle East; shipping
monthly to Mediterranean and Caribbean;
daily airfreight shipments of urgent
spares/equipment.

When replying
to adverts
please mention
the Waypoint &
Marina Guide

TUITION / SAILING SCHOOLS

**ASSOCIATION OF SCOTTISH
YACHT CHARTERERS**
7 Torimturk, Tarbert,
Argyll PA29 6YE
Tel/Fax: (01880) 820012
e-mail: info@asyc.co.uk
www.asyc.co.uk
Scottish Charter Companies & Sailing
Schools.

**BISHAM ABBEY SAILING &
NAVIGATION SCHOOL**
National Sports Centre, Bisham,
Nr. Marlow, Bucks SL7 1RT
Tel: (01628) 474960
www.bishamabbeysailing.co.uk
RYA recognised establishment. Dinghy
Sailing for adults and children. Shore-
based navigation, intensive and semi-
intensive - Dayskipper, Yachtmaster,
YMOcean. One day - 1st aid, VHF-SRC,
Radar, Diesel Engine, Electronic
Navigation, CEVNI, Boat handling,
Powerboat, IWHC, ICC. Boat Safety
Scheme.

CORSAIR SAILING
30 Wilmot Way, Banstead, Surrey
SM7 2PY
Tel: (01737) 211466
Fax: (01737) 211466
e-mail:
info@corsair-sailing.co.uk
www.corsair-sailing.co.uk
RYA shorebased and individual tuition in
South London and practical sail training
from Portsmouth and Chichester.

**HASLAR MARINA & VICTORY
YACHT CHARTERS**
Unit 16, Haslar Marina, Gosport
PO12 1NU
Tel: (023) 9252 0099
Fax: (023) 9252 0100
e-mail:
info@victorycharters.co.uk

www.victorycharters.co.uk
Quality bareboat & skippered charter all
year round from our Gosport base. Also
the full range of RYA theory and practical
courses. Corporate events also catered
for.

**HASLAR MARINA & VICTORY
YACHT CHARTERS**
Unit 16, Haslar Marina, Gosport
PO12 1NU
Tel: (023) 9252 0099
Fax: (023) 9252 0100
e-mail:
info@haslarseaschool.co.uk
www.haslarseaschool.co.uk
The full range of RYA theory and practical
courses on modern, comfortable yachts.
4:1 teaching ratio on practicals. Also,
bareboat & skippered charter.

**JP SERVICES -
MARINE SAFETY & TRAINING**
The Old Police House, Arundel
Road, Tangmere, Chichester,
West Sussex PO18 0DZ
Tel: (01243) 537552
Fax: (01243) 531471
e-mail: training@jpservices.co.uk
www.jpservices.co.uk
RYA and professional training for motor
yachts and work boats. Max 2 students
per practical course. Sea survival courses.
Safety Training and risk awareness to
MCA standards. Consultancy following on
the water accidents.

ADVENTURE
TRAIN
QUALIFY

Learning to sail, brushing up on your skills or aiming for qualifications is a whole lot easier with the UK's leading sea school.

- Complete beginners to Yachtmaster
- RYA practical and theory courses
- Flotilla weekends & refresher cruising
- Sea Survival, SRC, First Aid, Diesel engine & safety skills
- Celtic Venture milebuilder to Ireland, Scotland and Isle of Man

Cruising weekends from £160 all inclusive

For a brochure, ring 01248 670964

www.plasmenai.co.uk
plas.menai@scw.co.uk

Plas Menai, The National Watersports Centre, Caernarfon, Gwynedd LL55 1UE

PLAS MENAI
THE NATIONAL WATERSPORTS CENTRE

PLAS MENAI NATIONAL WATERSPORTS CENTRE
Caernarfon, Gwynedd LL55 1UE
Tel: (01248) 670964
Fax: (01248) 670964
e-mail: plas.menai@scw.co.uk
www.plasmenai.co.uk
Practical and shore-based RYA sailing courses, refresher & flotilla cruising weekends around the North Wales coast, Ireland, Isle of Man and southern Scotland Competent Crew to Yachtmaster and one-day shore-based safety and navigation skills courses.

PLYMOUTH SAILING SCHOOL
Queen Anne's Battery, Plymouth PL4 0LP
Tel: (01752) 667170
Fax: (01752) 257162
e-mail: school@plymsail.co.uk
www.plymsail.co.uk
One of the oldest established sailing schools in the country. Shorebased navigation, practical sailing, power cruising and power boating courses all the year round from a sheltered base in Plymouth Sound.

TILLER SCHOOL OF NAVIGATION
30 Wilmot Way, Banstead, Surrey SM7 2PY
Tel: (01737) 211466
Fax: (01737) 211466
e-mail: info@tiller.co.uk
www.tiller.co.uk
Distance Learning courses for RYA shorebased Day Skipper, Coastal Skipper / Yachtmaster Offshore and Yachtmaster Ocean. Well proven, highly rated and equally suited to power and sail. Ask for Free Information Pack.

WATERSIDE ACCOMODATION & RESTAURANTS

CAFÉ MOZART
48 High Street, Cowes, Isle of Wight PO31 7RR
Tel: (01983) 293681
Fax: (01983) 293681
e-mail: cafemozart@hotmail.com
www.cafemozart.co.uk
From sticky buns to fine dining!

HARBOUR LIGHTS RESTAURANT (Walton-on-the-Naze) Ltd
Titchmarsh Marina, Coles Lane, Walton-on-the-Naze, Essex CO14 8SL
Tel: (01255) 851887
Fax: (01255) 677300
www.titchmarshmarina.com
Open 7 days a week the Harbour Lights provides fine views overlooking the marina and a warm welcome. English/continental breakfasts and extensive bar meals are served daily. Summer evening barbecues and a la carte restaurant with traditional English fayre.

THE TAYVALLICH INN
Tayvallich, By Lochgilphead,
Argyll PA31 8PL
Tel: (01546) 870282
Fax: (01546) 870333
e-mail: tayvallich.inn@virgin.net
www.tayvallich.com
Bar and restaurant situated on the shores of Loch Sween. Fresh, local seafood a speciality, although plenty for the meat-eater and vegetarians.

WEATHER INFORMATION / METEOROLOGICAL

MARINECALL
iTouch (UK) Ltd, Avalon House,
57-63 Scrutton Street, London
EC2A 4PF
Tel: (0870) 600 4219
Fax: (0870) 600 4229
e-mail: marinecall@itouch.co.uk
www.marinecall.co.uk
Marinecall - weather at sea. Specialist weather forecasts for UK inshore / coastal and offshore areas. 5 day reports call 09068 505 200 (60p/min).

MET OFFICE
London Road, Bracknell,
Berkshire RG12 2SZ
Tel: (0845) 300 0300
Fax: (0845) 300 1300
e-mail: sales@metoffice.com
www.metoffice.com
Need an extra pair of hands on deck? The Met Office offers accurate weather information for planning or adapting to changing conditions at sea. For a free booklet detailing all our services please contact us.

WIND POWER

AMPAIR
Tel: (01425) 480780
www.ampair.com
Wind Chargers: Ampair specialise in wind, water and solar powered battery charging systems for boats of all sizes. We can also supply inverters, chargers, regulators and monitors. Technical information and catalogue.

MARLEC ENGINEERING CO LTD
Rutland House, Trevithick Road,
Corby, Northamptonshire
NN17 5XY
Tel: (01536) 201588
Fax: (01536) 400211
e-mail: sales@marlec.co.uk
www.marlec.co.uk
For wind and solar powered battery charging on the board talk to Marlec. We manufacture the Rutland Marine range of wind windchargers, and import and distribute Solarex photovoltaic modules. Manufacturer of Leisurelights - low energy high efficiency 12v lamps.

WOOD FITTINGS

SHERATON MARINE CABINET
White Oak Green, Hailey, Witney,
Oxfordshire OX8 5XP
Tel/Fax: (01993) 868275
Manufacturers of quality teak and mahogany marine fittings, louvre doors, grating and tables. Special fitting-out items to customer specification. Colour catalgoue available on request.

YACHT BROKERS

ABYA ASSOCIATION OF BROKERS & YACHT AGENTS
Wheel House, Petersfield Road,
Whitehill, Bordon,
Hants GU35 9BU
Tel: (0845) 0900162
Fax: (0845) 0900163
e-mail: info@ybdsa.co.uk
www.ybdsa.co.uk
Professional association for yacht brokers/dealers.

ARDFERN YACHT CENTRE LTD
Ardfern by Lochgilphead, Argyll,
Scotland PA31 8QN
Tel: (01852) 500247
Fax: (01852) 500624
e-mail: office@ardfernyacht.co.uk
www.ardfernyacht.co.uk
Boatyard and marina facilities in a picturesque natural harbour, comprehensive workshop facilities, extensive chandlery, diesel, gas.

BLUE BAKER YACHTS
Charter & Brokerage
Management.
Woolverstone Marina,
Woolverstone, Ipswich, Suffolk
IP9 1AS
Tel: (01473) 780111 / 780008
Fax: (01473) 780911
e-mail:
brokerage@bluebakeryachts.com
www.bluebakeryachts.com
Blue Baker Yacht Management, East Coast Brokerage and Charter Management for bareboat, skippered and corporate yacht charters. Sales of new and used yachts.

DICKIES OF BANGOR
36 Garth Road, Bangor,
Gwynedd LL57 2SE
Tel: (01248) 363400
Fax: (01248) 354169
e-mail: info@dickies.co.uk
www.dickies.co.uk
Full yard services, chandlery, brokerage and new boat dealers for Beneteau Sail and power boats and Lagoon power catamarans.

MIKE LUCAS YACHTING
Lymcourt Lodge, Middle
Lincombe Road, Torquay,
Devon TQ1 2HE
Tel: (01803) 212840
Fax: (01803) 212818
e-mail:
mike@mikelucasyachting.co.uk
www.mikelucasyachting.co.uk
Saga Sabler Starlight Specialized broker agent.

2 CLASSICS

Contests have long enjoyed a fine reputation among the cruising cognoscenti for building serious cruising yachts to the highest standards. Traditional interiors in teak and other woods are

allied with modern hull shapes and rigs to give comfort, ease of handling and performance. The yard is keen to tailor each yacht to its owner's needs while remaining keenly priced.

The traditional low coachroof range comprises 38, 42S, 44, 48 & 60 ft. The CS range with panoramic view from the saloon comprises (new) 44CS, 48CS, 55CS and 60CS.

Wauquiez have long been regarded as the doyen of French yachtbuilders. The Wauquiez Pilot Saloons offer unrivalled performance with perfect visibility even when sitting in the raised saloon.

The Pilot Saloon range comprises (new) 40PS, 43PS and 48PS. Larger Pilot Saloons can be custom built. The Centurion 48S fast cruiser combines a beautiful classic profile with performance and superb accommodation.

For new and used Contests, Pilot Saloons and Centurions contact the UK & Irish agent.

ONE PORT OF CALL

CHARLES WATSON MARINE
3 THE SQUARE HAMBLE
HAMPSHIRE, U.K. SO31 4LS
TEL: (023) 8045 6505 FAX: (023) 8045 7773
EMAIL: CHARLESWATSON@CHARLES-WATSON.COM

YACHT CHARTERS & HOLIDAYS

407 RACING (YACHT CHARTER)
6 Conference Place, Old Orchards, Lymington, Hampshire SO41 3TQ.
Tel: (01590) 688407
Fax: (01590) 610407
e-mail:
407Racing@407YachtCharter.co.uk
www.407yachtcharter.co.uk
Beneteau 40.7 *firsts* for 100 guests or more for corporate outings. Numerous Sunseekers from 34' to 68'. 5 Luxury Swans from 48' to 60'. Where the best yachts just get better.

ASSOCIATION OF SCOTTISH YACHT CHARTERERS
7 Torimturk, Tarbert, Argyll PA29 6YE
Tel/Fax: (01880) 820012
e-mail: info@asyc.co.uk
www.asyc.co.uk
Scottish Charter Companies & Sailing Schools.

BLUE BAKER YACHTS
Charter & Brokerage Management.
Woolverstone Marina, Woolverstone, Ipswich, Suffolk IP9 1AS
Tel: (01473) 780111 / 780008
Fax: (01473) 780911
e-mail:
brokerage@bluebakeryachts.com
www.bluebakeryachts.com
Blue Baker Yacht Management, East Coast Brokerage and Charter Management for bareboat, skippered and corporate yacht charters. Sales of new and used yachts.

DOUNE MARINE
Doune, Knoydart, Mallaig, Inverness-shire PH41 4PL
Tel: (01687) 462667
Fax: (01687) 462667
e-mail: liz@doune-marine.co.uk
www.doune-marine.co.uk
Charter Eda Frandsen our 70ft traditional gaff cutter. Restaurant meals / showers / 2 free moorings. Shorebased holidays for walking, wildlife, photography and diving.

HASLAR MARINA & VICTORY YACHT CHARTERS
Unit 16, Haslar Marina, Gosport PO12 1NU
Tel: (023) 9252 0099
Fax: (023) 9252 0100
e-mail:
info@victorycharters.co.uk
www.victorycharters.co.uk
Quality bareboat & skippered charter all year round from our Gosport base. Also the full range of RYA theory and practical courses. Corporate events also catered for.

HASLAR MARINA & VICTORY YACHT CHARTERS
Unit 16, Haslar Marina, Gosport PO12 1NU
Tel: (023) 9252 0099
Fax: (023) 9252 0100
e-mail:
info@haslarseaschool.co.uk
www.haslarseaschool.co.uk
The full range of RYA theory and practical courses on modern, comfortable yachts. 4:1 teaching ratio on practicals. Also, bareboat & skippered charter.

INDULGENCE CHARTERS
20 High Street, Wendover, Buckinghamshire HP22 6EA
Tel: (01296) 696006
Fax: (01296) 624219
e-mail:
paul@indulgencecharters.com
www.indulgencecharters.com
Our luxury fleet of MCA coded Sunseekers offers charters with the privileges of a hotel suite combined with the excitement offered by a performance motor yacht that is yours to plan and play with.

SLEAT MARINE SERVICES
Ardvasar, Isle of Skye IV45 8RS
Tel: (01471) 844216
Fax: (01471) 844387
e-mail:
services@sleatmarineservices
www.sleatmarineservices.co.uk
Yacht Charter - we offer a choice of yachts in the 10-12 metre size range. Services to visiting yachts include: 15 ton hoist, general repairs, diesel, water, mooring and showers. We look forward to seeing you.

SLEAT MARINE SERVICES
Ardvasar, Isle of Skye IV45 8RS
Tel: 01471 844216
Fax: 01471 844387
E-mail: enquiries@sleatmarineservices.co.uk
Website: www.sleatmarineservices.co.uk
Bareboat or skippered charter from the beautiful Isle of Skye.
A selection of yachts in the 10-12 metre range available. Also at Ardvasar (Armadale):
15 tonne hoist, yacht repairs, moorings, diesel, water and shower facilities.

YACHT CLUB FACILITIE

ROYAL WESTERN YACHT CLU
Queen Anne's Battery, Plymou
Devon PL4 0TW.
Tel: (01752) 660077
Fax: (01752) 224299
e-mail: admin@rwyc.org
www.rwyc.org
Home of shorthanded sailing. Visiting yachtsmen welcome. Mooring facilities available.

YACHT CLUBS

Aberaeron YC	
Aberdovey	01545 5700
Aberdeen and Stonehaven SC	
Nr Inverurie	01569 7640
Aberdour BC Aberdour	01383 8606
Abersoch Power BC	
Abersoch	01758 7120
Aberystwyth BC	
Aberystwyth	01970 6245
Aldeburgh YC Aldeburgh	01728 4525
Alderney SC Alderney	01481 8229
Alexandra YC	
Southend-on-Sea	01702 3403
Arklow SC Arklow	00353 402 331
Arun YC Littlehampton	01903 7160
Axe YC Axemouth	01297 200
Ayr Yacht and CC Ayr	01292 4760
Ballyholme YC Bangor	028 912714
Baltimore SC	
Baltimore	00353 28 204
Banff SC Cults	01261 8152
Bantry Bay SC Bantry	00353 27 500
Barry YC Barry	01446 7355
Beaulieu River SC	
Brockenhurst	01590 6162
Bembridge SC	
Isle of Wight	01983 8726
Benfleet YC	
Canvey Island	01268 7922
Blackpool and Fleetwood YC	01253 8842
Blackwater SC Maldon	01621 8539
Blundellsands SC	0151 929 21
Bosham SC Chichester	01243 5723
Brading Haven YC	
Isle of Wight	01983 8722
Bradwell CC Bradwell	01621 8929
Bradwell Quay YC	
Wickford	01268 7765
Brancaster Staithe SC	01485 2102
Brandy Hole YC	
Hullbridge	01702 2303
Brightlingsea SC	
Colchester	01206 3032
Brighton Marina YC	
Peacehaven	01273 8187
Bristol Avon SC Bristol	01225 8734
Bristol Channel YC	
Swansea	01792 3660

stol Corinthian YC
ridge 01934 732033

xham YC Brixham 01803 853332

rnham Overy
ithe SC 01328 730961

rnham-on-Crouch SC
nham-on-Crouch 01621 782812

rnham-on-Sea SC
dgwater 01278 792911

rry Port YC
ry Port 01554 833635

bot CC 0117 9514389

ernarfon SC (Menai Strait)
ernarfon 01286 672861

mpbeltown SC
mpbeltown 01586 552488

rdiff Bay YC Cardiff 029 20226575

rdiff YC Cardiff 029 2046 3697

rlingford Lough YC
strevor 028 4173 8604

rrickfergus SC
hitehead 028 93 351402

stle Cove SC
eymouth 01305 783708

stlegate Marine Club
ockton on Tees 01642 583299

anonry SC Fortrose 01463 221415

ichester Cruiser and Racing Club
01483 770391

ichester YC
hichester 01243 512918

hristchurch SC
hristchurch 01202 483150

lyde CC Glasgow 0141 221 2774

o Antrim YC
arrickfergus 028 9337 2322

obnor Activities Centre Trust
01243 572791

oleraine YC Coleraine 028 703 44503

olne YC Brightlingsea 01206 302594

onwy YC Deganwy 01492 583690

oquet YC 01665 711179

orrib Rowing & YC
Galway City 00353 91 564560

owes Combined Clubs
01983 295744

owes Corinthian YC
sle of Wight 01983 296333

owes Yachting 01983 280770

ramond BC 0131 336 1356

reeksea SC
Burnham-on-Crouch 01245 320578

rookhaven SC
rookhaven 087 2379997 mobile

rouch YC
Burnham-on-Sea 01278 782252

Dale YC Haverfordwest 01646 636362

Dartmouth YC
Dartmouth 01803 832305

Deben YC Woodbridge 01394 385400

Dell Quay SC Chichester 01243 785080

Dingle SC Dingle 00353 66 51984

Douglas Bay YC
Douglas 01624 673965

Dovey YC Aberdovey 01654 767607

Dun Laoghaire MYC 00353 1 288 938

Dunbar SC
Cockburnspath 01368 86287

East Antrim BC Antrim 028 28 277204

East Belfast YC Belfast 028 9065 6283

East Cowes SC
Isle of Wight 01983 531687

East Dorset SC Poole 01202 706111

East Lothian YC 01620 892698

Eastney Cruising Association
Portsmouth 023 92734103

Eling SC 023 80863987

Emsworth SC Emsworth 01243 372850

Emsworth Slipper SC
Emsworth 01243 372523

Epic Ventures Ltd
Cowes 01983 291292

Essex YC Southend 01702 478404

Exe SC (River Exe)
Exemouth 01395 264607

Eyott SC Mayland 01245 320703

Fairlie YC 01294 213940

Falmouth Town SC
Falmouth 01326 373915

Falmouth Watersports Association
Falmouth 01326 211223

Fareham Sailing & Motor BC
Fareham 01329 233324

Felixstowe Ferry SC
Felixstowe 01394 283785

Findhorn YC Findhorn 01309 690247

Fishguard Bay YC
Lower Fishguard 01348 872866

Flushing SC Falmouth 01326 374043

Folkestone Yacht and Motor BC
Folkestone 01303 251574

Forth Corinthian YC
Haddington 0131 552 5939

Forth YCs Association
Edinburgh 0131 552 3006

Fowey Gallants SC
Fowey 01726 832335

Foynes YC Foynes 00353 69 91201

Galway Bay SC 00353 91 794527

Glasson SC Preston 01524 751089

Glenans Irish Sailing School
00353 1 6611481

Glénans Irish SC (Westport)
00353 98 26046

Gosport CC Gosport 02392 586838

Gravesend SC
Gravesend 01474 533974

Greenwich YC London 020 8858 7339

Grimsby and Cleethorpes YC
Grimsby 01472 356678

Guernsey YC
St Peter Port 01481 722838

Halfway YC 01702 582025

Hamble River SC
Southampton 023 80452070

Hampton Pier YC
Herne Bay 01227 364749

Hardway SC Gosport 02392 581875

Hartlepool YC
Hartlepool 01429 233423

Harwich Town SC
Harwich 01255 503200

Hastings and St Leonards YC
Hastings 01424 420656

Haven Ports YC
Woodbridge 01394 659658

Hayling Ferry SC; Locks SC
Hayling Island 023 80829833

Hayling Island SC
Hayling Island 023 92463768

Helensburgh SC Rhu 01436 672778

Helensburgh 01436 821234

Helford River SC
Helston 01326 231006

Herne Bay SC
Herne Bay 01227 375650

Highcliffe SC
Christchurch 01425 274874

Holyhead SC Holyhead 01407 762526

Holywood YC Holywood 028 90423355

Hoo Ness YC Sidcup 01634 250052

Hornet SC Gosport 02392 580403

Howth YC Howth 00353 1 832 2141

Hoylake SC Wirral 0151 632 2616

Hullbridge YC 01702 231797

Humber Yawl Club 01724 733458

Hurlingham YC London 020 8788 5547

Hythe SC Southampton 023 80846563

Ilfracombe YC
Ilfracombe 01271 863969

Iniscealtra SC
Limerick 00353 61 338347

Invergordon BC 01349 877612

Irish CC 00353 214870031

Island CC Salcombe 01548 531176

Island SC Isle of Wight 01983 296621

Island YC Canvey Island 01268 510360

Isle of Bute SC
Rothesay 01700 502819

Isle of Man YC
Port St Mary 01624 832088

Itchenor SC Chichester 01243 512400

Keyhaven YC Keyhaven 01590 642165

Killyleagh YC
Killyleagh 028 4482 8250

Kircubbin SC
Kirkcubbin 028 4273 8422

Kirkcudbright SC
Kirkcudbright 01557 331727

Langstone SC Havant 023 92484577

Largs SC Largs 01475 670000

Larne Rowing & SC
Larne 028 2827 4573

Lawrenny YC 01646 651212

Leigh-on-Sea SC 01702 476788
Lerwick BC Lerwick 01595 696954
Lilliput SC Poole 01202 740319
Littlehampton Sailing and Motor
Club Littlehampton 01903 715859
Loch Ryan SC Stranraer 01776 706322
Lochaber YC Fort William 01397 772361
Locks SC Portsmouth 023 92829833
Looe SC Looe 01503 262559
Lossiemouth CC
Fochabers 01348 812121
Lough Swilly YC Fahn 00353 74 22377
Lowestoft CC
Lowestoft 01502 574376
Lyme Regis Power BC
Lyme Regis 01297 443788
Lyme Regis SC
Lyme Regis 01297 442800
Lymington Town SC
Lymington 0159 674514
Lympstone SC Exeter 01395 264152
Madoc YC Porthmadog 01766 512976
Malahide YC
Malahide 00353 1 845 3372
Maldon Little Ship Club
01621 854139
Manx Sailing & CC
Ramsey 01624 813494
Marchwood YC
Marchwood 023 80666141
Margate YC Margate 01227 292602
Marina BC Pwllheli 01758 612271
Maryport YC 01228 560865
Mayflower SC Plymouth 01752 662526
Mayo SC (Rosmoney)
Rosmoney 00353 98 27772
Medway YC Rochester 01634 718399
Menai Bridge BC
Beaumaris 01248 810583
Mengham Rythe SC
Hayling Island 023 92463337
Merioneth YC
Barmouth 01341 280000
Monkstone Cruising and SC
Swansea 01792 812229
Montrose SC Montrose 01674 672554
Mumbles YC Swansea 01792 369321
Mylor YC Falmouth 01326 374391
Nairn SC Nairn 01667 453897
National YC
Dun Laoghaire 00353 1 280 5725
Netley SC Netley 023 80454272
New Quay YC
Aberdovey 01545 560516
Newhaven & Seaford SC
Seaford 01323 890077
Newport and Uskmouth SC
Cardiff 01633 271417
Newtownards SC
Newtownards 028 9181 3426
Neyland YC Neyland 01646 600267

North Devon YC
Bideford 01271 860367
North Fambridge Yacht Centre
01621 740370
North Haven YC Poole 01202 708830
North of England Yachting
Association Kirkwall 01856 872331
North Sunderland Marine Club
Sunderland 01665 721231
North Wales CC
Conwy 01492 593481
North West Venturers YC
(Beaumaris) Beaumaris 0161 2921943
Oban SC Ledaig by Oban
01631 563999
Orford SC Woodbridge 01394 450444
Orkney SC Kirkwall 01856 872331
Orwell YC Ipswich 01473 602288
Oulton Broad Yacht Station
01502 574946
Ouse Amateur SC
Kings Lynn 01553 772239
Paignton SC Paignton 01803 525817
Parkstone YC Poole 01202 743610
Peel Sailing and CC
Peel 01624 842390
Pembroke Haven YC 01646 684403
Pembrokeshire YC
Milford Haven 01646 692799
Penarth YC Penarth 029 20708196
Pentland Firth YC
Thurso 01847 891803
Penzance YC Penzance 01736 364989
Peterhead SC Ellon 01779 75527
Pin Mill SC Woodbridge 01394 780271
Plym YC Plymouth 01752 404991
Poolbeg YC 00353 1 660 4681
Poole YC Poole 01202 672687
Porlock Weir SC
Watchet 01643 862702
Port Edgar YC Penicuik 01968 674210
Port Navas YC Falmouth 01326 340065
Port of Falmouth Sailing Association
Falmouth 01326 372927
Portchester SC Portchester 01329
376375
Porthcawl Harbour BC
Swansea 01656 655935
Porthmadog & Trawsfynydd SC
Talsarnau 01766 513546
Portrush YC Portrush 028 70 823932
Portsmouth SC
Portsmouth 02392 820596
Prestwick SC Prestwick 01292 671117
Pwllheli SC Pwllheli 01758 613343
Queenborough YC
Queenborough 01795 663955
Quoile YC Downpatrick 028 44 612266
R Towy BC Tenby 01267 241755
RAFYC 023 80452208
Redclyffe YC Poole 01929 557227

Restronguet SC
Falmouth 01326 3745.
Ribble CC
Lytham St Anne's 01253 7399.
River Wyre YC 01253 8119.
RNSA (Plymouth)
Plymouth 01752 55123/.
Rochester CC
Rochester 01634 8413.
Rock Sailing and Water Ski Club
Wadebridge 01208 8624.
Royal Dart YC
Dartmouth 01803 7524.
Royal Motor YC Poole 01202 7072.
Royal Anglesey YC (Beaumaris)
Anglesey 01248 81029.
Royal Burnham YC
Burnham-on-Crouch 01621 78204.
Royal Channel Islands YC (Jersey)
St Aubin 01534 74578.
Royal Cinque Ports YC
Dover 01304 20626.
Royal Corinthian YC
(Burnham-on-Crouch)
Burnham-on-Crouch 01621 78210.
Royal Corinthian YC (Cowes)
Cowes 01983 29260.
Royal Cork YC
Crosshaven 00353 21 83102
Royal Cornwall YC (RCYC) Falmouth
01326 312126
Royal Dorset YC
Weymouth 01305 78625.
Royal Forth YC
Edinburgh 0131 552 300.
Royal Fowey YC Fowey 01726 83357.
Royal Gourock YC
Gourock 01475 63298.
Royal Harwich YC
Ipswich 01473 78031.
Royal Highland YC
Connel 01546 510261
Royal Irish YC
Dun Laoghaire 00353 1 280 9452
Royal London YC
Isle of Wight 019 83299727
Royal Lymington YC
Lymington 01590 672677
Royal Mersey YC
Birkenhead 0151 645 3204
Royal Motor YC Poole 01202 707227
Royal Naval Club and Royal Albert
YC Portsmouth 023 9282 5924
Royal Naval Sailing Association
Gosport 023 92521100
Royal Norfolk & Suffolk YC
Lowestoft 01502 566726
Royal North of Ireland YC
028 90 428041
Royal Northern and Clyde YC
Rhu 01436 820322
Royal Northumberland YC
Blyth 01670 353636

al Plymouth Corinthian YC
outh   01752 664327

al Scottish Motor YC
  0141 881 1024

al Solent YC
outh   01983 760256

al Southampton YC
thampton   023 8022 3352

al Southern YC
thampton   023 8045 0300

al St George YC
Laoghaire   00353 1 280 1811

al Tay YC Dundee   01382 477516

al Temple YC
nsgate   01843 591766

al Torbay YC
quay   01803 292006

al Ulster YC
gor   028 91 270568

al Victoria YC
bourne   01983 882325

yal Welsh YC (Caernarfon)
ernarfon   01286 672599

yal Welsh YC
narfon   01286 672599

yal Western YC
mouth   01752 660077

yal Yacht Squadron
e of Wight   01983 292191

yal Yorkshire YC
dlington   01262 672041

e Harbour SC Rye   01797 223136

Caernarvonshire YC   01758 712338

alcombe YC Salcombe01548 842593

altash SC Saltash   01752 845988

alloway BC Lerwick   01595 880409

arborough YC
carborough   01723 373821

chull SC Schull   00353 28 37352

cillonian Sailing and BC
t Mary's   01720 277229

easalter SC
Vhitstable   01227 264784

eaview YC
le of Wight   01983 613268

horeham SC Henfield   01273 453078

kerries SC
arlingdford Lough   00353 1 849 1233

laughden SC Duxford   01223 835395

ligo YC Sligo   00353 71 77168

olva Boat Owners Association
ishguard   01437 721538

olway YC
irkdudbright   01556 620312

outh Caernavonshire YC
bersoch   01758 712338

outh Cork SC   00353 28 36383

outh Devon Sailing School
Newton Abbot   01626 52352

outh Gare Marine Club - Sail
Section Middlesbrough   01642 453031

outh Shields SC
South Shields   0191 456 5821

South Woodham Ferrers YC
Chelmsford   01245 325391

Southampton SC
Southampton   023 80446575

Southwold SC   01502 716776

Sovereign Harbour YC
Eastbourne   01323 470888

St Helier YC
St Helier   01534 721307/32229

St Mawes SC St Mawes01326 270686

Starcross Fishing & CC (River Exe)
Starcross   01626 891996

Starcross YC Exeter   01626 890470

Stoke SC Ipswich   01473 780815

Stornoway SC
Stornoway   01851 705412

Stour SC   01206 393924

Strangford Lough YC
Newtownards   028 97 541883

Strangford SC
Downpatrick   028 4488 1404

Strood YC Aylesford   01634 718261

Sunderland YC
Sunderland   0191 567 5133

Sunsail Portsmouth   023 92222224

Sussex YC
Shoreham-by-Sea   01273 464868

Swanage SC Swanage   01929 422987

Swansea Yacht & Sub-Aqua Club
Swansea   01792 469096

Tamar River SC
Plymouth   01752 362741

Tarbert Lochfyne YC
Tarbert   01880 820376

Tay Corinthian BC
Dundee   01382 553534

Tay YCs Association   01738 621860

Tees & Hartlepool YC   01429 233423

Tees SC Aycliffe Village   01429 265400

Teifi BC - Cardigan Bay
Fishguard   01239 613846

Teign Corinthian YC
Teignmouth   01626 772734

Tenby SC Tenby   01834 842762

Tenby YC   01834 842762

Thames Estuary YC   01702 345967

Thorney Island SC
Thorney Island   01243 371731

Thorpe Bay YC   01702 587563

Thurrock YC Grays   01375 373720

Tollesbury CC Tollesbury01621 869561

Topsham SC Topsham   01392 877524

Torpoint Mosquito SC -
Plymouth Plymouth   01752 812508

Tralee SC Tralee   00353 66 36119

Troon CC Troon   01292 311908

Troon YC Troon   01292 315315

Tudor SC Portsmouth   023 92662002

Tynemouth SC
Newcastle upon Tyne   0191 2572167

Up River YC Hullbridge   01702 231654

Upnor SC Upnor   01634 718043

Wakering YC Rochford   01702 530926

Waldringfield SC
Wickham Market   01728 736633

Walls Regatta Club
Lerwick   01595 809273

Walton & Frinton YC
Walton-on-the-Naze   01255 675526

Warrenpoint BC
Warrenpoint   028 4175 2137

Warsash SC
Southampton   023 80583575

Watchet Boat Owner Association
Watchet   01984 633736

Waterford Harbour SC
Dunmore East   00353 51 383230

Watermouth YC
Watchet   01271 865048

Wear Boating Association
  0191 567 5313

Wells SC
Wells-next-the-sea   01328 711190

West Kirby SC
West Kirby   0151 625 5579

West Mersea YC
Colchester   01206 382947

Western Isles YC   01688 302371

Western YC Kilrush 00353 87 2262885

Weston Bay YC
Portishead   01275 620772

Weston CC
Southampton   07905 557298

Weston SC
Southampton   023 80452527

Wexford HBC
Wexford   00353 53 22039

Weymouth SC
Weymouth   01305 785481

Whitby YC Whitby   01947 603623

Whitstable YC
Whitstable   01227 272343

Wicklow SC
Wicklow   00353 404 67526

Witham SC Boston   01205 363598

Wivenhoe SC
Colchester   01206 822132

Woodbridge CC
Woodbridge   01394 386737

Wormit BC   01382 553878

Yarmouth SC Yarmouth 01983 760270

Yealm YC
Newton Ferrers   01752 872291

Youghal SailingClub
Youghal   00353 24 92447

YACHT DESIGNERS

**DAVID M. CANNELL &
ASSOCIATES**
River House, Quay Street,
Wivenhoe,
Essex CO7 9DD.
Tel: +44 (0) 1206 823 337
Fax: +44 (0) 1206 825 939
e-mail: enquiries@dmcmarine.com
www.dmcmarine.com
Design of yachts and commercial craft to
80m. Newbuilding and refit overseeing.
condition surveys, valuations, MCA Code
of Practice Compliance and Stability,
Expert Witness. Members: Royal
Institution of Naval Architects, Yacht
Designers and Surveyors Association.

MARINE SUPPLIES AND SERVICES

YACHT CLUBS – YACHT DESIGNERS

OWEN CLARKE DESIGNS LLP
Lower Ridge Barns, PO Box 26, Dartmouth, Devon TQ6 0YG
Tel: (01803) 770495
e-mail:
info@owenclarkedesign.com
www.owenclarkedesign.com
Yacht design, naval architects, surveyors.

YACHT MANAGEMENT

407 RACING
(YACHT CHARTER)
6 Conference Place, Lymington Hampshire SO41 3TQ
Tel: (01590) 688407
Fax: (01590) 610407
e-mail:
407racing@407yachtcharter.co.uk
www.407yachtcharter.co.uk
Where the best yachts just get better.

SWANWICK YACHT SURVEYORS
Swanwick Marina, Lower Swanwick,
Southampton SO31 12L
Tel: (01489) 564822
Fax: (01489) 564828
e-mail: swanwickys@aol.com
www.swanwickys.co.uk
Pre-purchase surveys. MIIMS & BMF member.

YACHT VALETING

KIP MARINA
The Yacht Harbour, Inverkip, Renfrewshire PA16 0AS.
Tel: (01475) 521485
Fax: (01475) 521298
www.kipmarina.co.uk
Marina berths for vessels up to 75' LOA, full boatyard facilities including travel hoist, crane, on-site engineers, GRP repairs etc. Bar, restaurant, saunas, launderette and chandlery. Distributors for Moody & Elan, Fairline, Searanger, Rodman & Revenger.

MARINE GLEAM
14 Fromond Close, Lymington, Hants SO41 9LQ
Tel: 0800 074 4672
e-mail:
enquiries@marinegleam.biz
www.marinegleam.biz
A full cleaning programme to meet your specific requirements from a one off, or a regular clean to a full exterior polish, teak, canopy and covers, anti-fouling, full interior, engine & bilges cleaned.

When replying to adverts please mention the Waypoint & Marina Guide

This Advertisers' Index is provided free of charge and whilst every care is taken to ensure accuracy, the Publishers cannot accept any responsibility for errors.

MARINE SUPPLIES AND SERVICES

YACHT DESIGNERS – YACHT VALETING